W9-CTQ-775

當代美國俚語及常用口語

CONTEMPORARY AMERICAN SLANG
AND USEFUL EXPRESSIONS

（修 訂 版）

鄭 愛 倫 編著

文鶴出版有限公司
THE CRANE PUBLISHING CO.,LTD.

CONTEMPORARY AMERICAN SLANG
AND USEFUL EXPRESSIONS
當代美國俚語及常用口語

版權所有・翻印必究
（修訂版）

中華民國七　十　年四　月　初　版
中華民國七十一年五　月　二　版
中華民國七十二年五　月　三　版
中華民國七十三年六　月　四　版
中華民國七十五年十七月　修訂版
中華民國七十七年七　月　再　版
中華民國七十八年五　月　三　版
中華民國八　十　年六　月　四　版
中華民國八十一年七　月　五　版
中華民國八十二年十　月　六　版
中華民國八十四年四　月　七　版

新聞局登記證局版台業字第1452號
定價：新台幣貳佰元

著　　　者：鄭　愛　倫
發　行　人：戴　奕　煌
負　責　人：張　富　恭
發　行　所：文　鶴　出　版　有　限　公　司
地　　　址：台北市和平東路一段１０９號６樓
電　　　話：３９３－４４９７・３９４－１７９１
郵　　　撥：０１０７９２６１號
出版登記證：行政院新聞局局版台業字第１４５２號
法律顧問：文　聞　法　律　事　務　所
電　　　話：３９５－７９２８
印　刷　者：普　賢　王　印　刷　廠

ISBN: 957-9463-03-4

序

記得早幾年，在我赴美求學的時候，那時很少聽到有人談論美國俚語的事，所以當初赴美時，蠻以為自己背得滾瓜爛熟的一些對話可以應付得足足有餘了。誰知到了美國，發現自己常常是鴨子聽雷——有聽沒有懂，然而他們使用的並不是什麼艱深的難字。當年我在德州大學奧斯汀校區一所女生宿舍餐廳打工時，那些調皮的大男生，因日久混熟了，常愛開玩笑，所以一見人就會來上一句 "Hi, Turkey." 雖然心裏知道鐵不是什麼好話，但實在不知道他真正的意思。因為當時在台灣只聽到過 chicken 知道那是罵人胆小、懦弱的意思。但 turkey 却是從來沒聽過，心想：感恩節還早，怎來的 turkey 呢？諸如此類的事多如牛毛不勝枚舉。

美國是一個活潑、幽默的民族，雖然我們也有俚語（像：你少"蓋"啦！別"驢"了！……），但不如美國人用的多，他們日常生活中常透過了美式的幽默，大量的使用俚語，也常常是一語雙關。學習英文會話，若不懂得這些，還是學得不完全，不道地的，而這一類的知識，是很難在一般傳統的會話課本中學到。所以，很多人下了好幾年功夫學習英文，但還是聽不懂電影、電視上的對話，體會不出他們的幽默來！所幸，近年來大家已開始對「俚語」這東西，感覺到它的存在與重要了，今天我執筆寫這本書，也是希望能盡自己一點棉薄之力，提供有志學習英文的朋友，一些資料，以便能夠跨越過這個學習障礙，把口語英語學得更真實、更道地。

在本書裏，我除了竭力的做最詳盡的說明外，每一個解釋，還附有一則以上的例句，例句多採用對話方式，生動風趣，俾期學者在瞭解字義之後，更能進一步使用。使英文的學習能由機械式被動的記誦而達到主動的活用。書中俚語，夾雜了一些不能登大雅之堂的「三字經」及「粗俗俚語」，這一類字眼，在美國日常生活中，電視、電影上不乏人使用。作者以為這類字眼不妨也去瞭解一下，免得那天出國留學，被人消遣了還不知道。況且，這類的字，知道了，並不代表就是要去使用。再說，在電視、電影上一知半解的聽來之後，如果能知道它是一個粗俗的字句，我們反而可以避免「道聽塗說」式的去使用它，以免「一鳴驚人」，鬧出笑話來。

今天本書能夠與各位見面，首先，我要感謝我的老友吳慧君小姐，感謝她在各方面給予我的支持與鼓勵。其次，要感謝我的幾位美國朋友：Mr. Jon Kanisely, Mr. Nyr Indictor, Mr. Charles Newman 賜予我的各種寶貴意見及協助我做英文的校對工作。還有，我要謝謝徐華麗、王朝榮、吳荻吉、黃孟蘭、簡文參，及李慧群等同學協助我做校對及編整的工作。最後，我要感謝我的家人、及朋友，在這段著書期間給予我的鼓勵與幫助。沒有他們就沒有這本書，我衷心的感謝他們。

本書匆匆寫成，希望能對各位學習英文的朋友有所裨益，然而個人才識有限，匆忙之處，誤漏必定不少，還望各位先進、朋友不吝指正。謝謝。

鄭　愛　倫

修 訂 序

　　本書在第五版做了小幅度的修訂，刪去了一些老舊的說法，也修改了一些句子，俾使本書更合時宜，並在書後增加了索引，以便讀者查用。

　　此次修訂承蒙Mr. Morton W. Belcher Ⅲ，吳慧君小姐及陳鈺貞同學協助校對及編整的工作，在此特予致謝。

　　本書自出書以來承蒙大家喜愛支持，此次修訂之後，仍盼各位先進、朋友一本初衷，不吝指正，謝謝。

　　　　　　　　　　　　　　　　鄭　愛　倫

編 輯 體 例

1. 俚語及常用口語的選擇：本書去蕪存菁選用了美國當今最新，最常用的俚語及常用口語。總計收錄二千餘則，每則俚語下，並有例句說明使用法。

2. 俚語及常用口語的排列：為便於查閱，本書後面有索引如同字典依照字母A～Z的順序排列。

3. 音標：本書採用K.K.音標。

4. 例句：每個俚語，及常用口語之下，依其不同的意義，附有一則以上的例句。例句多採自然生動，風趣幽默的對話方式。

5. 符號：本書採用了以下的幾種符號：

    (a) ＝表示意義相同，或可互相換用，如

     blend (＝match) 在此表示blend 與 match 意義相似。

     get (＝have) cold feet, 在此表示可說成get cold feet, 也可說成 have cold feet.

    (b) or 相當於＝，表示可代換使用，如：

     cast (or throw) pearl before swine 表示 cast pearl before swine 及 throw pearl before swine 均可。

    (c) ／ 表示任選一個均可，如

     give (someone) a call/ring/buzz, 表示 give me a call ＝ give me a ring＝give me a buzz, 都是「打個電話給我」的意思。

    (d) （ ） 表示（ ）內的字可用，可不用，如：

     take (a) French leave, 表示take a French leave 與 take French leave, 均可。

6. 特別註釋：若遇有特別需要解釋及補充說明的地方，在例句之後，均有特別註釋。

1. **a bunch of**

①一群②許多

① ● "They are a bunch of nuts."
「他們是一群瘋子。」

② ● "I got a bunch of friends."
「我有一票朋友。」

● "She gave me a bunch of bananas."
「她給我一大堆香蕉。」

2. **a little too far**

有點太過份了！（批評別人的言行過份）

● "You have gone a little too far this time."
「這次你是有點太過份了。」

3. **a lot you know!**

你知道的真不少！

● "This is the best Cantonese restaurant in town."
「這是本市最好的廣東菜館。」

"A lot you know!"
「你知道的真不少啊！」

4. **a lousy choice of words.**

[`lauzɪ]

口不擇言；出口不遜

● "He called you a bitch? That was a lousy choice of words."
「他叫妳母狗？他真是口不擇言啊！」

5. **(He's) a man who needs no introduction.**

[ˌɪntrə`dʌkʃən]

（他是）一個家喻戶曉的人物（或是好名，或是惡名）

● "And now, I'd like to introduce a man who needs no introduction, Calvin Costner."
「現在，讓我介紹一個家喻戶曉的人物凱文寇斯納。」

6. **A promise is a promise.**

   [ˋprɑmɪs]

   答應的事不許反悔。（或不會黃牛）

   ● "You said you would come...."
      「你說你會來的。」

   "Yes, a promise is a promise."
      「說話算數，絕不黃牛。」

7. **accounts differ**

   [əˋkaunts]

   各執一詞（雙方說詞不一）

   ● "What happened here?"
      「這裏發生了什麼事？」

   "Accounts differ. I didn't get here until after it was all over, so I don't know who hit who first."
      「（他們）各執一詞，我是事情過後才來的，所以我也不知到底是誰先動手的。」

8. **acid** （如LSD）

   [ˋæsɪd]

   迷幻藥

   ● "My roommate took some acid last weekend and said he saw God."
      「我的室友上週末吃了一些迷幻藥，然後說他看到上帝了。」
      註：drop acid 是注射。take acid 是服用。

9. **act your age**

   穩重一點；不要像個小孩一樣

   ● "Act your age, don't act like a child."
      「穩重一點，別表現得像個小孩一樣。」

   ● "Act your age, not your shoe size."
      「表現得像你的年齡一樣，不是像你的鞋子號碼一樣大。」

註：在美國鞋子的尺寸通常是由 5 ─ 1 2 號，在此引申鞋子號
碼爲歲數。

10. **ad. [æd] (=advertisement)**

廣告

● "Let's put an ad in the newspaper."
「讓我們登個廣告在報紙上吧。」

11. **after you**

請你先走。（譬如兩人同時出門，讓對方先走，以示謙讓）

● "You first." "No, after you."
「你先請。」「不，你先請。」

12. **after (someone)**

催人（做某事）

● "He's been after me for months to marry him."
「他已經催了我好幾個月，要我嫁給他。」

13. **(It goes) against my grain.**

[gren]

違背（不合）我的個性

● "To tell even a little fib goes against my grain."
「即使撒點小謊也違背我的個性。」

14. **album (=record)**

['ælbəm]

①唱片　②相簿

① ● "This is Air Supply's best album."
「這是Air Supply's 最好的唱片。」

② ● "Do you want to take a look at my family album?"
「你想不想看看我們家的相簿？」

15. **all gone**

①賣光了（少人用），②走光了，③沒有了；不見了

① ● "I'd like some eggs, please."

「我要買些蛋。」

"I'm sorry, the eggs are all gone."

「對不起,蛋已全賣光了。」

② ● "By eight o'clock, the guests had all gone."

「八點左右,客人全走光了。」

③ ● "Hey, my books are all gone! Did you take them?"

「嘿,我的書全不見了,你有沒有拿?」

16. all done in

累壞了!

● "Boy, I'm all done in."

「老天,我真累壞了。」

17. All's fair in love and war.

在情場及戰場上,一切是不擇手段的。

● "You know I was going to ask Lily out tonight. Why did you call her? You no good son of a bitch."

「你知道,我今晚要邀 Lily 出去,你為什麼還打電話邀她呢?你這狗養的。」

"Well, you should know. – All's fair in love and war."

「哦,你該明白—— 在情場上是不擇手段的。」

● "Don't be such a sore loser. You know all's fair in love and war."

「別這麼酸溜溜的。你知道,在情場及戰場上,一切是不擇手段的。」

18. ALL SALES ARE FINAL!

　　　　[selz]　　　　['faɪnl]

貨物出門,概不退還!

● "Excuse me ma'am, this shirt is too big for me. Can I have my money back?"

「小姐（女士）打擾一下，這件襯衫太大了，是不是可以退錢？」

"I'm sorry, ALL SALES ARE FINAL."
「對不起（我們）貨物出門，概不退還。」

19. **all set**
一切準備好了

- "How is everything?"　　"Don't worry. It's all set."
「怎麼樣了？」　　　　　「別擔心，一切都已經準備好了。」

20. **All sold out**
[sold]
①客滿　②賣光了

- "Sorry, It's all sold out."
「對不起，客滿了／賣光了。」
註：汽車旅社及一般出租公寓外頭常見 "No　Vacancy" 也是表示客滿。

21. **All that glitters is not gold.**
　　　　　　　['glɪtəz]
（發光的東西未必是金子）中看未必中用。

- "I didn't expect Jim to be so stupid."
「我沒想到 Jim 會那麼笨。」
"Yeah, all that glitters is not gold."
「是啊，中看的東西未必中用。」

22. **all the same**
①無所謂，都一樣　②外表一樣無法辨別　③ (=nevertheless)
雖然如此，但是

① ● "Would you like a cup of coffee or tea?"
「你要咖啡還是茶？」
"Either will be fine, it's all the same to me."
「都可以，反正對我說來都一樣。」

② ● "Which one is real? They look all the same."

「那一個是眞的？他們看上去都是一樣的。」

③ ● "The movie downtown is supposed to be really good."

「據說市中心上映的電影很棒。」

"All the same, I'd rather stay home and study."

「雖然如此，我還是情願留在家裏唸書。」

23. **all the time**

經常的

● "I think of you all the time."

「我經常想到你。」

24. **all the way**

①從……（來），②極端的轉變

① ● "She came to Taipei all the way from New York."

「她遠從紐約來到台北。」

② ● "He went all the way from a member of the Democratic Party to the head of the Republican Party in five years."

「五年之內，他從一名民主黨的黨員，變成共和黨的領袖。」

25. **(To be) all thumbs**

[θʌmz]

笨手笨脚

● "I'm all thumbs. Could you help me tie this knot?"

「你能幫我打這個結嗎？我眞是笨手笨脚的。」

26. **all wet (=completely mistaken)**

[wɛt]

完全搞錯了！完全誤會了！

● "He's all wet. He thinks Ronald Reagan can solve all our problems."

「他完全搞錯了。他以爲 Ronald Reagon 能解決我們一切的問題。」

27. **All-American**

①美國國家代表隊。②典型的美國理想型的人物（高壯漂亮、出風頭等等，通常指男的）

① ● "John Smith is going to Tokyo with the All-American basketball team."

「John Smith 將跟美國國家籃球代表隊去東京（賽球）。」

② ● "He's not only a three-letter man, he's also a straight A student, you know, one of those All-American types."

「他不僅僅代表三個球隊，他的學業成績也是全部甲等，你知道，他就是那種人人都想成爲的美國理想型的人物。」

28. **All-star game**

明星隊（美國職業球隊由各隊所選出最傑出球員組成的明星隊。）

● "This will be Peter's last chance to play in the All-star game."

「這將是 Peter 最後一次打明星隊的機會。」

29. **allow me**

[əˈlaʊ]

請讓我來（如幫女士開門，拿重的東西）

"Allow me."　　　"Thank you."

「讓我來。」　　　「謝謝。」

30. **ambulance chaser**

[ˈæmbjələns] [ˈtʃesə]

專辦交通事故損害賠償的律師（指凡是意外事件發生——墜機、車禍——湧到現場找生意的律師，這些律師爲了賺打官司錢，常常將小事化大，遊說受害者打官司，控告對方。）

● "After the plane crashed, all the ambulance chasers showed up at the emergency room."

「在墜機之後，所有的專辦交通事故賠償的律師都出現在急診處。」

31. **amusing**

[ə'mjuzɪŋ]

有趣，真精彩（也可用來做反話）

● "John got drunk last night, and chased a blonde all over the party."

「John 昨晚喝醉了。在宴會裏滿場追逐一個金髮女郎。」

"That's amusing."

「真有趣。」

32. **An eye for an eye (and) a tooth for a tooth.**

以牙還牙，以眼還眼。

● "You shouldn't try to get revenge."

「你不該試圖報復的。」

"Even the Bible says an eye for an eye and a tooth for a tooth. I'll get even with him."

「即使聖經上也說以眼還眼，以牙還牙。我要跟他扯平才行。」

33. **anchor man**

['æŋkə]

①敬陪末座；倒數第一名。②電視新聞主播

① ● "He is the anchor man of the class of 1985."

「他是 1985 年班的倒數第一名。」

② ● "I don't like the anchor man for Action News."

「我不喜歡（ABC）新聞的主播」

註：Action News 是美國廣播公司（ABC）的新聞節目名稱。

34. **Another day, another dollar.**
    又是一天（不喜歡自己的工作，爲生活而工作的怨言）
    - "Time's up; we can go now. Another day, another dollar."
      「時間到了，我們可以下班了。唉！又是一天！」

35. **any better?**
    好一點沒有？有沒有起色？
    - "Are you any better?"   "Much better."
      「好一點了沒有？」   「好多了。」
    - "Is your new landlord any better?"   "Not really."
      「你的新房東比以前那個好一點吧？」   「不見得。」

36. **any time**
    隨時（不要客氣，請隨時開口。）或隨時奉陪（譬如有人找你打架，你可說 "any time."）
    - "You can use my car any time you want."
      「你可以隨時使用我的車。」
    - "Thanks for helping me do my homework."
      「謝謝你幫助我做功課。」
      "Any time."
      「不要客氣隨時都可以效勞。」

37. **Anything you say. (=Whatever you say.)**
    一切聽你的。
    - "Let's go to dinner first, then go to buy tickets for the movie."
      「讓我們先吃飯再去買電影票。」
      "Anything you say."
      「一切聽你的。」

38. **ape**
    [ep]
    大猩猩（塊頭很大，如一般運動員）

- "Her boyfriend is a big ape."
  「她的男朋友是個大猩猩。」

39. apple polisher　　(=ass kisser, brown noser, shoeshine boy,
    [ˋæpl] [ˋpɑlɪʃɚ]　　shoeblack)
    馬屁精

    - "He got that raise because he's a real apple polisher."
      「他得到升遷是因為他是個馬屁精。」

40. apples and oranges
    [ˋɔrɪndʒɪz]
    兩碼子事（不可混為一談）

    - "You can't add apples and oranges."
      「兩件事不相關連，不能說說這個又說說那個。」（如「天黑要下雨了」及「Mary 要畢業了」。）

41. Do you follow me?
    你有沒有聽清楚（跟得上我的話）？

    - "Do you follow me?"　　"Yes, Sir."
      「你聽清楚我的話沒有？」「聽清楚了。」

42. Are you sick?
    你瘋了嗎？（sick 是心思不正，或瘋了。）

    - "You're going to give up the inheritance? Are you sick or something?"
      「你要放棄繼承的遺產？你瘋啦？還是白痴？」

43. Are you through?
    [θru]
    你講完沒有？用完了沒有？

    - "Are you through? Now, listen to me."
      「你講完沒有？好，現在聽我說。」
    - "Are you through with the saw? Could you pass it over to me?"

「鋸子你用完了吧？可否把它遞給我？」

44. **Are you trying to kill me? (=Trying to get me killed?)**
想害死我嗎？

- "Boy, this soup is really hot. Are you trying to kill me?"
「乖乖，這湯眞燙，你想謀財害命啊？」

- "Watch what you're doing with that knife. Are you trying to kill me?"
「小心那把刀（別亂比劃）。你想殺我嗎？」

45. **around the clock (=24 hours)**
全天候的；日以繼夜的

- "All the 7-Eleven stores are open around the clock."
「 所有的 7-Eleven 商店是 24 小時營業的。 」

46. **around the corner**
[ˈkɔrnɚ]
即將來臨；就在眼前

- "Christmas is around the corner now. Have you bought any gift yet?"
「聖誕節就在眼前，你買了禮物嗎？」
註：歐美國家，在聖誕節親友有交換禮物的習慣。

47. **as easy as pie**
易如反掌；很容易

- "Breaking a brick with one hand is as easy as pie for me. I'm a black-belt in Karate."
「單手擊破一塊磚，對我說來易如反掌。因爲我是空手道黑帶。」

48. **as far as I know**
據我所知（聽來的，或看來的）

- "As far as I know, he hasn't left yet."
「據我所知，他還沒走。」

49. **As you/people say. . .**

正如你／人們所說的（‥後面常接一句名言）

- "As you say, life is tough."

  「正如你所說的，人生是艱苦的。」

- "As people say, time is money."

  「正如一般人所說的，時間就是金錢。」

50. **As you wish. (=It's up to you.)**

隨你的便

- "You guys just go ahead; I want to be alone."

  「你們儘管去吧；我想靜一下。」

  "As you wish."

  「隨你的便。」

51. **ask for**

①要求；請求　②罪有應得；自找的

① ● "The poor little girl asked for help."

　　「那個可憐的小女孩請求援助。」

② ● "You asked for it; it serves you right."

　　「你自找的，罪有應得。」

52. **ass** [æs]

①固執　②討厭鬼（ = asshole ）③屁股

① ● "Don't be such an ass."

　　「別那麼固執！」

② ● "He's such an ass."

　　「他是個討厭鬼。」

③ ● "Move your ass."
　　「（把你的屁股挪開）滾開。」

　● "Haul ass!"
　　「快點去！快點走！」

53. **associate**

① [ə'soʃɪt], ② [ə'soʃɪ,et]

①同事；②來往

① ● "Jerry, I want you to meet my associate, Mr. David Lee."
　　「Jerry，我要你見見我的同事，李大偉先生。」

② ● "I wouldn't associate with that crowd of people too much if I were you."
　　「如果我是你的話，我不會跟那一票人來往。」

54. **at a loss**

[lɔs]

茫然（不知所措）

● "When she found out she was kicked out of school, she was at a loss what to do."
　「當她發現她被學校開除了，她茫然不知所措。」

55. **at odds**

[ɑdz]

合不來；吵架

● "Why are you two always at odds?"
　「你們兩個為什麼老是吵架呢？」

56. **at the end of one's resources**

[rɪ'sorsɪz]

山窮水盡

● "I need a car, but I'm at the end of my resources."
　「我需要一部車，但我已經是山窮水盡（身無分文）。」

57. **At the moment, that's it.**

目前也只有這個法子了（表示別無良策）

● "What are we going to do now?"

「我們現在該怎麼辦？」

"Before the doctor arrives, let's keep her awake. I think at the moment, that's it."

「在醫生來前，我們要一直讓她保持清醒。我想這是目前我們唯一能做的事。」

1. **back-seat-driver**

   [bæk sit draɪvɚ]

   後座司機（坐在司機後，指揮司機開車的人）

   ● "Turn left, slow down, watch the red light, you're speeding. ..."

   「左轉，慢點，小心紅灯，你開得太快了。」

   "Don't be a back-seat-driver, Pete."

   「Pete，別當後座司機！」

2. **back up**

   ①支持；掩護。②和聲。③慢一點

   ① ● "Go, I'll back you up."

   「去，我會掩護你。」

   ② ● "If I get the contract, you can be my back up vocalist."

   「假如我得到那張合同，你可以幫我合聲。」

   "Really?"

   「真的嗎？」

   ③ ● "Back up. You're talking too fast."

   「慢一點，你說得太快了。」

3. **bag**

   [bæg]

   ①老太婆。②下眼泡浮腫。③放棄；不抱希望。

   ① ● "You're going out with an old bag like her?"

   「你要跟像她那樣的老太婆出去？！」

   ② ● "I have bags under my eyes from working too much."

   「因爲工作過度，我的下眼泡都腫了起來。」

   ③ ● "That test was so hard I bagged it."

   「那考試太難，我對它不抱希望。」

4. **bail out**

   [bel]

   救人出困難

   - "Will you bail me out of this trouble?"

     「你願意救我出困境嗎？」

5. **ball**

   ①舞會。②玩得盡興，開心

   ① ● "He asked me to go to the school graduation ball with him."

     「他要我跟他一起去參加學校的畢業舞會。」

   ② ● "We sure had a ball last night."

     「我們昨晚玩得真開心啊！」

6. **balls (=nuts)**   （較粗鄙的俚語）

   睪丸

   - "She kicked me right in the balls."

     「她一脚踢中我的下體。」

7. **bang up**

   ①撞壞了。② bang-up (adj.)做得很好的

   ① ● "He banged up his new car right after he bought it last week."

     「上個星期，他才買了一部新車，就撞壞了。」

   ② ● "That's really a bang-up job! I'm really proud of you, Rick."

     「幹得好！我真以你爲榮，Rick。」

   ● "Look at the crowd! You must do a bang-up business here. I'm really happy for you, Sis."

     「瞧瞧那堆人！你的生意一定做得不錯。我真爲你高興，老妹。」

8. **barge (right) in (to)**

   [bardʒ]

   擅自闖入

- "Next time don't barge into my room. Knock!"

  「下次別再亂闖進我房間，進來之前先敲門。」

- "When I was changing my clothes, all of a sudden he barged in."

  「我正在換衣服的時候，他忽然闖了進來。」

9. **(one's) bark is worse than his bite. (=Great barkers are no**
       [bɑrk]   [baɪt] **biters.** 會叫的狗不咬人。)

   指某人色厲內荏，只會虛張聲勢

   - "Don't be afraid. His bark is worse than his bite."

     「別害怕，他只會虛張聲勢。」

10. **bastard**

    [ˋbæstɚd]

    ①私生子。②差勁的傢伙。

    ① - "You bastard!"

        「小野種！」

    ② - "I told him to come at six and he didn't show up
        till eight. What a bastard!"

        「我叫他六點來，他一直到八點才露面，真是個差勁的
        傢伙。」

11. **bawl/yell (one's) head off (=to cry very hard)**

    [bɔl]

    哭得很大聲

    - "The child bawled his head off when his mother hit him."

      「當他的母親揍他的時候，他哭得驚天動地。」

12. **bawl (someone) out**

    責罵；痛罵

    - "Your father is going to bawl you out, so just be careful."

      「你爸爸將會痛罵你一頓，所以小心點。」

13. **Be a good sport.**

（要有團隊精神，尊重隊友的決定）不要自私，要合作。

- "Be a good sport and come with us to the movies."

「合作點，跟我們一起去看電影。」

14. **Be a man**

拿出大丈夫氣慨來

- "Be a man; just tell her you want to go to that party with her."

「拿出大丈夫氣慨來，告訴她你想邀她一起去參加那個宴會。」

15. **(Please) be brief.**

[brif]

請扼要的說；說得簡短些

- "O.K. now tell me what happened, and please be brief."

「好，現在告訴我到底發生了什麼事，請長話短說。」

16. **be good**

要乖；要守規矩；別亂來

- "I'll see you tomorrow. Be good."

「明天見，乖別亂來哦！」

17. **Be my guest.**

①請便。②我請客。(=It's on me.)

① ● "Can I bum a cigarette?"

「我可以借根煙嗎？」

"Be my guest."

「請便。」

② ● "Be my guest."

「我請客。」

"The coffee is on me."

「咖啡由我請。」

18. **to be on the spot**
    被逼表明態度
    - "He was on the spot. There was nothing he could do. So, he agreed."
      「他被迫表明態度，他沒有其他的法子，只好同意了。」

19. **be reasonable**
    [ˈrɪznəbl]
    講理點
    - "You want me to be home before 10? Be reasonable, Mom."
      「你要我十點前回家？講講理好不好，媽？」
    - "Come on, be reasonable."
      「唉呀，講講理好不好？」

20. **(be) smart (=wise up)**
    放聰明點
    - "Be smart, she is just using you."
      「放聰明點，她只是在利用你罷了。」

21. **Be tactful (=be diplomatic)**
    [ˈtæktfəl]
    圓滑點；技巧點（活一點，別那麼呆板）
    - "When you talk to customers, be tactful."
      「當你跟顧客談話時，要技巧一點。」

22. **beat**
    [bit]
    ①難倒（我）了。②比 … 好。
    ① - "Pete, do you know how far it is from New York to Washington D.C.?" "Beats me."
        「Pete，你知道紐約跟華盛頓之間有多遠嗎？」「這你可難倒我了。」

② ● "This beats paying!"

　　「免費比付錢好！」

　● "Taking the train sure beats taking the bus."

　　「搭火車當然比搭巴士好。」

23. **beat it**

[bit]

滾開

● "I don't need you. So, beat it."

　「我不需要你。滾開！」

24. **to beat (or punch, or kick) the shit out of (someone)**

把（某人）打得半死；揍扁

● "If I find out who did it, I'll beat the shit out of him."

　「如果我找出是誰幹的，我會揍扁他。」

25. **beat (someone) to a pulp.**

　　　　　　　['pʌlp]

打得稀爛；揍扁

● "If he comes again, I'll beat him to a pulp."

　「假如他再來，我會把他揍扁。」

26. **beat up**

[bit]

①又舊又爛。②揍揍。

① ● "This book is pretty beat up."

　　「這本書又舊又爛。」

② ● "He was beaten up badly outside a bar last night."

　　「昨晚他在一家酒吧外面被揍得相當慘。」

27. **beating around the bush**

　　　　　　　[buʃ]

兜圈子

● "Stop beating around the bush. I want to know the truth."
「別兜圈子，我要明白事情的真象。」

28. **beautiful (=great)**
棒透了！

● "Rudy has just finished his work. It's beautiful."
「Rudy 剛剛完成他的大作，做得真好！」

● "Beautiful! The refrigerator is full of cold beer."
「真棒！冰箱裏有一大堆冰啤酒。」

29. **beef**
①抱怨；怨言；發牢騷。②內容；細節。

① ● "Quit your beefing." (=stop complaining)
「別抱怨了。」

● "I had a beef with Linda this morning."
「今早我跟Linda 發了一頓牢騷。」

② ● "You said you had a new plan. What's the beef?"
「你說你有個新計劃。到底是什麼？」

30. **(he's/you've) been very helpful.**
（他／你）幫了很大的忙！

● "Thank you, Charlie. You've been very helpful these days."
「謝謝你，Charlie。這些日子，你真幫了不少忙。」

31. **Been waiting long?**
等了很久吧？（赴約遲到時，含歉意的問話。）

● "Sorry, I'm late, been waiting long?"
「對不起，我來遲了，等了很久了嗎？」
"No, I just arrived myself."
「沒有，我也是剛來。」

32. **behave yourself**

[bɪˈhev]

檢點一些；別亂來；自愛一點

● "Hey, behave yourself or I'll call the police."

「嘿，安份一點，否則我叫警察哦！」

33. **behind you**

①在你後面；請小心。（怕別人反身撞到你時可說）②支持。

② ● "I'll write this book."

「我將要寫這本書。」

"I'm behind you."

「我支持你。」

34. **bench warmer**

[bɛntʃ] [wɔrmɚ]

坐冷板櫈的球員；不出名的小球員（非主力球員）

● "Because of his bad performance, he became a bench warmer for the rest of the basketball season."

「因爲他的表現不好，剩下的籃球季他就被冷凍起來了。」

● "In last week's game, a bench warmer became a superstar."

「上週的比賽中，一個默默無聞的小球員變成了超級明星。」

35. **Better late than never.**

遲做總比不做好

● "I'll study hard from now on. I know I should have done it a long time ago."

「從今以後我會用功唸書，我早就該用功了。」

"Well, better late than never."

「嗯，遲做總比不做好。」

36. **better than nothing**

聊勝於無

- "You are going to have a raise this month, aren't you?"

  「你這個月要加薪了，不是嗎？」

  "Yes, only $50."

  「是啊，只加50元。」

  "Well, that's better than nothing."

  「聊勝於無啊！」

37. **BEWARE OF THE DOG!**

    [bɪ'wɛr]

    小心惡犬！

    "BEWARE OF PICKPOCKETS" ['pɪk,pɑkɪts]

    「小心扒手」

38. **beyond my control**

    超出能力範圍；無法控制；無法辦到。

    - "Would you ask them to be quiet?"

      「你能不能叫他們靜一點？」

      "I'm sorry, they're beyond my control."

      「對不起，我管不到他們。」

39. **big A (=acid, Vitamin A)**

    指LSD等興奮劑

    - "He ate some big A, and couldn't fall asleep for 2 days."

      「他吃了一些興奮劑，結果兩天無法入睡。」

40. **(a) big bore**

    討厭鬼

    - "He is a big bore."

      「他眞是個討厭鬼。」

41. **big deal**

    [dil]

    ①有什麼了不起。②大驚小怪；小題大作。

① ● "I just won a thousand dollars." "Big deal."
　「我剛贏了一千塊。」　　　「有什麼了不起！」

② ● "I don't think you should make such a big deal of what he's done."
　「我想你不應該對他所做的事表現得那麼大驚小怪。」

42. (a) big flop
　　　　[flɑp]
大失敗；大紕漏；很糟。

● "How was the party?"
　「宴會怎麼樣啊？」

"Don't mention it. It was a big flop."
「別提了，糟透了。」（例如請了40個人，只來了8個人。）

43. Big frog in a small pond
山中無老虎，猴子稱霸王。（大青蛙在小池塘中很威風，若換在大池中就不見得神氣了！）

● "He thinks he's a big shot at his company but he's just a big frog in a small pond."
　「他以為在他公司裏，他有多了不起，他只不過是山中無老虎，猴子稱霸王罷了。」

44. big hand
鼓掌

● "Here he is, Mr. John Denver. Let's give him a big hand."
　「Johe Denver 先生（名歌星），讓我們為他鼓掌。」

45. big idea
①什麼意思，怎麼回事？②餿主意。

① ● "What's the big idea?"
　「什麼意思啊？」

② ● "Who's big idea is this?"
「誰出的餿主意？」

46. big mouth
長舌的人；大嘴巴

● "You are a big mouth!"
「你真是個大嘴巴！」

● "If you open your big mouth, I'll beat you up."
「你如果開口講話，我就揍你。」

47. big shot
[ʃɑt]
大亨（有時有輕視的意味）

● "Do you know who that big shot is?"
「你知道那個大亨是誰嗎？」

"Yes, he is a Rockefeller."
「知道，他是洛克斐勒家的一份子。」

48. big-spender
闊佬；出手大方的人

● "He left a 5 dollar tip. What a big-spender."
「他留下五塊小費，真是個闊佬啊。」

註：也有人用 big-tipper 但 big-spender 較常用到。

49. big talk
吹牛

● "Don't give me that kind of big talk."
「別跟我吹那種牛。」

● "Big talk is easy, you know."
「你知道，吹牛是件容易的事。」

50. big-brother
政府，政權（有諷刺政府過份干涉自由之意。）

- "Big brother is watching you!"
  「政府當局在注意你了！（小心點）」
  註：此字來自一本書叫 "1984"。

51. **bike (=bicycle)**

[baɪk]

①脚踏車。②騎脚踏車

① • "Could I borrow your bike for a minute?"
  「我能不能借一下你的脚踏車？」

② • "How long will it take to get there?" "About five minutes if we bike over."
  「到那要多久？」「如果騎脚踏車大約要 5 分鐘。」

52. **bill (=cash)**

[bɪl]

①現鈔；錢。②帳單（＝check）。③把賬單寄來。

① • "I don't have any bills on me. Can you pay it for me now and I'll pay you back tomorrow?"
  「我現在身上沒錢，你可以幫我先付一下嗎？我明天還你。」

  • "Give me a fifty dollar bill."
  「給我一張 50 元的大鈔。」

② • "Waiter, could I have the bill?"
  「先生，賬單。」

③ • "How much?" "Don't worry, I'll bill you later."
  「多少錢？」　「別擔心我以後會把賬單寄給你。」

53. **bingo**

['bɪŋgo]

猜中；碰上了；成功了！

- "O.K. let's try it again."
  「好，讓我們再試一次。」

(The car starts.)　　"Bingo."

（車子發動了！）　　「成功了！」

54.　**Birds of a feather flock together.**

['fɛðə] [flɑk]

物以類聚

● "Those jocks are always hanging out together."

　「那些運動狂總是常常在一起。」

"Well, birds of a feather flock together."

　「嗯，物以類聚嘛。」

55.　**bite the bullet**

[baɪt]　　['bʊlɪt]

忍耐痛苦（因為以前沒有麻醉藥，開刀時叫病人口咬一個子
　　　　　彈以忍受痛苦。）

● "We're going to have to bite the bullet until Friday."

　「在禮拜五以前我們必須忍耐（節省）。」

56.　**blabber mouth (=big mouth)**

['blæbə]

多嘴婆；長舌婦

● "Here comes the blabber mouth."

　「多嘴婆來了。」

57.　**black market**

[mɑrkɪt]

黑市

● "He sold his money at black market prices and made
a 100% profit."

　「他把他的錢以黑市價格賣出，並且賺了一倍。」

58.　**black out**

①停電（=power　failure）。　②（=pass out）昏過去。

① ● "A lot of stores were robbed during the black out."
「在停電中許多商店遭到搶劫。」

② ● "He blacked out for 5 minutes."
「他昏過去大約五分鐘。」

● "He drank too much, and blacked out."
「他喝得太多以至昏倒了。」

59. blast that (name)

[blæst]

該死的（人名）

● "Blast that Ivan, he is such a creep."
「那個該死的 Ivan，他眞是一個討厭鬼。」

60. blend (=match)

[blɛnd]

①相配 (=match=compatible) 。②沒入（人群）。

① ● "I can't understand why Lisa talks to Jimmy. They don't blend at all."
「我不明白 Lisa 爲什麼會跟 Jimmy 聊天，他們倆一點也不相配。」

② ● "I'll talk to you later. I'm going to blend into the crowd."
「以後再聊，我要（沒入人群去了）走了！」

61. blind date

[blaɪnd det]

盲目約會（別人替你代訂的約會，見面前不知對方是誰）

● "I have a blind date this weekend. Wish me luck."
「這個週末我有個盲目約會，祝我好運吧！」

62. on the blink (=go kaput)

[blɪŋk] [kɑ'put]

壞了。

● "My refrigerator is on the blink."

「我的冰箱壞了。」

● "My phone is on the blink."

「我的電話壞了。」

63. **block**

[blɑk]

①擋住（路）。②坊（四方區域）

① ● "You're blocking my light; please move!"

「你擋住我的光了，請讓開。」

② ● "She lives on my block."

「她與我住在同一（街）區。」

64. **blonde (or blond)**

[blɑnd]

金髮（女郎）

● "She is 5 feet 4, 26 years old, and blonde."

「她 5 呎 4 吋，26 歲，金髮。」

● "He likes blondes."

「他喜歡金髮美女。」

註：褐髮女郎是 brunette [bruˈnɛt]。

65. **blood in one's eyes.**

[blʌd]

生氣

● "Who said I was angry?"

「誰說我生氣了？」

"Well, everybody said they could see blood in your eyes."

「每一個人都這麼說，他們可以看到你眼中的血絲。」

66. **blood sucker (=leech)**

[blʌd] [ˈsʌkɚ] [litʃ]

吸血鬼（指放高利貸的人）

● "You blood sucker, leave my father alone."

「你這吸血鬼，別煩我爸爸。」

67. **blow (it)**

[blo]

①搞砸了；弄僵了。②滾開。③討厭；厭惡（語氣強烈）。
④令人意外（好/壞）。⑤胡說八道；滾開。

① ● "Don't blow it."

「別搞砸了！」

● "You just blew it."

「你搞砸了。」

② ● "Go blow."

「滾開。」

③ ● "This test blows."

「這考試眞討人厭。」

④ ● "This test blew me away."

「這考試眞出乎我意外之外的（好/壞）。」

⑤ ● "Blow it out **your** ass/ear."

「滾開！」

68. **blow off steam**

做 … 以洩心頭的怒氣

● "After fighting with his wife, he went out for a walk to blow off steam."

「在跟他太太吵過之後，他出去散步以洩心頭之怒。」

69. **blow the whistle on. . . .**

[blo]　　[hwɪsl]

告發，打小報告，揭發醜聞

● "If you don't give me $5,000, I'll blow the whistle on you."

「你如果不給我五千塊，我就揭發你的事。」

● "I know who blew the whistle on us."
「我知道是誰打我們的小報告。」

70. **(to) blow up**
①炸掉。②突然生氣。

① ● "He blew up a bank in Hawaii."
「他在夏威夷炸了一家銀行。」

② ● "He blew up over nothing."
「他突然無緣無故的發起脾氣來。」

71. **blow your head off**
打爛你的頭（用槍射）

● "If you say one more word, I'll blow your head off."
「你再說一句，我就打爛你的頭。」

72. **blowout**
①吵鬧的宴會。②爆（胎）

① ● "They had a big blowout for Kevin's birthday."
「爲了慶祝Kevin 的生日，他們開了一個狂歡會。」

② ● "I'm sorry I'm late. One of my tires had a blowout."
「對不起來遲了，我的車胎有一個爆了。」

73. **blue**
①憂鬱。②黃色電影(skin flick, X-rated movies, **porno**
films)

① ● "I feel blue today."
「我今天心情欠佳。」

② ● "The movies on 42nd Street are mostly blue movies."
「在 42 街上放映的大部份是黃色電影。」

74. **blue streak**
[strik]
講話像機關槍一樣又快又久（希望對方能早早閉嘴）

● "He talks a blue streak."

「他講話像機關槍一樣。」

75. **bluffer**

['blʌfɚ]

蓋仙；說謊專家。

● "He is really a big bluffer."

「他真是個大蓋仙。」

76. **bluffing**

['blʌfɪŋ]

吹牛；唬人

● "I got 3 Aces."

「我有三個 Ace 。」

"You're just bluffing."

「你在唬人。」

77. **boast**

[bost]

蓋、吹牛、喧染、誇張

● "Chrissie is going out with me tonight."

「Chrissie 今晚要跟我出去。」

"Don't boast."

「少蓋。」

78. **baloney**

[bə'lonɪ]

吹牛；胡說

● "He said he could fly a plane?"　　"What baloney."

「他說他會開飛機？」　　　　　「真是吹牛。」

● "He is full of baloney."

「他滿口胡說。」

註：baloney 又當 bologna 講，bologna 是一種大型的義大利
　　香腸，通常用來夾麵包吃。

79. **bonehead (=cement head)**
    笨蛋；傻瓜

    ● "You are really a bonehead, can't you understand what I mean?"
      「你眞是個笨蛋，你難道不明白我的意思嗎？」

80. **boo-boo**
    [bu bu]
    ①不嚴重的錯誤。②小擦傷。
    ① ● "I made a boo-boo talking to Bill last night."
      「我昨晚對Bill 說了不該說的話。」
    ② ● "I'm going to put a bandage on your boo-boo."
      「我要在你的小傷口貼一塊繃帶。」

81. **boogie**
    ['bugɪ]
    ①跳舞。②快點走。
    ① ● "Let's get down and boogie."
      「讓我們下去盡情跳舞吧！」
    ② ● "It's late; let's boogie."
      「天色不早，我們快走吧！」
    註：跳舞古老的說法是 cut a rug 。

82. **book**
    [buk]
    ①登記、訂（房間）。②逮捕。
    ① ● "Have you booked the room in advance?"
      「你有沒有先訂好房間？」
      ● "I'm sorry, it's all booked."
      「對不起，所有的（房間、機票）都已被訂了。」
    ② ● "Book him, murder 1."
      「逮捕他，一級殺人罪。」
    ＊一級殺人罪名是美國最重的殺人罪。

83. **booty**

[ˈbutɪ]

①屁股（＝ass；butt）。②錢財（＝loot）。

① ● "Shake your booty!"

「扭動你的屁股！」

② ● "I want a fair share of the booty."

「我要公平的分享這筆錢。」

84. **boozer (=lush; drunk; alcoholic)**

[ˈbuzɚ]　[lʌʃ]　[drʌŋk]　[ˌælkəˈhɔlɪk]

酒鬼

● "My old man is a real boozer."

「我老頭是個道地的酒鬼。」

85. **bossy**

[bɔsɪ]

有官架子；官僚氣（擺老闆的架子，愛打官腔。）

● "He is very bossy."

「他很官僚。」

● "Don't be so bossy, give us a break."

「別老打官腔，讓我們清靜一下。」

86. **bother**

①困擾。②麻煩。

① ● "What's bothering you?"

「什麼事困擾著你？」

② ● "Do you want anything to drink?"

「你要喝什麼？」

"Don't bother. I'll be leaving in a minute."

「不用麻煩，我馬上就走了。」

87. **(the) bottle (=booze)**

酒類

- "He's hit the bottle for comfort in his misery."
  「他憂傷時就借酒澆愁。」

88. **bottom line.**

    底價（本錢）

    - "$5,000 is the bottom line. After that, it's all profit."
      「五千塊是本錢，剩下的全是淨利。」

89. **from the bottom of my heart**

    [ˋbɑtəm]

    心靈深處，打自心底

    - "I like her from the bottom of my heart."
      「我打自心底喜歡她。」

90. **Bottoms up!**

    乾杯

91. **(to) bounce a check**

    開空頭支票（絕大部份不是有意的，只因爲忘了自己還存有多少錢。）

    - "I bounced a check at the supermarket."
      「我在超級市場開了一張空頭支票。」
    - "My check bounced because I forgot to put money in my checking account."
      「我的支票退票了，因爲我忘了在我的（甲存）戶頭裡存錢。」

92. **bound for (=leave for)**

    [baund]

    開往 … 的

    - "Bus No. 101 is bound for Dallas."
      「101 巴士開往 Dallas 。」

93. **Boy**
   乖乖；老天
   - "Boy, it's really something."
     「乖乖，這東西真是不同凡響啊！」

94. **brace yourself**
   [bres]
   振作點；打起精神來（面臨挑戰）。
   - "Brace yourself; I don't think you'll make it."
     「打起精神來，（否則）我想你不會成的。」

95. **brag**
   ['bræg]
   吹噓（老掉牙的英勇事蹟）
   - "Are you bragging again about your high school basketball team? Come on, that was years ago."
     「你又在吹噓你高中的籃球隊？算了吧！那已經是好幾年前的事了。」

96. **brainwash**
   洗腦
   - "He was brainwashed by the enemy."
     「他被敵人洗腦了。」

97. **brains** [brenz]
   有才能；有腦筋
   - "He's got brains, so why doesn't he have money?"
     「他腦筋很好，為什麼發不了財呢？」

98. **brainstorm** ['bren,stɔrm]
   集思廣益
   - "We'll have to have a brainstorm on how to raise the money for next month's rent."
     「我們一定要想出一個法子來，看看如何籌下個月的房租。」

"They've been brainstorming for a week and still haven't come up with a solution."

「他們已想了一個禮拜但是還是沒想出一個解決的辦法來。」

99. brand new

[brænd]

全新的

● "John just bought a brand new car."

「John 剛買了一輛全新的車子。」

100. brazen hussy

['brezn 'hʌsɪ]

賤貨（罵女人的話）

● "Don't fool around with that brazen hussy."

「別跟那個賤貨鬼混。」

101. bread

[brɛd]

錢

● "I need bread."

「我需要錢。」

● "I got to have some bread."

「我一定要設法拿到一點錢。」

102. break

[brek]

①找開零錢。②機會。③休息一下。④喘口氣。

① ● "Can you break a hundred?"

「一百塊錢你找不找得開？」

② ● "Never give a sucker an even break."

「不必給一個傻瓜任何公平的機會。」

（如：一部有毛病的新車，本欲賣 $1000，一個笨蛋進來看上了，試車後，讚不絕口，問你賣多少錢，你說 $1500。）

③ ● "Let's take a break."
「讓我們休息一下。」

④ ● "Give me a break, will you?"
「讓我喘口氣，好嗎？」

103. break the ice
①化解誤會。②打破僵局。

① ● "Why don't you break the ice with Linda? She didn't mean to hurt you."
「你為什麼不跟 Linda 化解你們之間的誤會呢？她不是存心要傷害你的。」

② ● "Let's break the ice at this party and introduce ourselves to those girls over there."
「讓我們打破舞會的僵局，過去跟那些女孩來個自我介紹。」

104. break up
分開；分手

● "They broke up a couple of years ago."
「他們早幾年就分手了。」

105. breathe easy
[brið] ['izɪ]
解脫；輕鬆

● "She could breathe easy after her last final."
「她最後一堂考完就可以輕鬆了。」

106. breathing room / space
給我一點空間

● "Move over. Give me some breathing room/space."
(Give me some room to breathe)
「挪開一點，給我一點空間。」

107. **bring down the house**

博得滿堂采

● "Her show was very successful; she brought down the house."

「她的演出十分成功，她贏得滿堂采。」

108. **broad (=dame, chick)**

[brod] [dem] [tʃɪk]

馬子（對女人輕視的說法）

● "Who was that broad Jeff was with last night?"

「昨晚跟Jeff 在一起的那個馬子是誰？」

109. **to broaden one's horizons**

[ˈbrɔdn] [həˈraɪznz]

增廣見聞

● "You should read books to broaden your horizons."

「你該看點書，增廣一下你的見聞。」

110. **broke**

[brok]

破產；一文不名

● "I can't go to the movies with you tonight, because I'm broke."

「我不能跟你們去看電影，因爲我身無分文。」

111. **brownie points**

[ˈbraʊnɪ]

印象分數

● "He racked up a lot of brownie points by volunteering to help the teacher after school."

「由於志願課後留下來幫老師的忙，他積了不少印象分數。」

112. brush off

[brʌʃ]

敷衍

- "Don't brush me off, give me an answer, yes or no?"

「別敷衍我，給我一個回答，好還是不好？」

- "I asked him for money for gas, but he brushed me off, that SOB (=son of a bitch)."

「我向他要錢買汽油，但他一味敷衍我，那個混蛋！」

註：He brushed me off. = He gave me the brush off.

113. brute

(brut]

兇暴的傢伙（身高體壯）

- "What a brute."

「真是一個兇暴的傢伙。」

- "He's a brute to his wife."

「他對他的太太很兇暴。」

114. buck

[bʌk]

①（汽車）顛簸地行駛。②為（升官，利益）而努力。②一塊錢。

① • "The car bucked down the hill."

「車子一路顛下山去。」

② • "She's bucking for a raise."

「她為升等而努力。」

③ • "Do you have five bucks?"

「你有五塊錢嗎？」

115. buckle down

['bʌkl]

用心點；用功

● "You'd better buckle down, or you will flunk."
「你最好用功點，否則你會被當了。」

116. buck tooth

[bʌk] [tuθ]

暴牙

● "He has buck teeth."
「他有暴牙。」

註：假牙是false teeth 。

117. buddy

['bʌdɪ]

朋友

● "Hi, buddy."
「嗨，老友。」

118. bug [bʌg]

①困擾。②偷聽（＝tap）；竊聽。③找碴兒。④纏（人）；死盯不放

① ● "What's bugging you?"
「什麼事讓你煩心啊？」

② ● "We have been bugged. Did you know that? "
「我們被竊聽了。你知道了嗎？」

③ ● "He bugs me all the time."
「他一直找我的碴兒。」

④ ● "Stop bugging me."
「少纏我。」

● "If he says no, you know what I'll do?"
「假如他不答應的話，你知道我會怎辦？」
"No, what?"
「不知道，你怎麼辦？」
"Bug him."
「死纏一陣。」

119. **bull　(=baloney=bullshit=shit)**

　　胡扯；瞎蓋

　　● "I just ran a mile in four minutes."

　　　「我剛剛在四分鐘之內跑完了一哩。」

　　　"Bull."

　　　「瞎蓋。」

　　● "That's a lot of bull."

　　　「胡說八道。」

　　● "Don't give me that bull."

　　　「別跟我胡扯。」

120. **bull's eye　(=hit the bull's eye)**

　　對了；完全正確（正中目標）

　　● "What's the capital of Italy?"

　　　「義大利的首都在哪？」

　　　"Rome?"

　　　「羅馬？」

　　　"Bull's eye!"

　　　「完全正確！」

121. **bullshit**

　　[ˈbʊlˌʃɪt]

　　①廢話；瞎扯；無聊的事。②胡說八道；說謊；放屁。③聊
　　天。④混過去

　　① ● "He gave me all this bullshit about how sorry he was
　　　　until I told him to shut up."

　　　　「他跟我廢話了半天，說他有多抱歉，直到我叫他閉嘴
　　　　為止。」

　　　● "Stop bullshiting me."

　　　　「少跟我廢話。」

② ● "You are really nice."　　　 "Bullshit."

「你眞好。」　　　　　　　　 「放屁。」

③ ● "We used to sit and bullshit about life."

「我們以前常常坐下來閑聊人生。」

④ ● "He bullshited his way through college."

「他混過了大學四年。」

122. bully

['buli]

①難以相處的人。②逼迫；強迫；欺凌。

① ● "She's really a bully."

「她眞是一個難以相處的人。」

② ● "Don't let her bully you. I told her off one time, and she hasn't bothered me since."

「別讓她欺侮你。自從我叫她滾開過一次後，她再也不敢來惹我了。」

123. bum (=hobo, tramp, vagrant)

[bʌm] ['hobo] ['træmp] ['vegrənt]

①流浪漢；無賴；討厭鬼。②屁股。③借。

① ● "His uncle is a bum."

「他的叔叔是個流浪漢。」

● "You're a bum."

「你是個討厭鬼。」

② ● "He was kicked right in the bum."

「他被人在屁股上踢了一脚。」

③ ● "Can I bum 5 bucks from you?"

「我能向你借五塊錢嗎？」

124. bum out

失望；不高興；沮喪

● "I was really bummed out when I heard they cancelled

the concert."

「當我聽到音樂會被迫取消時，我感到非常地失望。」

125. bummer (n.)

[ˋbʌmɚ]

①可惜；倒霉。②討厭的人；無聊的傢伙。

① ● "He lost his eye sight? What a bummer!"

「他看不見了？眞可惜！」

② ● "He's a real bummer."

「他是一個討厭的無聊傢伙。」

126. burning your money

[ˋbɝnɪŋ]

浪費

● "Why did you order so many dishes? We can't eat that much; you're burning your money."

「你爲什麼點這麼多菜？我們又吃不完，你是錢多燒的啊！」

127. bush [buʃ]

鬍鬚

● "Do you know that tall guy with the bush on his face?"

「你認識那個個子高高的，臉上有鬍鬚的傢伙嗎？」

128. bust

[bʌst]

①（個人）破產。②因販毒而被捕；逮捕。

① ● "I'm busted."

「我破產了。」

② ● "There was a drug bust."

「有一個搜捕販毒的行動。」

註：公司破產用 bankrupt 。

129. busybody

['bɪzɪ/badɪ]

雞婆；愛管閒事的人

● "Do you know that you are a busybody?"

「你知道嗎？你是個雞婆。」

130. but how?

但如何去做呢？

● "I would like to have a new car free, but how?"

「我當然願意得到一部免費的新車，但怎麼做呢？」

● "I'd like to meet her, but how?"

「我當然願意見她，但怎麼才能見到她呢？」

131. butt (=ass=bottom)

[bʌt]　　　[batəm]

屁股

● "Hey, move your butt."

「嘿，把你的屁股挪開！（閃開！）」

● "You're a pain in the butt."

「你是個讓人頭疼的討厭鬼。」

註：cigarette　butt　是煙屁股。

132. butt in

[bʌt]

打岔；插嘴

● "It doesn't matter who he's talking to. I've got to butt in to tell him about that long distance phone call."

「我不管他在跟誰講話，我必須去打個岔告訴他長途電話的事。」

133. butt out

[bʌt]

滾開；走開

● "We don't need you here, why don't you just butt out?"

「這裏不需要你，你爲什麼不滾開？」

134. butter (someone) up

['bʌtɚ]

拍馬屁

● "If you need to use the car this Sunday, I think you should butter Mom up a little bit."

「假如你這個星期天需要用車的話，你要稍稍拍媽媽的馬屁。」

135. buy

相信（接受的意思）

● "I didn't buy his explanation for a minute."

「我壓根不相信他的解釋。」

● "I don't buy what he is saying."

「我才不相信他說的。」

136. buy (someone) a (drink; meal; dinner)

請客（喝酒、吃飯、吃晚飯）

● "Do you have a minute? Let me buy you a drink."

「你有空嗎？讓我請你喝一杯。」

● "When you get the money, I'll let you buy me a dinner."

「當你拿到錢後，我會讓你請我吃晚飯。」

137. buy low, sell high

[lo] [sɛl]

賤買貴賣（從中取利）

● "How can he make that much money within a year?"

「他怎麼可能在一年內賺那麼多錢呢？」

● "Buy low, sell high, you know."

「你知道的嘛，賤買貴賣！」

138. don't buy (someone's) story

不相信（某人）的鬼話

● "I don't buy your story, I've heard it a hundred times before."

「我才不相信你的鬼話，我已聽過上百遍了。」

139. by a hair (=just squeak by)

些微之差（勉強通過；險勝；勉強及格之意）

● "We won the game by a hair."

「我們險勝了對方。（如 51：50）」

140. by hook or by crook

[huk]　　　[kruk]

決心要成功（可能會不擇手段）

● "He intends to win Helen's heart and he'll do it by hook or by crook."

「他決心要贏得Helen 的芳心，而且他一定會做到。」

141. by the same token (=in the same manner; likewise.)

[ˈtokən]

同樣的；同理的

● "Many Americans don't like spicy food because they're not used to it.　By the same token, many Chinese don't like cheese."

「很多美國人不喜歡辣的菜，因爲他們不習慣。同樣的道理，很多中國人不喜歡乳酪。」

1. **cab (=taxi)**

   [kæb]

   計程車

   - "Let's hail a cab."

     「我們叫輛計程車吧！」

2. **cabby (=taxi driver)**

   [kæbɪ]

   計程車司機

   - "I worked as a cabby for the summer."

     「在夏天我當計程車司機。」

   - "Being a cabby can be lucrative, but it's hard to get a license."

     「當計程車司機很容易賺錢，但很難拿到駕照。」

3. **a piece of cake**

   真容易；簡單（如你在中綫投入一球，故作輕鬆狀說 "cake!"）

   - "Can you help me with this math problem, Tim?"

     「Tim, 你能幫我解這個數學難題嗎？」

     "Sure, it's a piece of cake."

     「當然，簡單得很！」

4. **call girl**

   應召女郎

   - "She worked as a call girl to support her habit."

     「她以當應召女郎來負擔她的毒癮（所需的金錢）。」

   註 habit 在此指吸毒上癮。

5. **call it square/even**

   扯平（互不相欠）

   - "I prefer to give you the cash and call it square."

     「我情願給你錢，然後雙方扯平。」

6. call me [a bad] name (= call me names)
          [an awful]

用下流話罵我

- "Why did you hit him?"

  「你為什麼打他？」

  "He called me [a bad / an awful] name."

  「他用下流話罵我。」

7. call the roll
          [rol]

點名

- "He already called the roll."

  「他已點過名了。」

8. (Can/Will) you give me a light?

借個火好嗎？（點香煙）

- "Can you give me a light?"

  「借個火好嗎？」

  "Sure."

  「好。」

9. Can you settle for less? (=Can you come down a little?)

少一點行不行？（價錢）

- "$25? It's too expensive; can you settle for less?"

  「25塊？太貴了，少一點行不行？」

  "I'm sorry, Ma'am. We have set prices"

  「對不起，女士，我們這兒是不二價的。」

10. Can we talk?

我們能不能談一談？

- "Robert, are you free now? Can we talk?"

  「Robert，你現在有空嗎？我們能不能談一談？」

11. **Can't you read?**

    你難道不識字嗎？（不依指示牌，而遭斥責）

    ● "Knock before you enter. Can't you read?"
    「進來前先敲門，你看不懂嗎？」

    ● "Do not disturb. Can't you read?"
    「請勿打擾。你不識字嗎？」

    ● "No parking. Can't you read?"
    「不准停車，你不識字啊？」

12. **cancer stick (=coffin nail)**
    ['kænsɚ] [stɪk]
    香烟

    ● "What do you smoke those cancer sticks for? Every one you smoke is just another nail in your coffin."
    「你幹嘛抽那些香煙呢？你每吸一根香煙，就等於在你的棺材上加上一根釘子。」

13. **candid camera**
    ['kændɪd/'kæmərə]
    可洞識一切的攝影機（指可疑的事，或醜態）

    ● "Smile, you're on candid camera!"
    「笑一個，你的一切行動已被看到了！（這是節目中的一個名句）」

    註：在美國有一個電視節目叫 "Candid Camera" 街上的人生百態盡入眼底。

14. **The cap fits.**
    [kæp]
    還可以

● "How's the married life?"

「新婚生活如何？」

"The cap fits."

「還可以。」

15. **car-pool**

[kɑr/pul]

自從 1975 年能源危機以來，美國總統卡特即呼籲全國人民共同響應一項「共同乘自用轎車上下班」案。

● "I find that I have been saving about $10 a week since I joined a car pool."

「自從加入共同乘車（政策）以來，我發現每個禮拜我可以省十塊錢。」

16. **care for a drink**

願意來杯（酒）嗎？

● "Do you care for a drink before dinner?"

「晚飯前，你願意來一杯嗎？」

17. **career woman**

[kə'rɪr]

職業婦女（地位較高，有升遷機會，待遇較好）（普通一般工作的婦女叫 working woman ）。

● "My mother is both a career woman and a housewife."

「我媽媽是個職業婦女，同時也是個家庭主婦。」

18. **carry on**

['kærɪ]

①滔滔不絕地說。②與人有染。

① ● "She carried on with her story for about half an hour."

「她滔滔不絕地說了大約有半個鐘頭。」

② ● "Mike is carrying on with Bill's ex-girlfriend Nancy."

「Mike 跟 Bill 的前任女友 Nancy 有染。」

19. **the case is closed**

[kes]

事情已過去；到此爲止；不必再提（如打官司時，案子已定讞）

● "The case is closed. We don't need to talk about it anymore."

「事情已過去，我們不必再談它。」

20. **cash in**

[kæʃ]

①佔便宜（分配不公平；做事不公平）。②贏大錢；把籌碼換成現鈔。③把值錢的東西換成錢。

① ● "He tried to cash in on me."

「他想佔我的便宜。」

② ● "He really cashed in at the race track last week."

「上個星期的賽（馬、狗）中，他眞贏了大錢。」

③ ● "My uncle wants to cash in his insurance policy and move to Hawaii."

「我叔叔想要把他的（零存整付式的）保險換成錢，然後搬到夏威夷去住。」

21. **(to) cast (or throw) pearls before swine**

[swaɪn]

對牛彈琴（有糟蹋東西的意思）

● "He doesn't appreciate good art. Giving him that painting for his birthday would be like casting pearls before swine."

「他不懂得如何欣賞藝術。給他那幅畫作爲生日禮物，簡直是糟蹋了。」

●She read us Byron's poems, but it was casting pearls to swine.

「她對着我們朗誦拜倫的詩，那真是對牛彈琴。」

22. **casual**

['kæʒuəl]

①隨便的；非正式的。②隨和的(=easy)

① ● "It's only a casual party; you don't have to dress up."

「這只是一個隨隨便便的小宴會，你不必穿得太正式。」

② ● "He's a very casual sort of a person."

「他是一個很隨和的人。」

23. **cat**

可鄙的女人（個性、行爲不好、差勁、自私的小人）

● "Susan and Debbie are a couple of cats. I don't know anyone who wants to room with them."

「Susan 和 Debbie 是差勁的女人，我不知道誰會願意跟她們住在一起。」

24. **Cat got your tongue?**

你的舌頭給貓咬了嗎？（怎麼不說話呢？）

● "What are you planning to do about Linda?"

「你打算怎麼解決 Linda 的事？」

" ······ "

"What's the matter, cat got your tongue?"

「怎麼回事，舌頭給貓咬啦？」

25. **cat house (=bordello; whore house; house of ill-repute)**

[bɔr'dɛlo] [hor]　　　　　　　[ɪl -rɪ'pjut]

綠灯戶；妓女戶

● "I went in there thinking it was a hotel. It turned out to be a cat house."

「我走進去以爲那是一家旅社。結果却是一間妓女戶。」

26. **catch one's eye (=attract)**

    [kætʃ]

    吸引人的注意

    - "She caught everyone's eye at the dance."

      「在舞會中她吸引了大家的注意力。」

27. **catch some Z's**

    小睡片刻；打個盹

    - "Excuse me, I want to catch some Z's."

      「對不起，我要去打個盹。」

28. **certainly not**

    ['sɚtənlɪ]

    當然不！

    - "Janet, will you sleep with me tonight?"

      「Janet，妳今晚願意跟我睡嗎？」

      "Certainly not."

      「當然不！」

29. **(have) no chance (=not a chance)**

    沒辦法；沒機會；休想；沒希望；不可能

    - "The Yankees have no chance of winning the World Series if Reggie Jackson is sick."

      「假如Reggie Jackson病了，洋基隊就休想贏得世界棒球賽冠軍了。」

30. **(the) chances are**

    ①失敗與成功之比是 … 。②成功的機會

    ① ● "The chances are fifty-fifty that he will pass the test."

      「他考試及格的機會是一半一半。」

    ② ● "The chances are good that he will pass the test."

      「他及格的機會很大。」

31. **change**

①零錢。②換換（環境，口味…）

① ● "Could I have some change?"

「我能不能換點零錢？」

● "Do you have any change?"

「你有零錢嗎？」

● "Keep the change!"

「不用找（零錢）了！」

② ● "I need a change."

「我需要換一換環境。」

● "Let's have pizza this evening for a change."

「今晚我們換換口味改吃義大利脆餅吧。」

● "They painted the house yellow for a change this year."

「他們今年把房子漆成黃色。」

32. **change the channel**

[ˈtʃænl]

①轉變話題。②換一個電視台

① ● "When we talk about marriage, he always changes the channel."

「每當我們談到結婚，他總是轉變話題。」

② ● "Roy, change the channel, I don't want to watch this soap opera."

「Roy 換一個電視台，我不想看這個茱電視劇。」

33. **charge**

[tʃɑrdʒ]

①記賬（在美國通常指以信用卡記賬，不付現）。②費用。

① ● "Charge it, please."

「請記賬。」

② ● "It's free of charge."

「那是免費的。」

34. **chasing girls**

[tʃesɪŋ]

追女孩子

- "He is really a heck of a playboy. He loves chasing girls."

「他眞是個花花公子，喜歡追女孩子。」

35. **cheap**

[tʃip]

①低賤；下賤。②小氣。③破；劣質。

①②"She is cheap."

「她眞下賤（小氣）。」

③ ● "This is really a cheap watch. It broke the first week I bought it."

「這手錶眞破，才買一星期就壞了。」

36. **(cheap) joint**

小吃店（沒有豪華裝潢的餐館）

- "This place is a real cheap joint; that's why I like to eat here."

「這眞是個價廉物美的小吃店，這就是我喜歡來這兒吃飯的原因。」

37. **cheap skate**

[sket]

小氣鬼；吝嗇鬼（例如不給小費的人）；壞蛋

- "What a cheap skate! He only left me a 10¢ tip."

「眞是個吝嗇鬼（壞蛋），他只留給我一毛錢的小費。」

38. **No cheating**

[tʃitɪŋ]

不要作弊

- "The monitor wrote 'No cheating' on the blackboard."

「監考員在黑板上寫着＂請勿作弊＂。」

39. **cheerleader**

['tʃɪrlidəʳ]

啦啦隊員

● "The Dallas Cowboys have the most beautiful cheer-leaders in the United States."

「Dallas Cowboys 隊擁有全美最漂亮的啦啦隊員。」

註：Dallas Cowboys 屬德州是美國有名的職業足球隊，擁有美女如雲的迷人啦啦隊。

40. **cheer up**

①打起精神；振作；別灰心。②加油打氣。

① ● "Cheer up! Don't be so sad."

「振作起來，別太難過。」

② ● "We gave Mary a birthday party to cheer her up."

「我們爲Mary 開了個生日宴會以替她加油打氣。」

41. **cherry**

處女膜（開玩笑時用）

● "Does she still have her cherry?"

「她還是處女嗎？」

42. **chic**

[ʃik]

①秀氣；清秀。②時髦。

① ● "She's chic."

「她眞秀氣。」

② ● "That's a chic dress you're wearing, Mary."

「Mary 這件衣服眞時髦啊！」

"Thanks."　「謝謝！」

註：chick [tʃɪk] 當少女講，此語稍有輕浮之意，如

"Look, Jack.　What a cute chick."

「Jack 瞧，多可愛的一個小妞啊！」

43. **chicken**

['tʃɪkən]

胆小；懦弱

- "You're so (such a) chicken, if you don't agree with him, why don't you tell it to his face?"

  「你眞是個胆小鬼，如果你不同意，你爲什麼不當面告訴他呢？」

- "I'm afraid he'll chicken out."

  「我擔心他會害怕退出。」

44. **chiseler (n.); chisel (v.)**

['tʃɪzlɚ]　　　['tʃɪzl]

n. 騙子　v. 詐欺；騙取

- "He chiseled me out of $10."

  「他騙了我 10 元。」

- "He's a real chiseler.　Be careful!"

  「他是個不折不扣的騙子，小心點！」

45. **chop-chop (=hurry up)**

[tʃɑp]

快點（據說來自中文）

- "We're late, chop-chop."

  「我們已經晚了，快點！」

46. **chuck it (=shelve it, dump it)**

[tʃʌk]

扔掉

- "Why don't you chuck it?　It's no good anyway."

  「你爲什麼不扔掉它呢？反正它也壞了！」

47. **chuckle**

['tʃʌkl]

咯咯而笑（聲短）

● "What are you chuckling about?"

「你笑什麼？」

48. **ciao (=good-bye)**

再見（義大利文）

● "I better go now. See you tomorrow. Ciao."

「我該走了。明天見，再見！」

● "Ciao."

「再見！」

49. **no class**

格調低；不高尙

● "I don't like John, he has no class."

「我不喜歡 John ，他格調太低了。」

50. **clean**

①無罪。②身上沒有你要找的東西（武器、毒品、信、錢等）。
③乾淨。

① ● "He's clean."

　　① 「他無罪。」　② 「他身上沒有你要找的東西。」

③ ● "Give me a clean sheet."

　　「給我一件乾淨的衣服。」

51. **clean as a whistle**

非常地乾淨

● "Did you find anything?"

「找到什麼沒有？」

"No.　He's clean as a whistle."

「沒有，他身上啥也沒有。」

52. **clean (someone's) clock (=to beat them up)**

揍；打

● "If he doesn't pay me that money, I'm going to clean

his clock for him."

「假如他再不還錢，我就要揍他了。」

53. cleaned out

輸得乾乾淨淨

● "He was cleaned out in last night's poker game."

「昨晚他賭撲克，輸得光光的。」

54. (to) clear the air (=to be frank)

打開天窗說亮話，有話直說

● "O.K. let's clear the air; why are you mad at me?"

「好吧！讓我們有話直說，你為什麼生我的氣呢？」

55. clear sailing

一帆風順（開頭難，往後就順了）

● "How did you get to know Suzanne Summers?"

「你怎麼認識 Suzanne Summers 的？」

"Well, a friend introduced us, and it was clear sailing after that."

「一個朋友介紹的，在那之後一切就一帆風順了。」

● "This course is difficult until the midterm, but after that, it's clear sailing all the way."

「這門功課在期中考前一直是很難唸，但在期中考之後就一帆風順了。」

56. Clear so far?

聽懂了嗎（到目前為止）

● "Clear so far? If you have any questions don't be afraid to ask."

「聽懂了嗎？如果你有任何問題，別怕發問。」

57. clear up

①弄清楚。②放晴

① ● "I have a problem I was hoping you could clear it up

for me."

「我有個問題，我原是希望你能幫我解決的。」

② ● "It looks like the weather will clear up soon."

「看來天要放晴了。」

58. (a) clearance sale

出清存貨大拍賣

● "How much was your new color T.V. set?"

「你那架新的彩色電視機多少錢？」

"It was $295. I got it at a clearance sale; real cheap, huh?"

「295 塊，我是在一次出清存貨大拍賣中撿到的，真便宜，嗯？！」

59. clip-joint

[klɪp/dʒɔɪnt]

黑店

● "$10 for a cup of tea? This is a clip-joint. I'm never coming here again."

「10 塊錢 (美金也！) 一杯咖啡？這是黑店嘛！我再也不會來了！」

60. clobber

['klɑbə]

①痛揍。②慘敗。

① ● "Do as you're told, or I'll clobber all of you."

「照我的話去做，否則我會痛揍你一頓。」

② ● "The home team was clobbered in yesterday's game."

「地主隊昨天被打得很慘。」

61. a close call

好險啊！

● "I almost got hit by a car this morning. It was really a close call."

「今早我差點被車撞倒，真是好險啊！」

62. **close-up**

①特寫鏡頭。②特別介紹（文章；訪問）

① ● "Step forward; let me get a close-up of you."

「走前一點，讓我給你照個特寫。」

② ● "I got a close-up interview with John Travolta."

「我得到了一個 John Travolta 的特別專訪。」

63. **Clothes make the man.**

[kloz]

人要衣裝，佛要金裝

● "Mom, could you lend me some money? I want to buy
some suits for my new job; you know, clothes make
the man."

「媽，你能不能借我一點錢？爲了新工作我要買點新衣服，
你知道人要衣裝，佛要金裝。」

64. **(to be on) cloud nine**

飄飄然

● "After a few drinks, I was on cloud nine."

「幾杯下肚，我飄飄欲仙。」

● "After he proposed, she was on cloud ninc."

「當他向她求婚之後，她覺得飄飄欲仙。」

65. **clowning around (=fooling around)**

['klaunɪŋ]

嬉戲；不務正業；遊蕩

● "Stop clowning around, Joe."

「Joe 別再遊手好閒了。」

66. **clumsy**

['klʌmzɪ]

①笨手笨脚。②孟浪；冒失；唐突。

① ● "I'm sorry I broke your window. I've always been

clumsy.''
「對不起，我把你的窗戶打破了。我永遠是這麼笨手笨
　　腳的。」

● "Why do I feel so clumsy today?"
　「我今天爲什麼這麼笨手笨腳的？」

② ● "Sorry for being so clumsy."
　「對不起，我太冒失了！（拍錯人肩膀，認錯人）」

67. come around

①（昏倒後）醒來 (=come to) ②同意（別人的想法/做法）

① ● "I hope he will come around soon."
　「我希望他會很快醒過來！」

② ● "You think about it. I'm sure you'll come around to
　my way of thinking."
　「你再想想，我相信你將會同意我的想法。」

68. come in handy (=useful)

　　　　[hændɪ]

派上用場

● "Why are you buying those useless books?"
　「你爲什麼買那些沒有用的書呢？」

"Maybe someday they'll come in handy."
　「也許有一天會派上用場的。」

69. come on

①快　點(=hurry up!)。②算了吧！（別再來這一套）。
③餌（引人上鉤）。④勾引。

① ● "Come on, let's go now."
　　「快點，我們走吧！」

● "Come on, give me $10."
　「快給我10塊錢。」

② ● "Come on, I know you can afford more than that."
　「算了吧！我知道你能出更高的價錢！」

③ ● "What kind of come on did Terry use on you. Cindy?"

「Terry 在你身上用了什麼樣的釣餌？用了 Cindy 嗎？」

④ ● "I think he's coming on to me."

「我想他在勾引我。」

70. come to think of it

①突然想起來了！（原本想不起來的一件事）。②說到這，使我聯想起

① ● "Now, come to think of it, it was July 15th, not July 17th."

「現在，我突然想起來了。是七月十五日，不是七月十七日。」

② ● "I saw Robert yesterday. He borrowed some money from me. Come to think of it, he already owed me twenty bucks."

「我昨天遇到 Robert。他跟我借了一點錢。對了，說起這事，我想起來他還欠我二十塊錢。」

71. no comment

['kamεnt]

無可奉告；不予置評

● When the Sanator was asked about the scandal, he said, "No comment."

當參議員被問及對醜聞的看法時，他說：「不予置評」。

72. compose yourself

[kam'poz]

平靜下來（別生氣；別緊張）

● "We're in public. Compose yourself."

「我們是在公共場所。別生氣。」

● "It's only 2 minutes to curtain time; compose yourself."

「還有兩分鐘開幕了，別緊張！」

- "With great difficulty, she composed herself and answered the policeman's questions."

  「她好不容易才平靜下來，回答了警察的問話。」

73. **confound it! (=Damn!)**

    [kɑn'faund]

    該死的；他媽的！（粗話 confound 一字已過時，現在一般人較愛用 damn 這個字。）

    - "Confound it! This phone is out of order again!"

      「他媽的！這電話又壞了。」

    - "Close that confounded window."

      「把那該死的窗戶關了！」

74. **cool**

    ①冷酷。②很棒。③自己的人（不是外人）。④很有自己的風格（或浪漫，或冷漠，或時髦）。

    ①② - "She is cool."

      「她很冷酷／很棒。」

    ③"Don't worry about him. He won't tell. He's cool"

      「別擔心他，他不會洩密的。他是我們自己人。」

    ④ - "Jack Nicholson is cool."

      「Jack Nicholson 很性格。」

75. **cool as a cucumber**

    ['kjukəmbə]

    極其冷靜；不驚慌失措

    - "After they heard the company was going to lay off 50 employees, everybody was in a panic, but John was cool as a cucumber."

      「在他們聽到公司將解僱50名人員之後，大家都十分驚慌，但是John却極其冷靜。」

76. **cool down**
   [kul]
   ①冷靜一點；別太激動。②變冷；冷却下來。
   ① ● "Cool down; don't get too excited."
   「冷靜一點，別太激動。」
   ② ● "Stop the car and let the engine cool down."
   「停車，讓引擎冷却一下。」

77. **coop**
   [kup]
   監獄
   ● "The prisoner flew the coop last night."
   「犯人昨晚逃獄了。」

78. **copper (=cop)**
   警察（比較不正式，不甚尊敬的稱呼法，現在 cop 較常用，
   copper 已過時。）
   ● "Hi, copper. What's happening here?"
   「嘿，警察，這裏發生了什麼事？」

79. **cop**
   [kɑp]
   ①警察；條子。②偷東西；順手牽羊。
   ① ● "He is a cop."
   「他是個條子。」
   ② ● "I copped these sodas off the back of a truck."
   「我從一輛卡車後面偷來這些汽水。」

80. **copy**
   ['kɑpɪ]
   ①影印＝（xerox）。②照抄。③原稿（尚未付印）
   ① ● "Please make an extra copy for me."
   「請幫我多印一份。」

② ● "Copy it!"

　「抄下來！」

③ ● "Where is the copy for that newspaper article that I was writing?"

　「我爲那報社寫的文章的原稿在那裏？」

81. **cough up (the money)**
　[kɔf]

把（錢）吐出來（威脅話）

● "All right, you've owed me $100 for five years; it's about time you cough it up."

　「好，你欠我 100 塊已欠了 5 年；現在該是你拿出錢來的時候了。」

82. **could be**
　有此可能

● "Do you think Bill will be our new chairman?"

　「你認爲 Bill 會成爲我們的新任會長嗎？」

　"Could be."

　「可能吧。」

83. **Could you give me a discount?**
　可以算便宜一點嗎？　可以打點折扣嗎？

● "Could you give me a discount?"

　「能不能便宜一點？」

　"O.K. I'll give you 10% (off)."

　「好，打九折。」

84. **Could you knock off (or forget) the (15 cents)?**
　不要算行嗎？（去掉一毛五的零頭）

● "How much?"

　「多少錢？」

　"$200.15."

　「二百塊一毛五。」

"Could you knock off (or forget) the 15 cents?"

「零頭不必算了吧?」

85. **count me in**

[kaʊnt]

把我算進去;把我包括在內

- "Don't count me in on what you guys are doing."

「你們打算做的事別把我算進去。」

86. **countdown**

倒數(如選美,或發射太空艙等)

- "Now, we come in to final countdown, 10, 9, 8, . . . 3, 2, 1."

「現在我們進入最後的倒數計時,10.9.8. … 3.2.1.。」

87. **(of) course not**

[kors]

當然不!(口語,加重語氣否認一件事)

- "Are you deaf?"

「你聾了嗎?」

"(Of) Course not!"

「當然沒有!」

88. **crack a book (=hit the books)**

[kræk]

K書(crack 是打開新書時咔的一聲)

- "What are you doing? Jack."

「Jack,你在幹嘛?」

"What do you think? Cracking a book of course."

「你以為呢?當然是在K書囉!」

89. **to crack down (on) . . .**

嚴格執行(管束)…

- "It's getting hard to pay people off. The government

is starting to crack down on bribery."

「賄賂（政府官員）越來越難了，政府現在對收紅包的事查得很嚴。」

90. **crack up**

[kræk]

①（突然）大笑。②發瘋（＝go crazy）。③撞爛。

① ● "He cracks me up."

「他使我大笑。」

● "When I heard that funny story, I just cracked up."

「當我聽到那個可笑的故事，我（忍不住）大笑起來。」

● "Everybody cracked up when they heard the joke."

「當聽到那個笑話時，每個人都大笑不止。」

② ● "After his divorce he cracked up."

「離婚之後，他就瘋了。」

③ ● "He cracked up his car."

「他把車子撞爛了。」

91. **cracker**

[ˈkrækɚ]

小餅乾（美國吃生菜沙拉與喝酒時都吃）

● "Waiter, could you bring us some more crackers, please!"

「你能不能再多給我們一點小餅乾！拜託，先生。」

92. **credit**

[ˈkrɛdɪt]

①學分（＝hour）。②功勞。③掛賬。

① ● "How many credits are you taking?"

「你現在一共修幾個學分？」

"12."

「12 個。」

② ● "I did all the work, and he got all the credit."

「我做工，他却贏得全部的功勞（不公平也）。」

③ ● "Can you give me credit until payday?"
「你能不能讓我掛賬直到發薪？」

93. **creep**
[krip]

討厭鬼；混蛋

● "John??!! He's such a creep."
「（你說）John ？？！！他眞是一個討厭鬼。」

● "You creep."
「你，討厭鬼。」

94. **creep up on**
悄悄地來了

● "Fall semester is creeping up on us. Before we know it, it will be finals time."
「（秋季）學期悄悄地來了。也許我們還沒有來得及察覺，期末考就到了。」

95. **critical condition / situation**
病危；危險期；轉振點

● "How's Mary?"
「Mary 的情況如何？」

"She's still in a critical condition."
「她仍然在危險期。」

96. **crocodile tears**
[ˋkrɑkəˌdaɪl]

貓哭耗子，假慈悲

● "Jim, I'm sorry about you and Jane."
「Jim，對於你跟 Jane 的事我感到遺憾。」

"Don't shed your crocodile tears for me."
「別貓哭耗子，假慈悲了。」

97. **crook** [kruk]

壞人；歹徒

● "Don't worry, I'm not a crook."

「別擔心，我不是壞人。」

98. **to cross (someone)**

①激怒 ②生氣

① ● "Don't cross me. I know Chinese kung-fu."

「別激怒我，我懂得中國功夫。」

② ● "I'm cross with John."

「我在生 John 的氣。」

99. **cross (one's) heart (and hope to die)**

[krɔs]   [hɑrt]

發誓（有的人一邊講還一邊在心口畫個十字）

● "I didn't tell your mother; cross my heart."

「我沒有告訴你媽媽，我發誓。」

100. **cross up**

出賣（朋友，國家）

● "He crossed us up for $5,000."

「他因為五千塊出賣了我們。」

101. **cruising**

[ˈkruzɪŋ]

①開車兜風（沒目的）。②釣馬子／凱子。③感到愉快（如參加宴會，尤指喝酒七分醉，或吸大麻等）

① ● "We went cruising all over town today."

「今天我們開車兜遍了全城。」

② ● "This is the street where all the cruising occurs in this town."

「這是本城把馬子、釣凱子的街道。」

③ ● "We were cruising last night."

「我們昨晚玩得真愉快。」

102. crummy

['krʌmɪ]

劣質的；難看的；骯髒的；差勁的；不佳的

- "She lived in crummy slums."

  「她住在骯髒的貧民窟裏。」

- "What a crummy car!"

  「多麼破的車啊！」

- "He played crummy at tonight's game."

  「他今晚打（球）得眞破。」

- "What a crummy day!"

  「今天眞不順心。」

- "He's a crummy doctor."

  「他是個蒙古大夫。」

103. cry one's eyes out

哭腫了眼

- "After hearing the bad news, she cried her eyes out."

  「當她聽到那個壞消息之後，她哭腫了眼。」

104. curiosity killed the cat.

[ˌkjurɪˈɑsətɪ]

好奇易招禍

- "Don't feel too bad about not knowing what happened to her; you know, curiosity killed the cat."

  「別爲了不知道她的遭遇而感到太難過，你知道，好奇會招來禍害的。」

105. cut class（高中生說 **skip class; play hooky.**）

[skɪp]

蹺課；溜課

- "You've been cutting class too often."

  「你課蹺得太多了。」

106. cut (someone) down (=disparage)

雞蛋裏挑骨頭；挑錯

● "You never did appreciate me. All you've ever done is cut me down."

「你從未讚賞過我，你只會挑我的錯。」

107. cut in (=butt in)

插嘴

● "Mind if I cut in?"

「你可介意我打個岔？」

● "When people talk, don't cut in."

「當別人在講話時，別插嘴。」

108. cut (in line)

插隊

● "Please don't cut in line."

「請別插隊。」

109. cut it short. (=Be brief.)

長話短說，挑重點講

● "Time is running out. Please cut it short."

「時間不多，請長話短說。」

110. cute

[kjut]

可愛；嬌小可愛（通常用在女人及動物身上）

● "She is very cute."

「她真可愛！」

● "Your hat is cute."

「你的帽子真可愛。」

註：美國人很愛用這字，形容人、東西，等等。

111. cute, very cute

[kjut]

聰明，眞聰明（諷刺別人自以爲是的小聰明）

- "Cute, Marie, very cute."

  「聰明，Marie，你眞聰明！」

1. **damn (or God damn)**
   [dæm]
   ①他媽的。②該死。③非常的。
   ① ● "Damn, it's hot."
   「他媽的，真熱。」
   ● "Damn it."
   「他媽的。」
   ② ● "Damn you."
   「去你的。」
   ③ ● "The movie was damn good."
   「那電影真是棒透了。」
   ● "He's damn good."
   「他真棒！」
   ● "You're damn right."
   「你（的話）對極了！」
   ● "It's a damn stupid mistake."
   「這真是一個極端愚蠢的錯誤。」
   ● "It's a damn shame."
   「真是非常可惜。」

2. **Damn it! (=God damn it!)**
   他媽的！該死。
   ● "Damn it!"
   「他媽的！」
   "What's wrong?"
   「怎麼了？」
   "I forgot my car key again."
   「我又忘了我車子的鑰匙。」

3. **Damn you**
   你他媽的！你真該死。

- "Damn you, why don't you go to hell?"

  「你他媽的，你為什麼不去死？」

4. **date**

   [det]

   (n.) ① (男女之間的) 約會。② (男、女) 伴 ③ (v.) 約會。

   (n)① ● "I'm sorry I can't go with you. I've got a date tonight."

   「對不起，我不能跟你去，今晚我有約會。」

   ② ● "Here comes my date."

   「我的 (男/女) 伴來了。」

   (v)③● "Who are you dating tonight?"

   「你今晚跟誰約會？」

5. **day care center**

   托兒所

   ● "She works in a day care center."

   「她在一家托兒所工作。」

6. **day off**

   休假

   ● "This is my day off."

   「今天我休息。」

   ● "I have three days off."

   「我有三天的休假。」

   ● "I'm going to take a day off."

   「我將要請假一天。」

7. **(Someone's) days are numbered.**

   (某人) 活不長了。(也可用來威脅人)

   ● "He's a very sick man. His days are numbered."

   「他病得很重，他的日子不多了。」

8. **dead broke (=flat)**
   [dɛd brok]

   一文不名；身無分文

   ● "I lost all my money in the casino. I'm dead broke now."
   「我在賭場輸光了，我現在身無分文。」

9. **Dear John letter**
   絕交信

   ● "Charlies got a Dear John letter from Farrah."
   「Charlies 收到一封Farrah 寫的絕交信。」

10. **death trap (=fire trap)**
    [dɛθ] [træp]

    死亡的陷阱

    ● "Taiwan's movie theaters are all death traps."
    「台灣的電影院都是死亡的陷阱。」（如遇火災逃不出去。）

11. **debut**
    [ˋdebju]

    初次登台之女子

    ● "Lily is going to sing at the Hilton tonight. This is her debut. Are you going?"
    「Lily 今晚要在Hilton 演唱。這是他第一次登台作秀。你去不去看？」

12. **Decisions, decisions**
    [dɪˋsɪʒənz]

    眞難做決定！（左右爲難）

    ● "What do you like for dessert, ice cream or cheese cake?"
    「你喜歡什麼甜點，冰淇淋還是乳酪蛋糕？」
    "Decisions, decisions."
    「眞難決定！」（兩樣都喜歡！）

13. **deserve it**

   [dɪ`zɝv]

   活該；罪有應得

   ● "Mary got kicked out of school, because she cheated on the test."

   「Mary 因爲考試作弊被學校開除了。」

   "The only thing I can say is that she deserved it."

   「唯一我能說的就是她活該。」

14. **Did I say something wrong?**

   我是不是說錯了什麼？（看到別人突然變臉）

   ● "Why are you mad at me? Did I say something wrong?"

   「你爲什麼生我的氣？是不是我說錯了什麼？」

15. **different strokes for different folks**

   　　　　[stroks]

   人各有志；人各有所好

   ● "Why don't you like dancing?"

   「你爲什麼不喜歡跳舞呢？」

   "Different strokes for different folks."

   「人各有所好嘛！」

16. **dig**

   [dɪg]

   ①接受。②明白；了解；知道。

   ① ● "Can you dig it?"

   　　「你能接受嗎？」

   ② ● "Do you dig it?"

   　　「你明白嗎？」

   　　"Yes, I dig it."

   　　「我明白。」

17. **dip**
    [dɪp]
    ①沾（醬）。②醬。③泡水。④討厭鬼（因爲笨）
    ① ● "Here, you can dip it in this."
    「喏，你可以沾這種醬。」
    ② ● "Would you like to try this onion dip?"
    「你要不要嚐一嚐這洋葱醬？」
    ③ ● "We had a dip in the ocean yesterday."
    「我們昨天去泡海水。」
    ④ ● "He's a real dip."
    「他眞是個討厭鬼。」

18. **dirt cheap**
    便宜透頂
    ● "How much is this vacuum cleaner?"
    「這吸塵器多少錢？」
    "$9.50."
    「九塊半。」
    "It's dirt cheap."
    「眞是便宜透頂。」

19. **direct**
    [dəˈrɛkt]
    直爽；坦白
    ● "Boy, you look awful in that shirt."
    「老天，你穿那件襯衫可眞難看。」
    "You don't have to be that direct."
    「你不需要那麼坦白。」

20. **dirty look**
    白眼
    ● "What did she say?"
    「她說了什麼？」

"Nothing; she just gave me a dirty look."

「啥也沒說，只是給了我一個白眼。」

21. **disconnect**

①電話被電話局停話。②申請暫時停止使用電話（在美國，當你外出旅行一、兩個月時，可申請電話暫停使用，因此可以不必付電話費。）

① ● "Our phone has been disconnected."

「我們的電話被停話了。」

② ● "I want to disconnect my telephone from June 1 to August 31 please."

「自6月1日起到8月31日止我要暫停使用我的電話。」

22. **disgust (=disgusting)**

[dɪsˋgʌst]

討人厭的；令人作嘔的

● "Did you see that girl?"

「看到那個妞了嗎？」

"Yeah, how disgusting! Zits all over her face."

「看到了，真噁心！青春痘長滿了一臉。」

23. **Dixie (=Dixie Land)**

美國南部各州

● "He was admired by most black people in Dixie."

「他受到南部大多數黑人的敬仰。」

24. **dizzy**

[ˋdɪzɪ]

①頭昏。②糊塗

① ● "I feel a little dizzy."

「我感到有點頭昏。」

② ● "She's just a dizzy broad. Don't worry about what she said."

「她只是一個糊塗女人，別擔心她所說的話。」

25. **do a job on (someone)**
①揍（一個人）。②打敗。

① ● "I'll do a job on my kid brother; he stole my pocket money again."
「我要揍我的小弟弟，他又偷了我的零用錢。」

② ● "The Steelers did a job on the Oilers last year, but this year my money's on Houston."
「去年（匹茲堡的）Steelers 隊打敗了（休士頓的）Oilers 足球隊，但今年我仍賭 Oilers 贏。」

26. **do all the talking**
出面負責交涉

● "Why don't you go and do all the talking?"
「你何不出面負責一切的交涉！」

● "You just shut up, and I'll do all the talking."
「你閉嘴，我出面負責交涉。」

27. **Do as I say! (=Do as I told you.)**
照我的話去做

● "Shut up, and do as I say!"
「閉嘴，照我的話去做。」

28. **do (someone's) dirty work for him**
①爲某人做壞事。②煩忙費時的工作。

① ● "Jack, don't do Mack's dirty work for him; you might get yourself in trouble."
「Jack，別替 Mack 做壞事，你可能自己惹上麻煩。」

② ● "The new office-boy always gets stuck doing all the dirty work."
「新來的小弟總是被煩忙的工作，搞得頭暈轉向。」

29. **Do I have any other choice?**
我有其他的選擇嗎？（常是沒有選擇餘地時無可奈何的語氣。）

- "Why did you give up, Debbie?"
  「Debbie, 你爲什麼要放棄呢？」

  "Did I have any other choice?"
  「我還有其他的選擇嗎？」

30. **do (someone) in**
   送掉 (人) 的命；斷送前程。

   - "Don't play with that gun, it might do you in."
     「別玩槍，你可能送掉小命。」

31. **do that**
   照辦

   - "I'll do that!"
     「我會照辦！」

   - "You do that!"
     「你就這麼做！」

32. **Do you have any openings? = Do you have any job available?**
   請問有沒有工作？（找工作時用）

   - "I went to 3 companies and asked them if they had any openings, but thumbs down at all 3."
     「我去了三家公司，問他們有沒有工作，但是三家都說沒有。」

   註：openings 指「工作」。

33. **Do you have the time? (= What time is it?)**
   請問幾點？

   - "Excuse me, ma'am, do you have the time?"
     「對不起，女士，請問幾點？」

     "Oh, yes, it is 2:15."/"Yes, I have 2:15."
     「哦，現在是2:15。」

   註："Do you have the time?"是問「幾點鐘？」而不是「你有空吧？」可別鬧笑話！以爲人家要請你喝咖啡！

34. **Do you have your papers?**
    你有證件嗎？（任何證件，如：身份證、居留證、學生證等
    等。）

35. **doc. (= doctor)**
    醫生（當面口語稱呼用）
    ● "Hello, doc, are you free this afternoon?"
    「喂，大夫你今天下午有空嗎？」

36. **dock**
    [dɑk]

    扣薪

    ● "If you're late again, I'll dock your pay."
    「如果你再遲到，我將要扣你的薪水。」

37. **dog days**
    ①窮極無聊的日子　②八月中很熱的天氣。
    ①● "I wish I could find something to do to kill all these
    dog days."
    「我希望我能找到一些事做以打發這些無聊的日子。」
    ● "It's a dog day afternoon. I can't wait until dinner."
    「真是個無聊的下午。我不知怎麼才能捱到晚飯時間?」
    ②註：希臘神話中有一個獵人養了一隻狗，有一個星座因它
    　　而命名，在八月中，太陽下山時，在西邊水平線上可
    　　見到這顆星星，所以 dog days 指八月中的熱天。

38. **dog (or cat, or horse, or bird) person**
    喜歡狗的人
    ● "I don't like cats. I'm a dog person."
    「我不喜歡貓，我是個喜歡狗的人。」

39. **doggy (or doggie) bag**
    ['dɔgɪ]　　　　　　　　[bæg]
    裝剩餘飯菜用的袋子（在美國起先都是藉口把吃剩的東西帶

回去餵狗，事實上帶回去餵人的也不少！）

- "Excuse me, could we have a doggy bag to take this home?"

「對不起，能不能給我們一個袋子把這些東西帶回家？」

"Sure."

「當然（可以）。）

40. done

①做成了；做好了。②就這麼辦吧！一言爲定。③累壞了。

① ● "Is the soup ready yet?"

「湯好了嗎？」

"Yes, it's done."

「好了！」

② ● "I'll pay you $100 a month plus expenses."

「我每個月付你一百塊外加一切雜支。」

"Done."

「一言爲定。」

③ ● "I'm too done to say anything."

「我累得說不出話來。」

41. (I've/You've) done everything (I/you) can.

(=I've/You've done everything possible)

（我／你）已盡力了！

- "It's not your fault, you've done everything possible."

「那不是你的錯，你已盡力了。」

- "I'm sorry, I've done everything I can."

「對不起，我已盡力了。」

42. done for

完蛋

● "I'm done for."
「我完蛋了。」

43. **Don't be bashful!**
    ['bæʃfəl]
別害羞；別難為情；別不好意思
● "If you need any help, just let me know. Don't be
bashful."
「假如你需要任何的幫忙‧請告訴我，不要不好意思。」

44. **Don't be hasty. (=Take it easy.)**
    ['hestɪ]
別急；別催
● "I'm thinking of asking Gail to marry me."
「我想向 Gail 求婚。」
"Don't be hasty. You've only known her a month."
「別太急，你認識她才不過一個月而已。」

45. **Don't be modest!**
    ['madɪst]
別 (太) 謙遜，客氣
●"It's wonderful work."
「這作品真棒。」
"Oh, it's nothing."
「哦，算不得什麼。」
"Don't be so modest."
「別太客氣啦！」

86

註：美國常會回答"Thank you." 所以 Don't be modest 美
國人較少用到。

46. don't be silly
[ˈsɪlɪ]

別驢了！

- "Don't be silly; of course I'll pay you back."
「別驢了，我當然會還你。」
- "Thanks for everything."
「一切謝謝了。」
"Don't be silly."
「不必謝。」

註：美國人常會用"Sure." "Don't be silly." 來表示「我當
然會幫你。」「你實在不必謝我。」中國人乍聽之下也
許會覺得怪。

47. Don't be so cheap.
不要那麼小氣

- "It's only 50¢ more for seats in the front. Don't be
so cheap."
「（前座）只比後座貴五毛錢，別那麼小氣。」

48. Don't be so sure!
別太過於自信（表示事情變化難以預料）

- "Pamela is going to the Senior Prom with me."
「Pamela 要跟我去參加畢業舞會。」
"Don't be so sure."
「別太過於自信。」

49. Don't bother! (=Never mind =Forget it. =It won't be neces-
sary.)
不用費神了！不必麻煩了！

- "Let me get you something to drink."
「讓我幫你倒點喝的。」

"Don't bother; I'll be going soon."

「不必麻煩，我馬上就走了。」

50. **Don't count on me.**

別指望我，別依賴我（有自身難保之意）

- "If you want to pass the English exam this time, study hard. Don't count on me to help you."

  「如果這次你想英文考試及格，用功唸書，別指望我會幫助你。」

51. **Don't do this to me.**

別這樣對我（如：遺棄、欺騙、背叛）

- "Joel, please don't do this to me. You know that I can't live without you."

  「Joel 別這麼做，你知道的，沒有你我就活不下去！」

52. **Don't forget to give my love (or my best, or my regards) to (someone).**

（別忘了）代我問候（某人）

- "Don't forget to give my regards to your brother."

  「別忘了代我問候你老哥。」

  "I won't."

  「我不會忘的。」

53. **get fresh**

吃豆腐；毛手毛脚

- "Behave yourself; don't get fresh with my sister."

  「安份一點，別吃我妹妹的豆腐。」

54. **don't get me wrong**

可別把意思搞錯了！別誤會我的意思。

- "Hey, don't get me wrong; I didn't mean I don't want to go with you."

  「嘿，別搞錯了，我可不是說我不願意跟你去。」

55. **Don't get smart with me.**
少在我面前耍花樣

- "Tell me the truth; what happened?　And don't get smart with me."
「老實告訴我，到底發生了什麼事？別在我面前耍花樣。」

56. **Don't give me any lip.**
不要回嘴（命令語）

- "When I'm telling you something, don't give me any lip!"
「當我跟你講話，別回嘴。」

57. **Don't be sarcastic.**
　　　　　[sɑr`kæstɪk]
少說風涼話

- "I twisted my back last night."
「昨晚我扭到腰了。」
"I thought it was a new style of disco."
「我還以爲那是 disco 的新花招呢。」
"Don't be sarcastic.　It still hurts."
「別說風涼話，還痛得很呢！」

58. **Don't impose/force your opinions upon others.**
　　　　[ɪm`poz]
別硬要別人聽你的！（聽從你的意思）

- "He's got a very bad habit."
「他有非常壞的習慣。」
"What?"
「什麼（習慣）？」
"I just think that someone should tell him that he shouldn't impose his opinions on others. After all, he isn't king."
「我只是在想，應該有個人告訴他，別老要別人聽他的。
畢竟他不是皇帝。」

59. **jump to conclusions.**
　　　　[kən`kludʒənz]
遽下斷語；太早下定論

- "Bruce is going to lose."
  「Bruce 會輸掉。」
  "Don't jump to conclusions. It's only the 8th round."
  「別太早下定論，才第八回合呢！」（拳賽）
- "I don't think he likes me."
  「我不認為他喜歡我。」
  "Don't jump to conclusions. You only met once for a few minutes."
  「別遽下定論。你們才認識幾分鐘。」

60. **Don't just shake your head.**
             [ʃek]
    別光是搖頭（想點法子啊！）

    - "Don't just shake your head, do something."
      「別光是搖頭，想點法子啊！」

61. **Don't let me disturb you.**
                    [dɪˈstɝb]
    別讓我打擾（或妨礙）你的正事。（當你突然光臨而別人正在忙時。）

    - "You two go ahead; don't let me disturb you."
      「你們繼續（談吧！）別讓我打斷你們。」

62. **Don't mention it.**
    不必再提了；不用再提了；不必掛在心上

    - "Thanks for your help last night, Mark."
      「Mark，謝謝你昨晚的幫忙。」
      "Don't mention it."
      「不必掛在心上。」

63. **Don't move / utter a sound.**
    別動；別作聲（躲過追兵；跟踪歹徒；靜候獵物）

    - "Here he comes; don't move or utter a sound."
      「他來了，別作聲。」

64. **Don't overdo it.**

別做得太過火（表演得太誇張，太過火了！）

● "Chrissy, don't overdo it."
「Chrissy，別做得太過火。」

65. **Don't play dirty games.**

別玩花招；耍陰險

● "Don't play dirty games with me."
「別跟我耍陰險。」

66. **Don't push your luck.**

別太仗恃你的運氣

● "You got away with it once. Don't push your luck."
「你得以逃脫一次，但別太仗恃你的運氣。」

67. **Don't rock the boat.**

就保持現狀吧！（譬如你不想進一步由朋友變為情人。）

● "I'm very happy about the way we are now. Let's not rock the boat."
「我很滿意我們目前的關係，就保持現狀吧！」

68. **Don't sweat it.**

不要緊張

● "The car broke down and the repair shop is ten miles away."
「車子壞了，修車廠又在十哩外。」

"Don't sweat it, maybe we can fix it."
「不要緊張，也許我們自己可以修好它。」

69. **Don't take any chances**

不要冒險

●"Don't take any chances with him, he's completely un-reliable."
「別跟他去冒險，他完全不可信賴。」

- "Let's go check and make sure. I don't want to take any chances."

  「我們去檢查一下看看是不是確實沒問題，我可不想冒任何險。」

70. **Don't take it/thing so hard/bad. (=Don't take it so seriously.)**

   不要太難過；別想得太多；別想不開

   - "All my money was stolen yesterday. I'll commit suicide if my loan doesn't come through."

     「昨天我的錢全被偷了。如果我的貸款不獲准，我會自殺。」

     "Hey, don't take things so hard."

     「嘿，別那麼想不開。」

71. **nonsense!**

   [ˈnɑnsɛns]

   胡說八道；胡扯；瞎說

   - "I can't be your friend; you're pretty and rich, and I..."

     「我不夠資格做你的朋友，你長得漂亮又有錢，而我…」

     "Nonsense. What does that have to do with the price of beans?"

     「那兒的話，這跟我們現在談的事又有什麼關係？」

72. **Don't tell a soul/anybody. (=Just between us.)**

   不要對別人說；別洩露出去

   - "Don't tell a soul; I don't want other people know about this."

     「別洩露出去，我不希望別人知道。」

     "Don't worry, I won't tell anybody, not even my husband."

     「別擔心，我不會告訴任何人，連我先生我都不會告訴他。」

73. **Don't tell me ...**

   別告訴我；別說 …

- "Don't tell me you lost all your money again."

「別告訴我，你又把錢搞丟了。」

74. **think too much/so highly of yourself**.

自以為了不起

- "I can get along without you; don't think too much (=so highly) of yourself."

「沒有你我也可以活下去，別太自以為了不起。」

註：Don't belittle yourself.「別小看自己（自卑）。」

75. **"Don't trust anyone over 30."**

別聽信 30 歲以上人的話，因為①雙方有代溝。②對方可能會倚老賣老。（這是一句美國人常用的話）

76. **Don't you dare ...**

你敢 ⋯（表示不可以，否則 ⋯）

- "Don't you dare say it to me."

「你敢對我說那些話。」

77. **Don't you think you're a little old to be doing that/this?**

(=Aren't you kind of old for that sort of thing?)

做這種事，你難道不覺得嫌老了一點嗎？

- "Fighting with your kid brother again? Don't you think you're a little old to be doing that?"

「又跟你弟弟吵了？你難道不覺得以你的年紀做這種事有點太老了嗎？」

78. **dope** [dop]

①大麻。②毒品（鴉片、嗎啡）。③傻瓜、笨蛋。④情報；密告。

① ● "When his parents caught him smoking dope, he offered them some."

「當他的父母抓到他抽大麻時，他要他們也抽一點。」

② ● "He was arrested for peddling dope, mostly grass, but also some hard stuff."

「他因兜售毒品而被捕，他出售的大部份是大麻，也有一點海洛英」（ grass 是指大麻，hard stuff 是指會上癮的東西，如：海洛英。）

③ ● "You dope, when are you going to get your shit together?"
「你這個笨蛋，什麼時候你才會頭腦清楚？」

④ ● "We have a lot of dope on the murder case."
「關於這件謀殺案子，我們有很多密報。」

79. dope fiend
　　[find]

染上毒癮的人

● "Her husband is a dope fiend."
「她的先生是個有毒癮的人。」

80. dorm (=dormitory)
　　[dɔrm]

　　宿舍

● "I live in a girls' dorm."
「我住在一所女生宿舍裏。」

81. double-cross
　　['dʌbl] ['krɔs]

　　出賣；背叛

● "He double-crossed me, the bastard."
「那個小野種，他出賣了我。」

82. double talk

　　花言巧語

● "Don't believe a word of what he says. It's all double talk."
「半句話也別信他的，全是花言巧語。」

83. **dough**

[do]

錢

- "Let's figure a way to make some dough."

「讓我們想個法子去弄點錢來。」

84. **down**

情緒低潮；生意低落

- "I really feel down today."

「我今天情緒很低落。」

"What's wrong?"

「怎麼回事？」

- "Business is down. We'll have to get rid of some of the dead wood around here."

「生意走下坡。我們必須辭掉一些沒有用的人。」

註：down 的相反是 up。

85. **downhill**

①一帆風順。②走下坡

① ● "It's downhill from now on."

「從此以後，一帆風順。」

② ● "My English has gone downhill."

「我的英文已走下坡。」

86. **to be down on (someone)**

因為不滿意，所以批評某人，挑某人的錯。

- "My boss has been down on me lately."

「我的老闆近來常挑我的錯。」

註："Get" down on (someone) 則有「開始」找麻煩的意思。

87. **down payment**

[daun 'pemənt]

①分期付款的首款。②押金、定金。

● "How much should we pay for the down payment?"
「首款該付多少？」

88. **down the drain**
　　　　[dren]

泡湯了（變成泡影、付諸流水）

● "What happened to your trip to Europe?"
「你的歐洲之行怎麼了？」

"That went down the drain a long time ago."
「早就泡湯了。」

89. **down with**

打倒

● "Down with Mao."
「打倒毛（澤東）。」

90. **drag**

①牽連；連累。②吸一口香煙（或大麻煙）。②賽車。④長的路可賽車用。⑤無聊；討人厭。⑥男人穿女人的衣服。⑦拖延（長而無聊）。

① ● "Don't let him drag you into it."
「別讓他把你牽連進去。」

② ● "Do you want a drag?"
「你要吸一口嗎？」

③ ● "Do you want to drag?"
「你想賽車嗎？」

④ ● "They race cars on the drag strip."
「他們在路上賽車。」

⑤ ● "He is a real drag."
「他真討人厭。」

⑥ ● "The men at the gay bar were all dressed in drag."
「在同性戀酒吧中的男人都穿了女人的衣服。」

⑦ ● "The meeting was very boring. It dragged on for four hours."

「這會議眞乏味。前後拖了四個鐘頭。」

91. Drat! (=Darn=Doggone)

[dræt] [dɑrn][ˌdɔgˈgɔn]

糟糕

● "Drat! I forgot my umbrella again."

「糟了！我又忘了拿我的雨傘。」

92. drawback

[ˈdrɔˌbæk]

缺點

● "The only drawback to having the party at your house is that it's too far away."

「在你家開舞會的唯一缺點就是你家太遠了。」

93. drink in

欣賞（用眼睛看）

● "The scenery was beautiful. I sat there drinking it all in."

「景色眞美，我坐在那盡情欣賞。」

94. drive-in

①可開車進去存款的路邊銀行；或可開車去點東西的小吃店。
②露天電影院。

① ● "Let's go through the drive-in; it's faster."

「我們去路邊銀行存款，比較快些。」

② ● "During the day it's a swap shop, and at night it's a drive-in."

「白天這裏是個舊貨市場，在晚上則是個露天戲院。」

註：在美國，這是一地兩用的好方法。

95. drive (someone) nuts (=drive someone crazy)

逼（人）發瘋

● "You drive me nuts."

「你逼得我快發瘋了。」

● "I hate pop music; it drives me nuts."

「我痛恨流行歌曲，聽了叫我發瘋。」

96. **drop (someone) a line (=write me)**

①寫信。②通知

① ● "Drop me a line when you get there, will you?"

「到了那兒，給我來封信好嗎？」

② ● "In case something happens, we will drop your nearest relative a line."

「萬一有什麼意外發生，我們會通知你的至親。」

97. **drop in**

偶然來訪

● "Drop in sometime, will you?"

「有空來坐坐，好嗎？」

98. **(a) drop in the bucket (=a drop in the ocean)**

　　　　　　　[`bʌkɪt]

滄海一粟；九牛一毛

● "Let him pay, it's only a drop in the bucket to him."

「讓他付吧，對他來說只不過是九牛一毛。」

99. **drop me**

①讓我在 … 地方下車（搭便車時請求別人讓自己下車時用。）
②拋棄。

① ● "Drop me at the railway station, please."

「請在火車站停一下。」

② ● "Don't drop me."

「別拋棄我。」

100. **drop out**

①退學生；開除。②休學。

① ● "He is a high school dropout."

「他是一個高中退學的學生。」

② ● "She dropped out of school in fifth grade."

「她五年級時休學了。」

101. drown (one's) troubles

[draʊn]

借酒澆愁

● "After his girlfriend ran away with his best friend, he tried to drown his troubles at the local bar."

「他的女友跟他最要好的朋友跑了之後，他企圖在當地的酒吧借酒澆愁。」

102. drug addict

['ædɪkt]-n.　　　　v.-[əˋdɪkt]

煙毒蟲　　　　　　上癮；迷上 … 。

● "He is a drug addict."

「他是一個煙毒蟲。」

103. drugged (=doped)

[ˋdrʌgəd]　[dopt]

下毒；放藥

● "He has been drugged."

「他被人下毒了。」

104. drunk (=smashed, pickled, lit, loaded)

[drʌŋk]　[smæʃt]　[ˋpɪkld]　[lɪt]

喝醉

● "I'm drunk."

「我喝醉了。」

105. dry as a bone

形容東西很乾，沒有一點水份

● "It was raining outside my house but three blocks away the street was dry as a bone."

「我家這兒在下雨，但三條街外却是乾乾的一滴雨也沒有。」

106. dry humor

[ˋhjumɚ]

平淡；缺乏表情的幽默（聽了不會大笑的笑話，要三思才會會心一笑的）

● "The English are famous for dry humor. Americans like practical jokes."

「英國人以平淡的幽默出名；美國人却喜歡惡作劇。」

註：practical jokes 如踩香蕉皮摔一大跤或把蛋糕扔在別人臉上，「勞來、哈台式的笑話」看了會哈哈大笑的那種。

107. dynamite

[ˋdaɪnə͵maɪt]

很棒的！棒透了。

● "Are you going to make that dynamite stuffed pepper tonight?"

「你今晚要做那棒透了的青椒釀肉嗎？」

108. dum-dum

[ˋdʌm-dʌm]

笨蛋

● "He's a dum-dum."

「他是一個笨蛋。」

109. dumb

[dʌm]

笨

●"I'm not that dumb."

「我才沒那麼笨呢？」

●"Don't play dumb; you know what I mean."

「別裝傻，你明白我的意思。」

110. dummy

[ˈdʌmɪ]

笨蛋

- "What did you say to her, ˈdummy?"

  「笨蛋，你對她說了什麼？」

1. **ease up on**
   展開；施展

   ● "After he got to know her better, he decided he should ease up on the charm, but she wasn't interested, so he eased out the door."
   「在他更熟悉她之後，他決定對她施展他的魅力，但她不感興趣，所以他只好離去。」

   註：ease out 是離開。

2. **(someone is) easily dominated**
   ['dɑmə,netɪd]
   易受人指使；沒有主見

   ● "She is easily dominated."
   「她很容易受人指使。」

3. **easy**
   ①別太緊張。②慢點；小心點。

   ① ● "Easy (=Take it easy.) it will be O.K. in a minute."
   （拔牙時醫生說）：「放輕鬆一點，馬上就好。」

   ② ● "Go easy on those hairpin curves."
   「小心那些大轉彎。」

4. **easy come easy go**
   來得容易去得快（例如不義之財），到頭來仍是一場空。

   ● "I won $100 at poker last week and lost it all betting on the horses."
   「我上星期玩撲克牌贏了一百塊，結果賭馬時全輸了。」
   "Easy come, easy go."
   「來得容易，去得快。」

5. **eat (one's) heart out**
   羨慕死

- "If you meet Lisa's boyfriend, you will eat your heart out."

  「假如妳看到 Lisa 的男朋友，妳會羨慕死。」

- "Eat your heart out. She was the one who asked me out, and you know what that means."

  「羨慕吧！就是她約我出去，你該知道那代表着什麼？」

- "This is my new car. Eat your heart out."

  「這是我的新車，羨慕吧！」

6. **eating up=eat (Something) up**

   ①相信。②多吃一點。

   ① ● "I told him a whole bunch of stories about the beautiful girls in Taiwan, and he just ate them up."

     「我告訴他一大堆有關台灣漂亮女孩的故事，而他全信了。」

   ② ● "Eat up. I'm paying for it."

     「多吃點，我可是付錢買的。」

7. **emergency**

   [ɪmɝdʒənsɪ]

   緊急之事（例如生病、車禍 … ）

   - "Give me the hospital; it's an emergency."

     「請接醫院，這裏有緊急事。」

   - "If I don't get to the bathroom soon, I'm going to have an emergency."

     「假如我不馬上去 1 號，馬上會有緊急事發生。」（急於上廁所）

8. **end of the journey**

   ['dʒɝnɪ]

   大功告成

● "That's it, the end of the journey."
「好了，大功告成。」
"Yeah!"
「哇！（好棒哦！）」

9. **enough to turn (anyone's / Your) stomach**
足以倒盡人的胃口！

   ● "Why don't you like watching T.V.?"
   「你為什麼不喜歡看電視？」
   "All those soap operas are enough to turn anyone's stomach."
   「那些電視劇足以倒盡任何人的胃口。」

   ● "His disgusting stories are enough to turn your stomach."
   「他那些令人厭惡的故事，足以倒盡你的胃口。」

10. **equal**
    [ˈikwəl]
    ①勝任；能幹。②同輩；同類。

    ① ● "He is equal to anything."
       「他凡事都能勝任。」

    ② ● "Go and mix with your equals."
       「去跟你那一伙兒鬼混吧！」

11. **even**
    扯平；報仇

    ● "We're even now."
    「我們扯平了。」

    ● "I want to get even."
    「我要報仇。」

12. **Every cloud has a silver lining.**
    [ˈsɪlvɚ] [ˈlaɪnɪŋ]
    塞翁失馬焉知非福（每件不好的事情，可能含有好的一面。）

- "The doctor said I have to stay in bed for two weeks."
「醫生說我得在床上躺兩個星期。」

"Well, every cloud has a silver lining. Now you can read all those books you haven't had time for."
「塞翁失馬焉知非福，你現在可以趁機看完以前沒空看的書了。」

13. **(someone is) every inch a (man/woman/gentleman/lady)**
每一寸都是…（男人/女人/紳士/淑女）（指男人/女人味十足）

- "She is every inch a woman."
「她每一吋都是女人。」（散發着女人的魅力）

14. **Everything fell into place.**
[ples]

一切順利

- "How was your business trip?"
「你這趟生意跑得怎麼樣？」

"Everything fell into place."
「一切順利。」

15. **Everything's gone haywire.**
['he,waɪr]

亂七八糟，一團糟。

- "How's your new business?"
「你的新公司如何？」

"Everything's going haywire."
「一團糟。」

16. **E.S.P. (=The sixth sense)**
第六感

- "She must have ESP. She knew her mother was trying to reach her."
「她一定具有第六感，她知道她媽媽在找她。」

註：E.S.P. 是 Extra-Sensory Perception 的縮寫。

17. **to eye (somebody)**

用懷疑的眼光打量（某人）

- "The guard eyed that young man for a while and then let him pass."

「那個警衛打量了一下那個年靑人，才讓他過去。」

1. **face (the facts; the music; him)**
   面對（事實；責罵；他）

   - "Let's face it, we're lost."
     「讓我們面對事實，我們迷路了。」
   - "I can't face him; I feel so ashamed."
     「我無法面對他，我覺得好羞愧。」
   - "Let's face the facts. John is the better man for this job."
     「讓我們面對事實，John 比較適合幹這份工作。」
   - "If we fuck up, I don't want to face the music alone."
     「假如我們搞砸了，我可不願一個人承擔所有的責罵！」

2. **(to) face the music**
   去面對不愉快的（責罰；挨罵）

   - "If we are going to be punished, I don't want to face the music alone."
     「假如我們要受罰，我可不願一個人去承擔。」

3. **fair enough**
   [fɛr/ɪˋnʌf]

   公平得很！

   - "I'll pay for the meal, and you pay for the movie, how about that?"
     「我請吃飯，你請看電影，如何？」
     "Fair enough!"
     「很公平！」

4. **fair shake**
   [ˋfɛr][ʃek]

   公平；妥當的安排

   - "Be sure to give my little brother a fair shake. He's only 20, but he learns fast."
     「一定要給我的小弟一個妥善的安排哦！他雖然只有20歲，

　　　　　但是他學得很快。」

　　　　"OK."

　　　　「好。」

5. **(It's a) fairy tale!**
　　　['fɛrɪ/tel]

　　瞎掰；鬼話連篇；胡說八道

　● "Did you hear about how David went to Bermuda and met the Swedish prime minister's daughter and what they did?"

　　「你有沒有聽說 David 去百慕達遇到瑞典首相的女兒以及他們所做的事？」

　　"Aw! That's a fairy tale. He didn't even go to Bermuda."

　　「噢！那完全是瞎掰。他連百慕達都沒去過。」

6. **fake**
　　[fek]

　　①騙子。②騙局。③虛幌一招。

　　① ● "You are a fake."

　　　　「你是個騙子。」

　　② ● "It's a fake."

　　　　「那是騙局。」

　　③ ● "I faked left and went right."

　　　　「我向左虛幌了一下，就從右邊過去了。」

7. **fan (T.V. fan, movie fan, football fan)**
　　迷

　　● "He is a typical football fan."

　　　「他是個標準的足球迷。」

　　● "I'm a big fan of yours."

　　　「我是你忠實的（影、歌）迷。」

8. **fast food**
　　速食（如漢堡、熱狗、炸雞之類的食物）

- "There is a fast food store."
  「那邊有一家速食店。」
- "Fast food makes me sick."
  「速食令我倒胃口。」

9. **fast talker**

   蓋仙（口若懸河，却是滿口胡言的人）

   - "Don't listen to him; he's a fast talker."
     「別聽他的，他是個蓋仙。」

10. **Fasten your seat belt.**

    ['fæsn]　　　[sit] [bɛlt]

    請繫好安全帶（在美國坐自用車或搭飛機常聽到的話）

    - "Ladies and Gentlemen, we are going to take off in a few minutes. Please fasten your seat belts and observe the 'No smoking' sign. Thank you."
      「各位女士，各位先生，我們馬上就要起飛了。請繫好安全帶，並請不要吸煙。謝謝。」

11. **fatso**

    [fætsọ]

    胖子

    - "Hey, fatso."
      「嘿！胖子。」

12. **fatty (=fatso, pusgut)**

    ['fætɪ]

    胖子

- "Hey, fatty."
  「嗨，胖子。」

13. **fed up**
    [fɛd]

    受夠了

    - "I'm fed up with you and your mother."
      「我受夠你跟你媽媽了。」
    - "I'm fed up with studying English."
      「我受夠英文了。」

14. **feel like a fool**
    覺得像個傻瓜

    - "When I stood in the rain waiting for Caroline for two hours, I felt like a big fool."
      「當我站在雨中等 Caroline 等了兩個小時，我覺得自己像個大傻瓜。」

15. **(I) feel like hell**
    不舒服；很糗

    - "After drinking a whole case of beer, I felt like hell."
      「喝完了一整箱的啤酒，我覺得很不舒服。」

16. **feel no pain**
    很痛快（已達忘憂之境，微醉也！）

    - "How are you doing, Ed?"
      「Ed。你現在覺得如何，還好吧？」
      "What do you think? After 5 beers, I'm feeling no pain."
      「你以為呢？喝下了五瓶啤酒，我現在覺得很痛快。」

17. **(I) feel terrible**
    ['tɛrəbl]

    我覺得很不舒服（指身體或心情）

    - "I don't know why I feel terrible now."
      「我不知道為什麼，我現在覺得很不舒服。」

18. **(the) feeling is mutual**

['mjutʃuəl]

彼此，彼此（想法一樣）（同感）

● "Well, Mr. Wilson, it's really a pleasure to do business with you."

「哦，Wilson 先生，跟你做生意真是我們莫大的榮幸。」

"The feeling is mutual."

「彼此，彼此。」

● "I don't like you."

「我不喜歡你。」

"The feeling is mutual."

「彼此，彼此。」

19. **fib (=white lie)**

[fɪb]

小謊言（不傷大雅，無關輕重的小謊言）

● "Are you fibbing about your age?"

「你是不是虛報了自己的歲數？」

"Only a little bit."

「只隱瞞了一點點。」

● "It's only a fib."

「那只是一個小小謊言。」

● David: "Why don't you go to the movies with us?"

「你為什麼不跟我們一起去看電影？」

Kathy: "I'd love to, but I can't. I have class this evening. I'm sorry."

「我很樂意跟你們一起去，但我今晚要上課，真是遺憾。」

Lisa: "She's fibbing. She just doesn't want to go."

「她在撒謊，她只是不想跟我們一起去罷了。」

20. **fiend**

[find]

迷；狂

- "I'm a dance fiend."

  「我是個舞棍。」

- "She is an opium fiend."

  「她是個鴉片鬼。」

- "He's a sex fiend."

  「他是個色鬼。」

21. **(a) fifth wheel (of the cart)**

礙事者，電灯泡

- "We don't need him tagging along. He's a fifth wheel."

  「我們不需要他跟著。他是個電灯泡。」

22. **fifty fifty**

二一添作五；對半分

- "Let's split this bill fifty fifty."

  「讓我們二一分賬。」

23. **fight hand to hand**

赤手空拳對打

- "They are fighting hand to hand."

  「他們赤手空拳地在對打。」

24. **figure**

['fɪgjɚ]

①身材；曲綫。②料到了。③預料；想。

② ● "She has a good figure."

  「她的身材很好。」

② ● "I had him figured out a long time ago."

  「我早知道他是什麼樣的人。」

③ ● "What time do you figure you'll be getting back?"

  「你想你什麼時候會回來？」

25. **fill in**
   [fɪl]

   ①臨時僱員。②補充說明（以便追上進度，明瞭現況）③填寫。

   ① ● "He is just a fill in at the BBC Company."
      「他在ＢＢＣ公司只是一個臨時僱員。」

   ② ● "Fill me in on what I have missed."
      「請補充說明一下我沒聽到的部份。」

   ③ ● "Fill in this form and go to window #18."
      「填好這份表格，然後去18號窗口。」

26. **Fill 'er (=her) up please.**
   請加滿它（汽油）

   ● "Fill 'er with regular, please."
      「請加滿普通汽油。」

   註：車子以 her 代稱。

27. **filthy rich. (=rolling in dough)**
   有錢得要命

   ● "Just look at that car!"
      「瞧瞧那輛車。」
      "Yes, it's Tom's; he's filthy rich."
      「是的，那是Tom家的車，他有錢得要命。」

28. **final**
   ['faɪnl]

   ①期末考。②最後的決定（不願再談論這事）

   ① ● "Don't tell me finals are coming."
      「別告訴我期末考快到了。」

   ② ● "We are not going to the movies tonight and that's final."
      「我們今晚不去看電影，這是最後的決定。」

29. **fine weather/day for ducks**
   雨天

- "We're going to have fine weather for ducks."
「將要有一陣子雨天。」

- "Do you like rainy days?"
「你喜歡雨天嗎？」

"Well, it's fine for ducks."
「哦，鴨子喜歡。」（表示①不喜歡。或②不在意）

- "It looks like duck weather, don't forget to bring your raincoat."
「看來即將下雨，別忘了帶雨衣。」

30. **finicky**

['fɪnɪkɪ]

事事講究的人（如吃東西，買東西）

- "He's a finicky eater."
「他是一個講究飲食（美味）的人。」

31. **finish!** ˙

完蛋了！

- "He's finished."
「他完了。」

32. **fink**

[fɪŋk]

①打退堂鼓。②告密。③告密者，打退堂鼓的人。

① - "I heard you're no longer dating Chrissie."
「我聽說你不再約 Chrissie 了。」

"Yeah, I finked out, I was tired of competing with other guys."
「是啊，我退出了，我已厭倦跟其他的傢伙競爭。」

② - "He finked to the cop, so we have to leave."
「他向警察告密，所以我們必須離開。」

③ - "James is a fink. He set us up."
「James 是個告密者，他陷害了我們。」

33. **First come, first served.**
[sɜvd]

先來者先接受服務招待

- "Hey, you!"
  「嘿,老兄。」
  "What?"
  「什麼事?」
  "Don't try to butt in line. First come, first served."
  「不要插隊,按次序來。」

- "Don't push, first come first served."
  「別推,按次序來。」

34. **first things first**

重要事先做

- "Do you want to go to the pool with us?"
  「你要不要跟我們一起去游泳?」

  "I'd love to, but I've got a paper to write, and you know, first things first."

  「我很樂意跟你們去,但是我要寫一篇報告,你也知道,重要的事該先做。」

35. **fish (=turkey)**

笨蛋

- "He's a fish."
  「他是一個笨蛋。」

36. **fishy**

①奇怪;難以令人相信的。②難以瞭解的;難以捉摸的;可疑的。

① ● "It's a fishy story."
  「這故事真奇怪。」

② ● "He's a very fishy guy."
  「他令人難以瞭解。」

● "There's something fishy going on here."

「這裏有點怪怪的。」

37. **fit**

[fɪt]

合用；適合

● "Good morning, John. How's the shirt?"

「John，早啊，那件襯衫如何？」

"Great; it fits me perfectly."

「棒透了，十分合身。」

38. **fit (someone) to a T.**

合適；恰當（如工作，衣服…）

● "How's your new job?"

「你的新工作如何？」

"It fits me to a T."

「十分適合我。」

● "Your description of him fits him to a T."

「你對他的描述，十分恰當。」

39. **fitting room**

[ˈfɪtɪŋ]

試衣室（在服裝店中）

● "Excuse me ma'am, can you tell me where the fitting room is?"

「小姐，打擾一下，請問試衣室在那裏？」

40. **fix**

[fɪks]

①修理。②沖泡；調（酒）。③預謀（暗盤交易）

① ● "Can you fix it for me?"

「你能幫我修理一下嗎？」

● "I'm going to have my car fixed."

「我要去修一下我的車子。」

- It's all fixed."

  「已經修好了。」

② • "Can I fix you something to drink?"

  「要不要我幫你沖杯什麼？」

  "Martin, please." / "How about a cup of coffee?"

  「請來杯馬丁尼。」   「來杯咖啡如何？」

③ • "The boxing match was fixed."

  「這場拳賽的輸贏已經預謀好了。」

41. (to) fix (someone's) wagon

  [fɪks]   [ˈwægən]

  (=to get back at someone) 報仇

- "I'll fix his wagon someday."

  「有一天我會向他報仇的。」

42. flag down a cab (=hail a taxi)

  招一部計程車

- "Let's flag down a cab; I don't think we can walk there."

  「我們叫一部計程車吧，我想我們走不到那兒。」

43. flattery will get you nowhere

  [ˈflætərɪ]

  拍馬屁也沒用

- "Just give me back my money; flattery will get you nowhere."

  「把錢還給我，拍馬屁是沒有用的。」

44. flea market

  [fli/ˈmɑrkɪt]

  廉價舊貨市場（內有許多小攤子）

- "I bought this book for a nickel at a flea market."

  「這本書是我以五分錢在舊貨市場買來的。」

45. **flick**

['flɪk]

電影

- "We went to a 3-D flick last night."

「昨晚我們去看了一場立體電影。」

註：3-D 是 three-dimensional 之意。

46. **flip out**

[flɪp]

①非常（高興或生氣…），（反應強烈）。②發瘋。

① ● "After he heard the news, he flipped out."

「聽到那消息後，他非常生氣（高興）。」

② ● "He flipped out on a bad acid trip."

「他有一次在迷幻藥的幻覺中發了瘋。」

註： acid 指 LSD. 迷幻藥也， trip 指幻覺。

47. **flop**

[flɑp]

①廉價；廉價的。②大失敗。

① ● "Bill, do you know any flop houses around here?"

「比爾，你可知道附近有沒有廉價的房子？」

② ● "How was the surprise party for John last night?"

「昨晚為 John 開的驚喜宴會如何？」

"It was a real flop. He never showed up."

「大大的失敗，他沒來！」

48. **flunked**

[flʌŋkt]

被當（功課）。（不是 down ）

- "I flunked English."

「我英文被當了。」

- "If you miss class three times, you will be flunked."

「假如你三次不來上課，你就會被當掉。」

49. **folks**

[foks]

①父母。②(buddy) 老友。

① ● "How are your folks?"

「你爸媽好嗎？」

② ● "How is it going, folks?"

「老友，近來如何？」

50. **follow**

[ˈfɑlo]

聽懂了嗎？跟不跟得上？

● "Could you follow what the teacher said in class?"

「在課堂上，你跟得上老師所講的課嗎？」

51. **fool around**

①遊蕩；遊手好閑 ②調戲；胡搞 (=fuck around)

● "What's your brother doing lately?"

「你弟弟近來在幹些什麼？」

"Nothing, just fooling around."

「無所事事，只是閑蕩罷了。」

② ● "It is really true that they've started fooling around together?"

「他們彼此調戲的事是真的嗎？」

52. **for fun**

只爲了好玩

● "We did this just for fun."

「我們這麼做，只是爲了好玩。」

53. **forget it**

不必提了；算了

● I'll give you back the money tomorrow." "Oh, forget it."

「我明天會把錢還你。」　　　　　　「哦，算了。」

● "I'm sorry about what I said last night."

「對昨晚（我所說）的話，我感到抱歉。」

"Oh, forget it. I didn't mean what I said either."

「哦，不必再提了。我講的也是氣話，不是眞正心裏想的。」

54. **foul language (=dirty words)**

[faul]

髒話，髒字眼

● "Don't use that foul language with me."

「別對我說髒話。」

55. **foul out**

五次犯滿畢業（用於籃球或英式足球中）

● "Be careful; you don't want to foul out?"

「小心點，你可不想出局吧？」

56. **foul-ups (=fuck-ups)**

[foul]

①紕漏；漏子。②倒霉鬼；掃把。（凡事不成，老做錯事）。

③弄壞。

① ● "I want you all to do a good job; I don't want any foul-ups."

「我要你們大家好好幹，我不希望出任何紕漏。」

② ● "He is a fuck-up." (=foul-up)

「他是個掃把。」

● "He is all fucked up."

「他成事不足，敗事有餘。」

③ ● "He borrowed my car and fucked up the engine."

「他借用我的車，而把引擎搞壞了。」

57. **frame (=set up)**

[frem]

陷害

- "Somebody framed you." (=somebody set you up.)
  「有人陷害你。」

- "I was framed; I didn't do it."
  「我是被人陷害的，我並沒有做（那件事）。」

58. freak
[frik]

一時興起

- "We did it as a result of a mere freak."
  「我們只因一時高興就做了（那件事）。」

註：60年代至70年代初。freak 當 " 嬉皮 "（hippie）講。

59. freak out

發瘋（歇斯底里）

- "He freaked out when he saw his house burning down."
  「當他看到他的房子被燒掉，他就發了瘋。」

60. free

①免費。②自由；或隨便。

① ● "Would you like to try some of this sausage? It's free."
  「你要不要嚐一嚐這些香腸？免費的哦！」

② ● "He is free."
  「他是自由自在的。」

61. freeze (=stop)
[friz]

停止；別動

- "Freeze; don't move."
  「停，別動！」

62. freezing
['frizɪŋ]

凍死了！（比 cold 還冷，用在寒風刺骨，天寒地凍時）

- "It's only 32°F, but I'm freezing."
  「雖然是華氏 32 度，但把我凍死了。」

- "It's freezing out; I want some hot coffee."

「外面眞凍，我要點熱咖啡。」

63. **fringe benefits**

[frɪndʒ ˈbɛnəfɪts]

（公司的）一般福利

- "We have very good fringe benefits, and I hope you will like our company."

「我們公司有很好的福利，我希望你會喜歡我們的公司。」

64. **from way back**

打從很久以前。

- "I know her from way back."

「我打從很久以前就認識她了。」

65. **From what I know of. . .**

據我所知

- "From what I know of him, he seems to be a nice guy."

「據我所知，他好像是個好人。」

66. **(a) front**

[frʌnt]

掩飾（幹壞事時用來當做擋箭牌）

- "His grocery store is a front for a gambling joint."

「他的雜貨店是賭場的障眼法。」

67. **frustrated**

[ˈfrʌstretɪd]

沮喪（受到挫折後）

- "After they knew they lost the game, they felt very frustrated."

「知道他們輸了之後，他們感到非常的沮喪。」

68. **Fry in (one's) own grease.**

[fraɪ]   [gris]

自作自受；作繭自縛

● "I told him she was no good, but he's getting really deeply involved with her. One of these days, he's going to fry in his own grease."

「我告訴他，她不是個好東西，但他已陷得很深。總有一天，他會自作自受的。」

69. **fuck**

[fʌk]

操（英文有名的四字經── Four letter word）

● "Fuck you."

「操。」

70. **fuck a (duck, tree, wall)**

他媽的；去你的；（少煩我）

● "Why don't you go fuck a tree and leave us alone."

「他媽的，少煩我們。」

71. **fuck off/(go) fuck yourself**

①滾開；少惹我（我不喜歡你）。②遊蕩；聊天；不務正業。

① ● "I don't want to talk to you; why don't you fuck off."

「我不想跟你講話，你爲何不滾開！」

② ● "We're just fucking off."

「我們只是在閒聊。（不是在幹正經事）」

72. **fucking (moron, ass hole . . .)**

['morɑn] [æs/hol]

瘋子；討厭鬼…（在此 fuck 只是加強語氣，眞正的主要字是後面的 moron; ass hole . . .）

● "Billy is a fucking moron; don't pay any attention to him."

「Billy 是個瘋子，別理他。」

73. **fucker**

王八蛋

- "You fucker!"

  「你這個王八蛋。」

- "That fucker is at it again."

  「那個王八蛋又犯了。（你叫他不要做他又做了）」

74. fussbudget

['fʌsˌbʌdʒɪt]

碎嘴婆；多嘴婆

- "She's the world's No. 1 fussbudget."

  「她是天下第一號多嘴婆。」

75. fussy

[fʌsɪ]

挑剔的

- "Don't be so fussy."

  「別這麼挑剔。」

註： fusspot 是指愛挑剔的人。

76. fuzzy

['fʌzɪ]

不清楚

- "Don't be so fuzzy on the details. I need to know more before I can decide."

  「在細節上別那麼含糊不清，在做決定前我需要知道得更多一點。」

1. **gag**
   [gæg]
   ①令人作嘔。②笑話。
   ① ● "Cigarette smoke makes me gag."
   「香煙的煙味令我作嘔。」
   ② ● "His gags aren't really funny."
   「他的笑話不好笑。」

2. **gain ground**
   [gen/graʊnd]
   ①進展。②追上；趕上；佔優勢。
   ① ● "We can gain no ground in peace talks."
   「在和談中，我們可能會毫無進展。」
   ② ● "The Japanese are gaining ground on the Americans in computer chip technology."
   「在電腦工業方面，日本已經趕上美國了。」

3. **game**
   加入；算我一份
   ● "I'm game."
   「我也參加。」

4. **gangster**
   [ˈgæŋstɚ]
   歹徒（通常是一伙人 gansters ）
   ● "Did you see in the paper that the police busted up that gangster ring that was responsible for all the bank hold-ups recently?"
   「你看到報上登的嗎？警察拘捕了一夥兒歹徒，據說跟連日來的各個銀行的搶劫案有關。」

5. **gate-crasher**
   [get /ˈkræʃɚ]
   不請自來，看霸王戲的（白吃白喝之類的無賴，=freeloader）

● "Do you have any idea how to deal with those gate-crashers?"

「你可有法子對付那些看覇王戲的人？」

6. **give rein to one's fancy**
   [ren] ['fænsɪ]
   一味空想；不切實際

● "Work hard; don't just give rein to your fancy."
   「努力工作，別一味空想。」

7. **(Somebody) gave you too many vitamin pills!**
   ['vaɪtəmɪn] [pɪlz]

你實在精力過剩！（吃多了維他命丸）

● "Would you sit down? Somebody gave you too many vitamin pills this morning."
   「你能坐下來（靜一靜）嗎？今天早上你實在是精力過剩。」

8. **gay (=homosexual; bugger)**
   [ge]
   同性戀者

● "Have you been to a gay bar?"
   「你去過同性戀者的酒吧嗎？」

註：gay 是同性戀者本身也引用的字。"fairy"則是一般人
    用的字。但"faggot""fags"是憎惡同性戀的人對他們
    的稱呼。
    "straight"則是非同性戀的人。
    "lesbian"則指女同性戀者。

9. **gem**
   [dʒɛm]
   好心人（心地善良與衆不同的人）

● "Kay is a gem. I needed $50 to pay this month's rent, and she lent it to me right away."

「Kay 實在是個好心人。我需要 50 元付這個月的房租，她馬上就借給我了。」

"Yeah. She's not a bit like Anne."

「是啊，她一點也不像Anne 。（那麼狠）」

10. **get all (one's) debts off the book! (=to clear one's debts)**
償還債務

● "At the end of the semester, I'd like to get all my debts off the book."

「學期結束時，我希望還清所有的債。」

11. **(to) get carried away**
（因生氣、酒醉、高興而）做得太過火

● "I'm sorry I yelled at you like that. I got carried away."

「抱歉對你那樣大吼大叫，我做得太過火了。」

12. **get changed**
換衣服

● "Do you want to go out for dinner?"

「你想出去吃晚飯嗎？」

"Fine, let's get changed."

「好，換件衣服吧！」

13. **get cleaned out**
[klind]

輸得乾乾淨淨

● "I got cleaned out last time I was in Las Vegas."

「上次我在拉斯維加輸得光光的。」

14. **get clobbered**
①挨揍。②打敗；③慘敗。

① ● "Don't get involved or you'll get clobbered."

「別過問，否則你會挨揍。」

② ● "The basketball team got clobbered by U.C.L.A."

「（我們的）籃球隊被U.C.L.A 的球隊打得慘敗。」

15. **get (=have) cold feet**

害怕（腿軟）（有臨陣逃脫之意）

- "When I have to see a doctor, I get cold feet."
  「每當我必須要去看醫生時，我總是很害怕。」
- "He got cold feet right before his wedding day."
  「就在結婚的前一天，他感到非常害怕。」

16. **get cracking**

[krækɪŋ]

做快一點

- "Let's get cracking; maybe we can finish it before dark."
  「做快一點，也許天黑前我們可以做完。」

17. **get (something) down cold**

學習並且完全了解

- "You'd better get the lesson down cold; otherwise you will fail the test."

  「你最好把功課唸好，否則你會考不及格。」

18. **(don't) get (too) excited**

[ɛk'saɪtɪd]

別太興奮；別太激動

- "Hey, don't get too excited."
  「嘿，別太激動。」

19. **(to) get (one's) foot in the door**

打入（電影事業）；邁入第一步

- "His new job at the company isn't high paying, but at least he got his foot in the door."

  「他在那家公司的新工作待遇不高，但至少他進去了。」

20. **Get going!**

走開（不禮貌的話語）

- "Let's get going!"

「我們走吧！（因爲包括了本身，指的是「走吧！」而不是「走開！」

● "Get going; you are in my way."

「走開，你擋了我的路。」

21. **get (someone) in the end** (=to catch up to someone in the end)

終會有報應

● "Why don't you quit selling dope? It will get you in the end."

「你爲什麼不停止賣毒品呢？你遲早會有報應的。」

22. **get involved**

[ɪn'vɑlvd]

牽扯進去；牽連

● "I don't want to get involved."

「我不想被牽連進去。」

23. **get it off my chest**
    [tʃɛst]

吐實（懺悔自己做過的壞事）；一吐胸中怒氣/積鬱

● "Mary, I want to get something off my chest."

「Mary, 我眞想一吐胸中的積鬱。」

"What?"

「什麼事？」

"While you were on that trip to Europe, I was drunk one Friday night with Alice, and, well, you know what happened."

「當你去歐洲旅行時，我跟Alice 在星期五的晚上喝醉了酒，然後你知道發生了什麼事。」

"How could you?!"

「你怎麼可以那麼做？」

24. **get (me) into this**
    害我陷入困境

    ● "It was you who got me into this."
    「是你害我陷入困境的。」

25. **get lost (=beat it, vamose, hit the pavement, scram, take a**
    滾開　　　[bit]　[væ\mos]　　　　　[ˋpevmənt] [skræm]
    　　　　　　long walk on a short pier)
    　　　　　　　　　　　[pɪr]

    ● "I don't want to see you anymore. Just get lost."
    「我不願再見到你，滾！」

26. **get off my back (=don't bother me)**
    少惹我

    ● "I'm not in a good mood; just get off my back."
    「我心情不好，少惹我。」

27. **get on (=be hired)**
    被僱用

    ● "How did you get on there?"
    「你怎麼在那家公司被僱用的？」
    "My uncle has pull with the manager."
    「我叔叔跟經理交情很好。」

28. **get (someone) on the rebound**
    在某人與男友（或女友）分手後，在其空虛寂寞時乘虛而入

    ●"Dave and Jane broke up, and Bob got her on the
    rebound."
    「Dave 跟 Jane 分手了，Bob（在 Jane 空虛時）乘虛而
    入。」

29. **get on (one's) back**
    找我的麻煩；催我做事

    ●"I don't know why Mr. White always gets on my back."
    「不知爲什麼 White 先生老是找我的麻煩。」

● "John always gets on his brother's back."

「John 老是催他的弟弟做事。」

30. **get out**

滾出去

● "Get out of here."

「滾出去。」

31. **get out of my way**

滾開；別擋路

● "Get out of my way. I'm busy, can't you see?"

「別擋路，我正在忙，你難道沒看見嗎？」

32. **get ready (=on your mark)**

準備好；準備妥當

● "Get ready, get set, go!"

「（賽跑中）各就各位，預備，起跑。」

33. **get ready (or be prepared) for the worst**

作萬一的準備

● "How is she?"

「她如何了？」

"Not so good. The doctor said we had to be prepared for the worst."

「不太妙，醫生說我們得做最壞的打算。」

34. **get (one's) shit together**

頭腦清醒；行動正常

● "I've never seen you do a right thing. When will you get your shit together?"

「我從來沒看過你做對一件事。你什麼時候才會頭腦清醒？」

35. **get sore (=mad)**

[sor]

生氣

● "I got sore because of his bad manners."

「我因爲他的不禮貌而生氣！」

● "Don't get sore. I was only joking."

「別生氣，我只是在開玩笑。」

36. **get (something) straight**

[stret]

把話說清楚；把事情弄清楚。

● "Let's get it straight."

「讓我們把話（事情）說清楚。」

37. **get the ax**

[æks]

被開除；被解僱

● "He got the ax because of his bad manners."

「他因爲惡劣的態度而被開除了。」

38. **get (or have) the munchies (=to be hungry)**

[mʌntʃɪz]

有點餓了（嘴饞）

● "Let's get something to eat. I've got the munchies."

「我們吃點東西吧，我有點餓了。」

39. **get the rebound**

[rɪˈbaund]

搶到籃板球

● "Wonda Lee, No. 7, got 10 rebounds in the game."

「Wonda Lee，7號，搶到10個籃板球。」

● "John White jumps, shoots, and misses. David Snow gets the rebound."

「John White 跳起來投籃，沒進。Davie Snow 搶到籃板球。」

40. **get to the bottom (of something)**

探個究竟

- "I don't know who did this, but I'll get to the bottom of it."

  「我不知道是誰幹的，但我會查個水落石出。」

41. **get to the point (=come to the point)**

    說出重點；主題來

    - "Stop beating around the bush and get to the point."

      「別兜圈子了，說出你要說的話來。」

42. **get your act together**
    (=get your shit together)

    頭腦清醒；做點正經事

    - "When will you grow up and get your act together?"

      「你什麼時候才會長大，幹點正事？」

43. **get with it**

    ①接受（某一種新的流行）。②趕快做好。

    ① ● " t with it, Bill: disco is here to stay."

      「接受它吧！Bill, disco 在此已生根了。」

    ② ● "It's getting late. Let's get with it."

      「天色不早了。我們快點做吧！」

44. **(You're not) getting away with it.**

    你逃不掉；賴不掉的。

    - "You killed my husband, and you're not getting away with it."

      「你殺了我的丈夫，你逃不掉的。」

45. **gig**

    [gɪg]

    （暫時性的）工作（通常指娛樂工作）

    - "Hey, Bill. How are you lately? I heard you got a

new gig."

「嘿，Bill，近來好嗎？我聽說你找到一份工作了。」

● "We've got a gig Friday night at the club. They're having a dance and they want our band to play."

「星期五晚上我們在夜總會有份臨時工作，他們開舞會要我們去伴奏。」

46. **gigolo (=kept man)**
[ˈdʒɪgəˌlo]

吃軟飯的男人；小白臉（陪伴有錢女人的男人）

● "He is a gigolo."

「他是一個吃軟飯的小白臉。」

47. **gimmick**
[ˈgɪmɪk]

①新花招。②這玩藝兒（難懂的東西）

① ● "This company is giving away calendars as an advertising gimmick."

「這家公司正在贈送日曆作為廣告新花招。」

② ● "Would you explain how this gimmick works?"

「你能不能解釋一下這玩藝兒怎麼用？」

48. **girl**

女朋友

● "She is my girl."

「她是我的女朋友。」

49. **give (me, him) a break**

①給 … 一個喘氣休息的機會。②別惹我。

① ● "Give me a break, will you?"

「讓我喘口氣休息一下，好嗎？」

● "He's been working for 8 hours straight. Give him a break."

「他一連工作了八小時，讓他休息一下。」

② ● "Today just isn't my day. Give me a break."

「今天真不順，別惹我。」·

50. **give (someone) a call/ring/buzz**

打電話

● "Give me a buzz, will you?"

「記得打電話給我，好嗎？」

51. **give (me) a chance**

給我一次機會

● "How do you know I can't do it unless you give me a chance."

「你不給我一個機會，你怎麼知道我不能做？」

52. **(to) give a damn**

　　　　[dæm]

在乎；在意

● "I don't give a damn."

「我才不在乎。」

● "You didn't give a damn about me."

「你對我一點也不在乎。」

53. **give (someone) a hard (or bad) time**

讓（某人）日子不好過（找麻煩；為難他）

● "I had enough today, so don't give me a hard time."

「我今天已受夠了，所以別再找我麻煩。」

● "Are you trying to give me a hard time?"

「你想讓我的日子難過是嗎？」

54. **give (someone) a kick in the behind**

鼓勵別人去做（別人因為不願意或緊張而不敢做）

● "School has been out for three weeks and my son still

hasn't started looking for a summer job."

「學校已結束三個星期了，我兒子還沒去找暑期工作。」

"Maybe he needs a kick in the behind to get him going."

「也許他需要有人催他一下。」

註：behind 指屁股 butt, ass 。

55. give ground
[gɪv/graund]

讓步

● "He's so stubborn that he refuses to give ground on any issue."

「他是那麼的頑固，拒絕在任何爭議上讓步。」

56. give it to (someone) good and strong

好好的罵一頓

● "When Bill comes home tonight, I'll give it to him good and strong."

「Bill 今晚回來我要好好的罵他一頓。」

57. give me a hand

幫個忙（指體力上的）

● "Judy, give me a hand will you? Pass me that hammer."

「Judy, 幫個忙好嗎？把那個鎚子遞給我。」

58. give (someone) the finger (=fuck you)

伸出中指表示"操"的意思

● "That creep used to hang around my sister, but she gave him the finger, and told him to get lost."

「那個混蛋常常騷擾我妹妹，她伸出她的中指給他看，並叫他滾遠點。」

註：the finger 指中指，在美國伸出一隻中指示人，表示 fuck 的意思（這是一個粗野的動作，所以可別亂伸手指，小心挨揍！）

59. **give up**
    認輸；投降
    - "I give up; you win."
      「我認輸，你贏了。（下棋、玩牌中）」

60. **give (someone) what for**
    責備；指控；罵；打
    - "Did he really say that to you? O.K. I'll give him what for."
      「他真的對你那麼說嗎？好，我會罵他一頓。」

61. **go ahead**
    請便；去（做）吧！
    - "If you want to get killed, just go ahead."
      「如果你不想活了，請便！」
    - "Could I take a look at your notes?"
      「我能不能看一看你的筆記？」
      "Go ahead."
      「請便。」

62. **go all the way**
    幹到底
    - "She refused to go 'all the way'."
      （在此表示）「她拒絕上床的意思。」

63. **go all-out! (=Let's give it all we've got.)**
    努力拼命幹（來自運動術語）
    - "Let's go all-out."
      「讓我們努力拼命幹吧！」

64. **go away**

    走開；滾

    ● "Go away; I don't want to hear anything you say."
      「走開，我不想聽你說任何事。」

65. **go bananas (= go crazy; go nuts)**
    發瘋

    ● "I'll go bananas if I have to do it again."
      「假如我得重頭再做一遍，我會發瘋。」

    ● "If I stay with her for one more minute. I'll go bananas."
      「假如要我再跟她多待一分鐘，我會發瘋。」

66. **go down the line**

    深入下層去尋找

    ● I went down the line to find a new man for the vice
      president's job.

      （我是 1 號大老闆，2 號老闆離職，我不升用 3 號而去 4.
      5. 6. 7. 號中找。）

67. **go Dutch**

    各付各的（帳）

    ● "Let's go Dutch."
      「我們各付各的吧。」

    註：美國人與朋友外出時通常是各付各的，所以很少用這句話。

68. **go for it.**

    努力去做；努力打敗對方（球賽中用）

    ● "Is everybody ready? O.K. Let's go for it."
      「大家都準備好了吧？好！讓我們努力打敗他們。」

69. **go home**

    滾回去

    ● "Go home commie!"
      「共產黨滾回去！」

● "Yankee go home!"
「美國佬滾回去！」

70. **(to) go in one ear and come out the other**
左耳進右耳出

  ● "It's no use trying to convince him, whatever you say goes in one ear and comes out the other."
  「不用去說服他，你的話他是左耳進右耳出。」

71. **Go jump in a lake (=get lost, take a hike)**
滾遠點（少煩我）

  ● "Can't you see I'm busy? Why don't you go jump in a lake."
  「你難道沒看見我正在忙？滾遠點。」

  註：當你在工作時，有人在一旁煩你，你叫他 "Go climb a mountain." "Go take a hike." ... 都是叫他滾開少煩人的意思，但語氣沒有 "Go jump in a lake." 重！

72. **go off half-cocked**
輕舉妄動（操之過急）

  ● "Don't go off half-cocked. Let's ask Mr. Moreno's advice first."
  「別輕舉妄動，讓我們先去請教一下 Moreno 先生。」

73. **Go to hell!**
     [hɛl]
去死；少惹我；走開

  ● "Go to hell, will you? I don't need your free advice."
  「少惹我行不行？我不需要你的免費忠告。」

74. **(to) go to pieces**
崩潰；支離破碎（指心情，事情）

  ● "After Pete left, she went to pieces."
  「在 Pete 離開之後，她完全崩潰了。」

● "This office has gone to pieces since the last budget cut."

「自從上次開支被削減之後，辦公室變得設備不全工作效率低落。」

75. **go-between**

中間人

● "Mr. Smith will serve as the go-between for our two companies."

「Smith 先生將當我們兩家公司的中間連絡人。」

76. **go-getter**

[ˋgɛtɚ]

工作認眞的人（如：大家都在吃中飯，他仍然在工作）

● "He's a real go-getter. He's going to go for it."

「他是一個工作認眞的人，他會有前途的。」

77. **(You're) going nowhere**

不可能有發展前途與希望

● "Take it from me, son, you're going nowhere."

「就拿我做例子，兒啊，你不會有發展的。」

● "You're going nowhere with that girl."

「你跟那個女孩子不會有希望的。」

78. **going out (=going steady)**

固定下去做男女朋友

● "They are going out together."

「他們定下來了。」

79. **going-out-of-business sale**

[sel]

歇業大拍賣

● "Bang Bang is having a going-out-of-business sale, do you want to go and take a look? Maybe we can buy some shirts for low prices."

「Bang Bang 公司正在舉行歇業大拍賣，你要不要去瞧瞧
？說不定我們可以買到幾件便宜襯衫。」

80. **(a) goner**
[ˈɡɑnɚ]

無藥可救的人（事）；完蛋

● "He's a goner; don't waste your time."
「他是一個無可救藥的人，別浪費你的時間了。」

● "As soon as he hit the ball, I knew it was a goner."
「當他一擊中那個球，我就知道完蛋了。」

81. **good buy (= nice buy = good bargain)**
買得便宜；買得划算；好價錢

● "How much is this hair dryer?"
「這個吹風機多少錢？」
"$5.95."
「五塊九毛五。」

"It's really a good buy. I'll buy two. One for my sister."
「真便宜，我要買兩個，一個給我妹妹。」
註：相反的是 "bad buy"。

82. **(someone is) good for nothing**
（某人）是個廢物

● "He's good for nothing."
「他是個廢物。」

83. **Good for you**
好！對你會有益。（恭喜你如此做！）

● "I'll take your word and see a doctor."
「我會聽你的話去看醫生。」
"Good for you."
「好！」

● "I already quit smoking."

「我已經戒煙了。」

"Good for you."

「恭喜。」

84. **good grief**

[grif]

老天！

● "Good grief, Mary is going to marry Paul next week."

「老天，Mary 下禮拜要嫁給 Paul。」

85. **Good night, sleep tight.**

晚安，祝好夢

● "Good night, sleep tight, don't let the bedbugs bite."

「晚安，好好睡，別給臭蟲咬着囉！」

註：這是美國人常掛在嘴上的一句話。

86. **good old days**

過去美好的時光

● "Oh, I can still remember those good old days."

「哦，我仍然可以記得那些美好的日子。」

87. **good taste**

[test]

有好眼光（鑑賞力，品味）

● "He has good taste in food, wine, and women."

「他對食物，酒跟女人都很有眼光。」

註：bad taste 是低俗的眼光，格調不高也！

88. **goof off**

['guf]

①遊蕩。②整天閒蕩的人。

① ◉ "Where is Dick? Susan."

「Susan，Dick 在哪兒？」

"He is goofing off again, Mom."

「媽，他又去遊蕩了。」

② ● "Mary is a goof-off."

「Mary 整天只知遊蕩。」

89. **gook**

[guk]

黃種人（輕視語，本字因在越戰中流行起來，故多指越南人）

● "Hey, you gook."

「嘿，黃種人。」

90. **gooney bird (=doof; doofus)**

['gunɪ]

笨鳥；笨蛋！（呆頭呆腦，呆頭鵝）

● "Who's that gooney bird?"

「那個笨蛋是誰？」

91. **gopher**

['gofɚ]

跑腿

● "Bill is the gopher around this office. Whenever we need anything, he's the one who goes for it."

「Bill 是我們辦公室裏跑腿的，每當我們需要任何東西的時候，總是他去買。」

92. **gosh**

[gɑʃ]

天啊！老天！

● "Gosh, this apple sure is big."

「老天，這蘋果可眞大啊。」

93. **got**

①難倒。②騙到了！③抓到。

①② "You really got me this time."

「這次你眞難倒／騙到我了！」

③● "Got you."
　「抓到你了。」

94. **(someone) got/have a lot of nerve**
很有勇氣；膽子很大（抱怨時則指厚臉皮）

● "She's got a lot of nerve to say that."
　「她能說出那些話實在很有勇氣。」

● "Maggie borrowed my new dress without asking again. She's got a lot of nerve."
　「Maggie 再次沒問我一聲就穿走了我的新衣服，她膽子眞大。」

95. **(have) got an eye**
①打算要做。②注意一下，留意一下（某事）。③有鑑賞力；有眼光。

①● "He's got an eye to marry Helen."
　「他打算要娶Helen。」

● "She hasn't got an eye to marry John."
　「她還沒打算要嫁給John。」

②● "I've got an eye out for that book. If I find it, I'll tell you."
　「我已留意那本書了。如果我發現，我會告訴你。」

③● "He has an eye for art."
　「他對藝術很有眼光。」

96. **got it**
①成功了。②懂了。③挨揍。

①● "I got it."
　「我成功了。」

②● "Do you understand?" "Yes, I've got it."
　「你懂了吧？」　　「懂了。」

③● "You're going to get it."
　「你要挨揍了。」

97. **(I/you)'ve got nothing to lose**
[luz]

不會有什麼損失的（不做白不做，不去白不去）

- "Come on, go with us. You've got nothing to lose."
「快點，跟我們一起去吧。反正你也沒什麼好損失的。」
- "Why don't you call Linda and see if she is free tonight?"
「你為什麼不打個電話給Linda，看看她今晚是否有空？」
"O.K. why not? I've got nothing to lose."
「好吧！為什麼不 (打) 呢？我反正也沒什麼損失。」

98. **(You) got off on the wrong foot**
（你）打從開頭就做錯了。

- "I got off on the wrong foot when I went to college. I just never learned to study in high school, but I learned how to study in my freshman year."

「當我進入大學時第一步就走錯了。我在高中時從來不知道什麼是唸書，我在大一時才學會怎麼去唸書。」

- "My relationship with Pam got off on the wrong foot, but things are OK now."

「我跟Pam的關係一開頭就沒搞好，但現在一切已沒問題了。」

99. **(someone) got the magic touch**
手法靈活；技巧好

- "How did you get her?"
「你怎麼得到她的？」

"I've got the magic touch."
「我有特別的技巧。」

100. **(I) got the runs (=I got quickstep)**
['kwɪk,stɛp]

瀉肚子

"Probably because of food poisoning, I got the runs."

"Would you like some more coffee?"   "Yes, please."   "Say when."

● "Probably because of food poisoning, I got the runs."

「也許是因爲食物中毒（不乾淨之故），我今天瀉肚子﹏」

101. grand

[grænd]

一千元（複數不加 s ）

● "How much do you want?"

「你要多少錢？」

"50 grand."

「五萬元。」

102. G.O.P. (=Grand Old Party — the Republican Party)

[grænd]

（美國）共和黨

● "First he worked for the GOP; then he switched to the Democratic Party."

「他先是爲共和黨工作，後來又轉替民主黨做事。」

103. grass (=pot; cannabis; marijuana; mary jane; reefer; boo; dope; weed)

大麻煙（未捲好的）

● "Do you want to buy some grass?"

「你要買點大麻煙嗎？」

註：joint, bone, reefer, stick是指已捲好的，"high"是形容吸後飄飄欲仙的感覺。

104. (a) great ticket

['tɪkɪt]

有勝利；贏的希望

● " Clinton and Gore will be a great ticket. "

「克林頓與高爾聯手會有贏的希望。」

105. green (=new hand)

[grin]

①生手；沒有經驗的。②嫉妒。

① ● "I don't think I can handle it myself, I'm still pretty green."

「我不認為我能單獨應付這件事，我仍然是個生手。」

② ● "He was green with envy."

「他嫉妒了。」

註：Vet (=Veteran) 是老手。

106. greenback

['grin bæk]

美鈔（因一般美鈔都是綠色的）

● "Could you lend me a few greenbacks?"

「你能不能借我幾張美鈔？」

107. green light

綠燈，即獲准做某件事

● "I got the green light this morning to go to the U.S.; I got my I-20 in the mail."

「今早我收到了入學許可證，我獲准去美國了。」

註 I-20 是指美國大學入學許可證。

● "My old man gave me the green light to marry her."

「我老爸批准我娶她。」

108. (be) (greeted) with open arms

受到熱烈歡迎

● "When he went back to the school, he was greeted with open arms."

「他返回學校時，受到了熱烈的歡迎。」

109. groovy

['gruvɪ]

①很棒；很順利；很好。②他不是外人；可信賴的。

① ● "I like this song."

「我喜歡這首歌。」

"Yes, it's groovy."

「是的，真棒。」

② ● "Don't tell him."

「別告訴他。」

"It's O.K. He is groovy."

「沒關係，他不是外人。」

110. guess so

大概是吧！可能

● "Is she coming?"

「她會來嗎？」

"I guess so!"

「我想會吧！」

111. gun-fighter (=gun man)

槍手；狙擊手

● "He hired two gun-fighters to kill you, so be careful."

「他僱了兩個槍手要殺你，所以小心一點。」

112. gut

[gʌt]

勇氣；胆量（欽佩的口語）

● "You've got a lot of guts to say that."

「你說那些話，眞是有勇氣。」

註：若 gut 改成 nerve 則成責備口吻，「胆子不小」。

113. guys and gals (=guys and dolls)

[gaɪz]　[gælz]

諸位　（guy 是男生，gal 是女生）

● "Hey, guys and gals, let's all sing happy birthday to Charlotte."

「嘿，各位，讓我們一起爲 Charlotte 唱生日快樂歌。」

114. gyp (=cheat)

[dʒɪp]

騙人

● "This watch is a fake. I got gyped."

「這個手錶是假的，我受騙了。」

115. gyp joint

[dʒɪp/dʒɔɪnt]

黑店（敲竹槓的商店）

● "Big cities always have a lot of gyp joints."

「在大城市中總有許多黑店。」

1. **hack it**
   忍得了；熬得住；可以做
   - "This training is too tough. I can't hack it."
     「這訓練太辛苦了，我受不了。」

2. **(one's) hair stood (on end)**
   毛髮聳然
   - "He was so frightened his hair stood on end."
     「他嚇得毛髮聳然。」

3. **Half a loaf is better than none.**
   聊勝於無
   - "How much did they pay you?"
     「他們付你多少？」
     "$1.50 per hour."
     「一個小時一塊半。」
     "$1.50 per hour? Are you crazy or something? You're working for nothing!"
     「一塊半一個小時？你瘋了是不是？你白作了！」
     "Well, half a loaf is better than none."
     「哦，聊勝於無嘛！」
   註：bread 又作「錢」解。

4. **hands up**
   舉起手來（搶劫時常用）

● "Hands up and don't move!"
「手舉起來，別動！」

5. **handy**

['hændɪ]

①派上用場。②精通，在行。

① ● "Save it, it will come in handy."

「留着它，總有一天會派上用場。」

② ● "I'm not very handy with electrical things, but my little brother is."

「我對電器不是很在行，但是我的小弟弟却很精通。」

6. **hang around**

①逗留；停留。②遊蕩。

① ● "Hang around for a while, I want to tell you something."

「再多待一會兒，我要告訴你一些事。」

② ● "Don't just hang around. You can help me to do some cleaning."

「別在那兒幌。你可以幫我清掃一下吧。」

7. **hang in there (=don't give up)**

堅忍；死守；別放棄

● "Don't quit. Hang in there a minute. I'll be right back."

「別放棄，再忍一下，我馬上回來。」

8. **hang on**

①請等一下（別掛斷電話）。②抓緊。③堅強。④繼續做，想… 。

① ● "Hello, may I speak to Mr. White?"

「喂，White 先生在嗎？」

"Hang on, please."

「請等一下。」

② ● "He fell out the window, but was able to hang on to the window ledge until the firemen came."

「他從窗戶摔了出去，但是有足夠的力氣抓緊窗台，直到消防隊員來。」

③ ● "Hang on Paul, the ambulance will be here any minute."

「Paul，堅強點，救護車馬上就到了。」

④ ● "Why do you insist on hanging on to that bad habit of biting your nails?"

「你怎麼還不停止咬指甲的壞毛病？」

9. **hang out**

①聚集。②一個人常去的地方。

① ● "We're not doing anything special tonight, just hanging out at home."

「我們今晚並沒有什麼特別的節目，我們只是窩在家裏。」

② ● "I met him at our usual hang out downtown."

「我與他在我們常去的鬧區地方碰了面。」

10. **hang up**

①心理上有某種迷惘的想法，所以對某些事有抗拒性，不表贊成。

②掛電話。

① ● "You should get over that ridiculous hangup."

「你該除去那可笑而不正確的想法。」

● "Very conservative people usually have a lot of hangups about sex."

「非常保守的人，常常對「性」很迷惘。」

② ● "She hung up the phone on me."

「她掛斷了我的電話。」

11. **hangover(n.)   hung over (v.)**

宿醉未醒

- "He has a hangover."
  「他宿醉未醒。」
- "He was hung over all Sunday."
  「他整個星期天都宿醉未醒（因星期六酒喝多了）。」

12. **hanky-panky**
   亂來；胡來

   - "We don't allow any hanky panky around here."
     「在這裏我們不允許任何胡來的事。」

13. **Happy driving.**
   （開車）一路順風

   - "Happy landing."
     （搭機）
   - "Bon voyage." [bɔ̃vwaˈjaʒ]
     （搭機，搭船）一路順風。
   - "Have a nice trip."
     「旅途愉快。」

14. **a happy ending**
   圓滿的結局

   - I always like a happy ending."
     「我喜歡圓滿的結局。」
   - "Not all stories have a happy ending."
     「不是所有的故事都有快樂的結局。」

15. **(I'm) happy for you.**
   我真為你感到高興（當聽到別人的好消息時）

   - "I got the scholarship."
     「我申請到獎學金了。」
     "I'm happy for you."
     「我真為你高興。」

16. **hard-headed**
   頑固

"Are you trying to give me a hard time?"

"I don't want you to see my daughter any more. You two don't belong with each other. Have I made myself clear?"

"Quit clear, Mr. Huss."

—

- "Don't be hard-headed."
  「別頑固。」

17. **hard time**
    [hard]

    添麻煩；難過的時光；為難（一個人）使其不痛快或工作不順。

    - "Don't give me a hard time. I got enough shit from people today."
      「別再給我添麻煩，今天我已受夠了。」
    - "Are you trying to give me a hard time?"
      「你想找我的麻煩嗎？」
      "Yes."
      「是的。」

18. **hard up**

    手頭很緊（經濟拮据）

    - "I'm hard up lately; can you loan me some money?"
      「我近來手頭很緊，你能借我一點錢嗎？」

19. **(Someone) has no control over (himself)**

    不能自制

    - "He got drunk every night. He just has no control over himself."
      「他每晚都喝醉了，他實在不能自制。」

20. **has-been**

    過氣的（明星、歌星）

    - "She is a has-been movie star."
      「她是一個過氣的電影明星。」

21. **haste makes waste**
    [hest]   [west]

    性急易出錯

- "Don't rush; haste makes waste."
  「別急，性急易出錯。」

22. **(a) haul**

    [hɔl]

    收穫

    - "What a haul! I would never expect to catch 15 fish in a day."
      「眞是大豐收，我怎也沒想到一天之內會抓到15條魚。」

23. **have a ball**

    玩得很開心

    - "We sure had a ball last night."
      「我們昨晚玩得眞開心。」

24. **have a blast**

    [blæst]

    狂歡；玩得非常開心（宴會）

    - "Did we have a blast last night!"
      「我們昨晚的舞會算不算是狂歡啊！」（眞開心之意！）

    註：have a blast 非常流行，意思與 have a ball 近似。

25. **to have a bone to pick with (someone)**

    把不愉快的事情解釋清楚；澄清不愉快的事

    - "I have a bone to pick with him."
      「我要跟他澄清一下不愉快的事。」

26. **(to) have a chip on (one's) shoulder**

    憤世嫉俗；容易動怒

    - "He has a chip on his shoulder."
      「他很憤世嫉俗。」

27. **have a crush on (someone)**

    [krʌʃ]

    迷上（某人）

● "I've had a crush on Robert Redford since I was a little girl."

「打從我是個小女孩，我就迷上了勞勃雷福。」

28. **have a flat tire and no jack!**
    [flæt/taɪr]   [dʒæk]

倒霉透了！（屋漏偏逢連夜雨）。（jack 是換輪胎用的千斤頂）

● "I never have felt so helpless before. We have a flat tire and no jack. Even though we have a spare, it's of no use."

「我從來就沒有這麼絕望過。我們的車胎漏氣了，但沒有千斤頂，雖然我們有備胎，也是無濟於事。」

29. **have a go at (something) (=give something a go)**

初嚐試；試一下（新的方法、東西）

● "I'll have a go at it this way."

「我這樣試試看。（如不知怎樣換車胎，自己胡亂試一下）」

● "Have you ever gone horseback riding?"

「你騎過馬嗎？」

"No."

「沒有。」

"You ought to have a go at it someday. It's a hell of a lot of fun."

「你哪天該試一試。騎馬是很有趣的。」

30. **have a heart of gold**

心地善良

● "I like Judy. She has a heart of gold."

「我喜歡 Judy, 她心地善良。」

31. **have a word with you**

跟你說句話（通常是告訴對方自己的不滿）

- "Bonnie, I want to have a word with you. I don't like the way you've been acting around Bruce recently. He's my boyfriend. Hands off, OK?"

「Bonnie，我要跟你談談。我不喜歡你最近在 Bruce 面前的表現。他是我的男朋友，你少打他的主意，好嗎？」

32. **have an ax to grind**
    [æks] [graɪnd]

別有企圖（對事情不滿意）

- "You'd better watch out for Lionel. I think he has an ax to grind."

「你最好提防一點 Lionel，我想他別有企圖。」

33. **have an itch**
    [ɪtʃ]

躍躍欲試；有 … 衝動去做 …

- "When I see the swimming pool, I have an itch to jump into it."

「當我看到游泳池的時候，我有股衝動想跳進去。」

34. **(to) have ants in one's pants**

煩燥不安；坐立不安（好像褲內有螞蟻）

- "Why can't you sit still? Do you have ants in your pants?"

「你為什麼坐立不安，褲子裏有螞蟻啊？」

35. **(have) been had**

受騙；上當

● "Don't you know when you've been had?"
「上當時你不知道嗎？」

36. **to have diarrhea of the mouth**
   [ˌdaɪəˈrɪə]
   話太多了！太囉嗦

   ● "Would you shut up?　You've got diarrhea of the mouth."
   「你閉嘴好不好？你話太多了。」

37. **Have I made myself clear?**
   我的話說得夠清楚了吧？（你該聽懂了）

   ● "I don't want you to see my daughter any more. You two don't belong with each other. Have I made myself clear?
   「我不希望你再來找我女兒，你們兩個是不屬於對方的，我的話說的清不清楚？」

   "Quite clear, Mr. Huss."
   「夠清楚了，Huss 先生。」

38. **have it out**
   把話說出來（攤牌；說出心中不快）

   ● "What about me bothers you? Let's have it out."
   「我到底什麼地方惹了你了？讓我們把話說清楚。」

39. **have it your own way**
   隨你（生氣時用）

   ● "This is my final offer.　Take it or leave it; have it your own way."
   「這是我最後的出價，要或不要隨便你。」

40. **have nothing to worry about**
    無可憂之事

    ● "We have nothing to worry about, because we have nothing to lose."
    「我們沒什麼可擔心的，因為我們沒什麼好損失的。」

    ● "I'm on the pill, so I have nothing to worry about."
    「我已吃了避孕丸，所以我沒什麼好擔心的。」

41. **(to) have one foot in the grave**
    老了（一脚已踩進墳墓）

    ● "He's old and sick. He has one foot in the grave."
    「他又老又病，他已經是一隻脚踩進墳墓的人了。」

42. **have pull with (someone)**
    對 … （人）有影響力

    ● "His father has pull with the governor."
    「他爸爸對州長有影響力。」

    ● "Don't try to fight with him. He has a lot of pull with Senator Johnson."
    「別想跟他爭，他對 Johnson 參議員有很大的影響力。」

43. **have some plan up (one's) sleeve**
    　　　　　[plæn]　　　　　[sliv]
    袖裏乾坤，定有妙計

    ● "What are we going to do?"
    「我們該怎麼辦呢？」

    "I don't know, but I'm sure Mr. Chamot must have some plan up his sleeve."
    「我不知道，但我相信 Chamot 先生一定有妙計。」

44. **have the inside track**
    ①佔有利位置。②優於。

    ① ● "They won the race because they had the inside track."

「他們贏了這場比賽，因爲佔了有利的位置。」

② ● "You should invest in his company. He's got the inside track, what with that computer filing system and all."

「你應該投資他的公司的。他的公司優於其他的公司，因爲他們有一個電腦資料中心及其他的設備。」

45. **(someone) (to) have the makings of a (musician, . . .)**
天生是塊 … 料

● "He has the makings of a composer."
「他天生是塊作曲的料。」

46. **having an affair with (someone)**
與（某人）有染

● "Do you think Dick is having an affair with his secretary?"
「你想Dick跟他的秘書有一手嗎？」
"I don't know."
「我不知道。」

47. **(We're) having trouble.**
我們正在吵鬧（或正鬧離婚）

● "How're you and Joan?"
「你與Joan近來如何？」
"We're having trouble."
「我們正在鬧離婚。」

48. **hay (=sack)**
[he]
床

● "Let's hit the hay. (=Let's go to sleep.)"
「我們睡覺去吧！」

49. **health nut**

[hɛlθ/nʌt]

有潔癖的人

- "You are really a health nut."

「你真是個有潔癖的人。」

"Yes, I know. I can't help it."

「是，我知道，但我對自己也沒辦法。」

50. **(Someone's) heart is in the right place, (but his brain isn't).**

頭腦有問題，但心地很好

- "Sometimes, he is insane, but his heart is in the right place."

「有時，他真是瘋了，但他的心地還是很好的。」

51. **Heaven / God knows.**

天知道！鬼才知道；天曉得

- "Do you think John will give you back the money he owes you?"

「你想 John 會還你他欠你的錢嗎？」

"Heaven knows."

「天知道。」

52. **heavy smoker (=nicotine fiend)**

['nɪkətɪn find]

老烟槍

- "Jack is a heavy smoker."

「Jack 是個老烟槍。」

53. **heck**

[hɛk]

他媽的，狗屎。（ hell 的委婉語，粗話 ）

- "Heck, I feel the same way you do."

「他媽的，我的感覺跟你一樣。」

● "What the heck."
「管他三七二十一。」

54. **a heck (= hell) of a man / woman**
   [hɛk]　　[hɛl]
   了不起

● "He is a heck of a man."
「他眞是一個了不起的人。」

55. **The heck with it!**
   算了

● "I've asked him three times but he always forgets."
「我拜託過他三次，但他老是忘記。」
"The heck with it. We can ask someone else."
「算了，我們可以請別人幫忙。」

56. **Hey, you know what?**
   嘿，你知道嗎？（在告訴別人一件事前的開場白）

● "Hey, you know what?"
「嘿，你知道嗎？」
"What?"
「知道什麼？」
"I'm going to get married tomorrow."
「我明天要結婚了。」
"No kidding?"
「不是開玩笑？」
"No kidding!"
「不是開玩笑。」

57. **hi-test**
   [haɪ/tɛst]
   高級汽油

● "Give me five dollars worth of hi-test, please."
「請給我五塊錢的高級汽油。」

註：premium 也是高級汽油，regular 是普通汽油，unleaded (no lead) 是不含鉛的，diesel 是柴油。

58. **high**

吃大麻後飄飄然的感覺

- "Want to get high?"

「要過過癮嗎？」

59. **highbrow**

[ˋhaɪˏbrau]

①特別（好）的鑑賞力。②來自世家名門，自以為了不起。

① ● "I have a highbrow taste in music."

「對音樂我的鑑賞力很高。」

② ● "We asked him to go to the Donny and Marie show, but he said he only likes classical music. What a highbrow."

「我們邀他去唐尼‧瑪麗的音樂會，但他說他只喜歡古典音樂。真是一個自以為了不起的人。」

註:lowbrow是指胃口、喜好是一般大眾化的。

60. **high-tail**

[tel]

快去；快快跑（兔子跑快時，尾巴豎起來）

- "The dean is looking for you. You'd better high-tail it over to his office."

「院長在找你。你最好趕快去他的辦公室。」

61. **higher-up**

高級職員；上司

- "He is one of the higher-ups in a multi-national corporation."

「他是一家國際性大公司的高級職員之一。」

62. **highway robbery**

敲竹槓；勒索

● "$60 for a pair of shoes?! That's highway robbery."
「一雙鞋 60 塊？這簡直是敲竹槓。」

63. **hijack**
['haɪdʒæk]

搶劫

● "This is a hijack; don't move."
「這是劫機，別動。」

64. **hit and run**
[hɪt]

棒球中打帶跑，即是汽車撞人後逃離現場

● "Hit and run is a serious crime."
「駕車肇事後逃逸是項嚴重的罪。」

● "It was a hit and run accident."
「那是一件駕駛員撞了人跑掉的車禍。」

65. **hit the nail on the head**
①猜對了；答對了。②計劃很好；很恰當（會成功）

① ● "I think the real reason he won't change jobs is that he's afraid to try something new."
「我猜想他不肯換工作的真正原因是因為他怕嘗試新的東西。」

"You hit the nail right on the head."
「你完全答對了。」

② ● "Your plan hits the nail on the head."
「你的計劃很好！」

66. **hitch hike (v.)**
[hitʃ /haɪk]

搭便車（在公路上以豎起大姆指，或以大姆指指自己要去的方向，請求搭便車）

● "Did you know that hitchhiking is dangerous?"
「你知道搭便車是件危險的事嗎？」

67. **hog**

[hɑg]

①駕車覇佔車道的人。②貪婪的人。③豬。④獨佔。

① ● "What a road hog."

「眞是一個差勁的駕駛員。」

註：road hog 是開在兩綫中間不讓別人超車佔馬路的人。

② ● "He's a hog."

「他是一個貪婪的人。」

註：speed Demon 是快車手（Demon 是一魔鬼名），快車手技術未必高明。slow poke 是慢蝸牛。

③ ● "Don't be such a hog. Save some food for the others."

「別那麼貪吃，留點給別人。」

④ ● "Don't hog the sofa. We can both sit here."

「別一人獨佔這沙發，我們可以一起坐。」

68. **hold a candle to (someone)**

與 … 一樣地好 （永遠用在否定句中）

● "His Chinese is good, but he can't hold a candle to you."

「他的中文很好，但是不如你的。」

69. **hold a job**

待在一個職位上

● "I don't know what's wrong with me, I can't hold a job very long."

「我不知道自己是怎麼搞的，老是在一種工作上待不久。」

70. **Hold it (=wait a minute=stop)**

慢著；等一下

● "Hold it; don't move."

「（用槍指着）慢著，別動。」

75. **honky-tonk**

[haŋkɪ/taŋk]

低級酒店.

- "There are a lot of honky-tonks in that area."
  「那個地區有很多低級的酒店。」
- "She sings in a honky-tonk at night."
  「她晚上在一家低級的酒店裡賣唱。」

76. **hoof**

[huf]

走

- "Let's hoof it to the Kash and Karry."
  「讓我們走到 Kash and Karry 去。」

註："Kash and Karry" 音與 "Cash and Carry" 同，是美
國有名的小型連鎖雜貨店。

77. **hooker** [ˋhukæ]

妓女

- "There are lots of hookers on the streets at night in
  New York."
  「晚上在紐約街道上常有許多妓女。」

78. **hot**

①辣（＝spicy）②想與人交朋友。③好；棒；才藝特出。④
贓物（＝stolen）。⑤運氣來時城牆都擋不住。

① ● "Do you like hot food?"
  「你喜歡吃辣的東西嗎？」
  "Yes, I do."
  「是的，我喜歡。」

② ● "I've got the hots for that girl."
  「我想跟那個女孩做朋友。」

③ ● "I don't think she is so hot, though."
  「我不認爲她是那麼地特出。」

"Don't you know that hitchhiking is dangerous?"

"Do you like hot food?"
"Yes, I do."

註：在電視、電影中，當歹徒正要開槍射殺對方
會及時趕到，大叫「別動！」

71. **Hold it down (=pipe down).**

安靜一點

- "Hold it down in here. My mother is o
  from Taiwan."

  「請安靜一點。我媽從台灣打電話來。」

72. **hold up**

[hold]

搶劫

- "The bank was held up yesterday. One
  was stolen."

  「銀行昨天被搶，損失了一百萬元。」

- "This is a hold-up! Don't move."

  「這是搶劫。別動！」

73. **honeymoon**

蜜月（指雙方關係良好）

- "Their honeymoon is over."

  「他們的蜜月期已過。」（關係開始惡化

- "The President and Congress are still
  moon."

  「總統與國會仍在蜜月期中。」

74. **honkey**

['hɑŋkɪ]

白鬼子（黑人罵白人的說法）

- "I'm going to teach that honkey a les

  「我要給那白鬼一個教訓。」

註：nigger 則是黑鬼（白人罵黑人的說法

- "That's hot!"

  「那東西眞棒！」

④ ● "This is a hot car."

  「這是一輛贓車。」

- "Hey, do you want to buy a radio? Real cheap!"

  「嘿，你想買架收音機嗎？很便宜哦！」

  "Is it hot?"

  「是贓物嗎？」

⑤ ● "When you're hot, you're hot. When you're not, you're not."

  「當你運氣（星運、賭運 …）來時，一切事情皆順心如意。當你運氣過去時一切皆枉然。」

79. hot-headed

衝動的；血氣方剛的

- "He is a hot-headed young man."

  「他是一個血氣方剛的年輕人。」

80. hot number

①風騷；馬蚤；騷貨。②偷來的東西

① ● "She's a hot number."

  「她是個騷貨。」

② ● "He bought a hot number from a fence."

  「他從贓貨商那兒買了一些贓貨。」

81. hot potato

令人敏感的東西

- "That issue is a hot potato; none of the candidates want to discuss it."

  「那是個令人敏感的爭議，沒有一個候選人願意談論它。」

82. hot rod

[rad]

老爺車（但情況很好）

● "Where did you get this hot rod?"

「你從哪兒買來的老爺車？」

83. **hot spot**

[spɑt]

困境；麻煩

● "Get me out of this hot spot, and tell him I'm not here."

「救我出這個困境，告訴他我不在。」

84. **hot stuff (=hot shit)**

[stʌf]

①出名的，人人想一睹為快。②專家。③好；棒（常用來形容東西，或運動員）

① ● "That new band is really hot stuff."

「那個新樂隊真是有名。」

② ● "If you need your car fixed, come see my roommate. He's pretty hot stuff."

「假如你的車子需要修理，來找我的室友，他真是個專家。」

③ ● "What do you think of Joe Namath?"

「你認為Joe Namath 如何！」（美國足球明星）

"Oh yeah, he was hot stuff in his day."

「對，想當年，他真是棒透了。」

85.. **(to) house**

容納；可居住

● "This dormitory houses 100 people."

「這間宿舍可以住100個人。」

86. **how about a kiss (kiss=smooch)**

[smutʃ]

親一下如何？

- "What do you want for breakfast, darling?"

  「你早餐想吃什麼？」

  "How about a kiss?"

  「一個吻如何？」

- "O.K. it's about time, I've got to go. Now, how about a kiss?"

  「是時候了，我得走了。來，親一下如何？」

87. **How about a second round? (=How about another drink?)**

   再來一杯如何？

   - "How about a second round?"

     「再來一杯如何？」

     "No, thank you. I've had enough."

     「不了，謝謝你，我已夠了。」

88. **How about that?**

   不賴吧？不錯吧？（做完一件事向人誇耀時用）

   - "O.K. Done! How about that?"

     「好，做好了。不賴吧？」

     "Not bad!"

     「不壞。」

   - "I've got a date with Janet for Friday! How about that?"

     「星期五，我跟 Janet 有約，不錯吧？」

     "I envy you."

     「我羨慕你。」

89. How $\begin{cases} \text{are they} \\ \text{are you} \\ \text{is she} \\ \text{is he} \end{cases}$ getting along?

   近況如何（包括事業，健康情形等等）

● "How are you getting along?"

「近來如何！」

"Fine, and you?"

「很好，你呢？」

90. **how awful**

[ˈɔfʊl]

真不幸；真糟糕

● "He was hit by a bus."

「他被巴士撞了！」

"How awful."

「真不幸！」

91. **How can you be so sure?**

你怎麼能如此肯定呢？（對別人十足肯定語感到懷疑時用）

● "How can you be so sure that guy isn't John Rittes?"

「你怎麼能確定那個傢伙不是 John Rittes？」

"Because ——, I'm that guy's wife."

「因為…，我是那個傢伙的太太。」

● "It's going to rain tomorrow? How can you be so sure?"

「明天會下雨？你怎能如此肯定？」

92. **How can you joke at a time like this?**

這種時候你怎還有心情說笑？

● "She can get $500,000 from the insurance company. It's not so bad being a rich widow."

「她可自保險公司得到五十萬，當個有錢的寡婦還真不錯咧！」

"How can you joke at a time like this?"

「在這種時候，你還有心說笑？」

93. **how come? (=why)**

怎會呢？怎麼可能呢？

● "I'm dead broke now."

「我身無分文。」

"How come?"

「怎麼會呢？」

註：幾乎用 "why" 的地方都可用 "how come" 代替，而且
  "how come" 用的次數也較多。

94. **How could I say no?**

我怎能拒絕？

● "I heard you went to Olivia's house."

「聽說你去 Olivia 家玩？」

"Yes. She said her mother wanted to see me. How could I say no?"

「對。她說她媽媽要見我。我怎能說不去？」

95. **How dare you say that?**

你怎敢這麼說？

● "You're a creep! a creep! a creep!"

「你是個討厭鬼，討厭鬼，討厭鬼。」

"How dare you say that!"

「你竟然敢如此說！」

● "You don't owe me anything? How dare you say that?"

「你不欠我任何東西？你怎麼敢這麼說？」

96. **How dare you!**

膽子真大啊！

● How dare you kiss me! You don't even know me."

「你連認都不認識我，就敢親我！」

97. **How did it go?**

後來呢？如何？（追問下文，結局）

● "You went on a fishing trip last weekend?"

「你上個周末去釣魚了？」

"Yeah."

「是呀！」

"How did it go?"

「如何？」

98. How did your shopping go?
['ʃɑpɪŋ]

你們逛街收穫如何？

● "How did your shopping go?"

「你們上街採購得如何？」

"Great.　I got all I needed."

「很好。我需要的都買到了。」

註：go shopping　是指上街購物，如 "Let's go shopping."

99.. How do I look?

我看起來如何？（打扮後，或試新衣時）

● "How do I look?"

「我看起來如何？」

"Like death warmed over.　Have you been sick, or what?"

「像回鍋的隔夜菜。你是生病了還是怎麼了？」

100. How do you figure that?

你怎會有這種想法（說明有這種想法的原因）

● "I'm going to marry Mike?　How do you figure that?"

「我要嫁Mike？你怎麼會這麼想？」

● "Bill's the one who's responsible."

「Bill 該對這件事負責。」

"How do you figure that?"

「怎麼說？」

101. How do you like it?

①你覺得如何（喜歡嗎？）②如何煮法。

① ● "This light blue T-shirt looks very pretty. How do you like it?"

「這件淺藍色的 T 恤看起來很漂亮，你喜歡嗎？」

② ● "How do you like your eggs?"

「你的蛋要怎樣做？」

"Sunny-side up." 「只煎半邊」

"over easy" 「兩面皆煎（如我們的荷包蛋）」

"over hard" 「煎好一面將蛋黃戳碎，翻面再煎」

"scrambled" 「炒蛋」

"omelette" 「蛋包（內含火腿，或洋菇…）」

"poached" 「水煮蛋（不帶殼）或指蒸蛋」

"hard-boiled" 「水煮蛋（帶殼）」

102. How is business?

①近況如何。(=How are you?) ②生意如何？

①② ● "Hi, Mr. Smith. How is business?"

「嗨，Smith 先生。生意好嗎？（近來好嗎？）」

"Not bad, thank you."

「還不錯，謝謝你。」

103. How is everything?

近況如何？

● "Hi, Daniel, long time no see, how is everything?"

「嗨，Daniel, 好久不見，近來好嗎？」

"Not bad, how about you?"

「還不賴，你呢？」

104. How was I?

我表現得如何？（在表演過後，徵求別人的意見）

● "How was I? Not bad, eh?"

「我表現得如何？不賴吧？」

"Terrific."

「棒透了。」

105. How well do you know (him/her)?

①你對（他／她）的瞭解有多少？②你跟他有多熟？（打聽人時用）

① ● "So you want to marry Baldwin? How long have you known him?"

「你要嫁給 Baldwin？'你認識他多久啦？」

"3 weeks?"

「三個禮拜？」（反問語，有夠不夠久之意。）

"3 weeks! How well do you know him?"

「三個禮拜！你對他的瞭解有多少呢？」

② ● "Gina."

「Gina.」

"Yes."

「嗯。」

"Do you know Olivia?"

「你認識 Olivia 嗎？」

"Yes, I do."

「我認識。」

"How well do you know her?"

「你跟她熟嗎？」

"Quite well. We went to the same college, and she was my roommate for 2 years."

「相當熟。我們唸同一所大學，她還跟我同住了 2 年。」

106. hunch

[hʌntʃ]

預感

● "I had a hunch you would come tonight."

「我有預感你今晚會來。」

"I have a hunch something is going to happen."

"What do we get this evening?"
"Yesterday's leftovers."

- "I have a hunch something is going to happen."

    「我有預感將會有事情發生。」

107. **hung up (=delayed)**

    耽擱了

    - "We got hung up in a traffic jam."

        「我們因爲交通受阻而耽擱了。」

108. **no hurry (=no rush)**

    ['hɝɪ]   [rʌʃ]

    不急；慢慢來

    - "Hi, Bill. I'll finish in a second, have a seat and make yourself at home."

        「嘿，Bill, 我馬上好了。坐一下，別拘束。」

        "No hurry, just take your time."

        「慢慢來，不急。」

1. **I'm a taxpayer (=I'm a taxpaying citizen)**

   我是一個納稅人（當你去辦事，政府官員給你臉色看時，你就可以用這話，表示是我在養活你們，別給我臉色看，或要求他們合作。）

   - (to a policeman): "I'm a taxpayer in this town and I demand more protection for our school children."

     （對警察說）：「我可是個納稅人哦！我要求你們多派警察來保護學童。」

2. **I'm all ears.**

   洗耳恭聽

   - "What do you want to tell me? I'm all ears."

     「你想告訴我什麼？我洗耳恭聽。」

3. **I'm at a loss as to what to do.**
              [lɔs]

   我茫茫然不知道怎麼做才對

   - "Darn it! I'm at a loss as to what to do."

     「他媽的！我茫茫然不知該怎麼辦了。」

4. **I'm at your disposal. (=I'm at your service.)**
              [dɪ'spozl]

   我隨時聽候你的差遣（客套話）

   - "If you need anything, anything at all, I'm at your disposal."

     「如果你需要任何東西，不管是什麼，我隨時聽候你的差遣。」

5. **I'm beat. (=I'm exhausted.)**

   累慘了！累壞了！累死我了！

   - "Oh boy, I'm beat. Oh, my feet are killing me."

     「噢，老天，我真是累慘了，我的脚痛死了！」

6. **I'm busy on another line.**

   我正忙着聽另一個電話

- "Hi, Joy, I'm busy on another line.　Can you hang on a minute?"

「嗨，Joy，我正在接另一個電話。你能不能等一下？」

7. **I'm flattered**
   ['flætəd]

我真是受寵若驚；榮幸之至

- (Robert Redford):　"Would you like to dance?"
  　　　　　　　　　　(=May I have this dance?)

（勞勃瑞福）：「你願意賞光嗎？」

(You):　"I'm flattered."

（你）：「榮幸之至。」

8. **I'm not at home today.**

今天不在家（不會客，不接電話之意）

- "If anyone calls, just tell him I'm not at home today."

「假如今天有人打電話來，就告訴他我不在。」

9. **I'm not going to let (someone) go on like this.**

我不會就此放過（某人）

- "I'm not going to let him go on like this.　He has ruined my life."

「他毀了我一生。我不會就此放過他。」

10. **I'm not superman (=I only have two hands)**
    ['supə,mæn]

我又不是超人（工作太多，忙不過來）

- "Stop pushing me.　One thing at a time; I'm not superman, you know."

「別催我。一次只能解決一件事，你要知道，我也只有一雙手！」

11. **I'm not trying to offend.**
    [əˈfɛnd]

我不是有意要冒犯（你）

- "I'm not trying to offend, but you shouldn't talk that way to Henry."

「我不是有意要冒犯，但你實在不該對Henry 那樣講話。」

12. **I'm on my way.**

我這就去了！

- "Lisa, I told you to get me a pizza."

「Lisa, 我告訴妳幫我買一個義大利餅。」

"Yes, I'm on my way."

「嗯，我這就要去了。」

13. **I'm only human**
    ['hjumən]

我只是個常人（沒有三頭六臂）

- "How can you expect me to finish this by tomorrow? I'm only human, you know."

「你怎麼能期望我明天以前做完這件事呢？我只是個常人啊！」

14. **I'm sorry to inform you....**
    [ɪn'fɔrm]

我很（遺憾／難過／抱歉）得告訴你…的消息（通常指不幸或壞消息）

- "I'm sorry to inform you, your parents were killed in a plane crash yesterday."

「我很遺憾告訴你，你的父母在昨天的墜機意外事件中喪生了。」

15. **I'm starved, I could eat a horse.**
    [starvd]

我餓得可以吞下一匹馬（這是美國人表示很餓的說法）

- "Boy, I'm starved. I could eat a horse."

「乖乖，我好餓，我足可以吞得下一匹馬。」

"Me too."
「我也是。」

16. **I'm telling you for the last time.**
我這是最後一次警告你。

- "Leave my sister alone; and I'm telling you this for the last time."
「少惹我妹妹，這是我最後一次警告你。」

- "I'm telling you for the last time, if you read dirty books, I'll knock your block off."
「最後一次警告你，如果你再看黃色書刊，我就敲掉你的腦袋。」

17. **I am to blame**
　　　　　[blem]
責怪我好了（一切都是我的錯）

- "It's all my fault.　I am the one to blame."
「這全都是我的錯！我是該受責備的人。」

- "Who is to blame for this?"
「這件事該怪誰？」

18. **I can manage on my own.**
我能處理自己的事

- "I don't need your help, I can manage on my own."
「我不需要你的幫助，我能自己處理好。」

19. **I can never thank you enough.**
千言萬語也道不盡我心中的感激。」

- "Huntz, I can never thank you enough."
「Huntz，千言萬語也道不盡我心中對你的感激。」

"Oh, don't say that; we're friends, right?　What's a friend for?"
「哦，可別這樣說，我們是朋友，對不對？要不然要朋友幹嘛？」

20. **I can see your point** . . . .

我可以瞭解你（所述）的理由；我懂你的意思。（常用在爭辯時，後面常是接 but … 然後提出自己反駁的意見）

● "I can see your point, but money is not the major subject in this issue."

「我可以明白你的理由，但是在這件事上，錢不是主要的問題。」

21. **I dare you**

[dɛr]

我打賭你不敢（做某件事）

● "I dare you to go out with Sam. Joe's not coming back till tomorrow night."

「Joe 要到明晚才會回來，但我敢打賭，你不敢跟 Sam 出去。」

● "I dare you to ask her out on a date."

「我打賭你不敢約她出去玩。」

註："I bet you" 是「我跟你打賭 …」

22. **I don't blame you.**

[blem]

我不怪你（有諒解之意）

● "I'm sorry, I didn't win the game, Sir."
「對不起，我輸了那場比賽。」

"I don't blame you; you tried your best."
「沒關係，你已盡力了。」

● "I'm going to quit my job."
「我打算辭職不幹了。」

"I don't blame you. I would too."
「我不怪你，如果我是你我也會。」

23. **I don't catch your meaning. (=I don't get you.)**
我不懂你的意思

● "I don't quite catch your meaning, what do you mean you're in trouble?"

「我不太懂你的意思，你說你惹上麻煩了是什麼意思？」

24. **I don't feel well.**

我覺得不太舒服

● "What's wrong? You look pale."
「怎麼啦？你臉色看上去很蒼白。」

"Well, I don't feel too well."
「嗯，我覺得不太舒服。」

25. **I don't give a damn.**

[dæm]

我才不管呢！我才不在乎！

● "What happened to Linda Smith? I've lost track of her lately."
「 Linda Smith 近來如何？我最近跟她失去了聯絡。」

"I don't know, and I don't give a damn."
「我不知道，我才懶得管她的死活。」

26. **I don't know what came over (someone)!**
不知道中了什麼邪；不知被什麼迷住了！

● "He just started screaming for no reason. I don't know what came over him."
「他無緣無故的尖叫起來，我不知他中了什麼邪。」

27. **I don't know what's wrong (=the matter) with me.**
我也不知道自己那根筋不對？我也不知道自己怎麼搞的。我也不知道自己吃錯了什麼藥。

● "I know I shouldn't say that, I don't know what's the matter with me."
「我知道我不該那麼說，我也不知道自己吃錯了什麼藥？」

28. **I don't know what to say.**
我真不知該說些什麼才好

● "Thomas, thanks for your help. I really don't know what to say."

「Thomas, 謝謝你的幫忙，我真不知該怎麼謝你才好。」

● "Julie, what's wrong between you and Gary?"

「Julie, 妳跟Gary 之間怎麼了？」

"I don't know what to say, I think we are just not compatible."

「我不知該說些什麼，我想我們就是彼此不合適。」

29. **I don't know what you're talking about.**

我不知你在胡說些什麼？

● "I'm a thief? I don't know what you're talking about?"

「我是個小偷？我不知你在胡說些什麼？」

● "Separation? What are you talking about?"

「分居？你在胡扯些什麼？」

30. **I don't mean (it)**

①我不是有意的。②我不是這個意思。

① ● "I'm sorry, I don't mean to hurt you."

「對不起，我不是有意要傷害你。」

"It's O.K."

「沒關係。」

② ● "I didn't mean to kill him, I meant to stop him, you idiot."

「你這個笨蛋，我並不是說真要殺了他，我是說阻止他。」

31. **I don't mean to (=I'm not trying to) offend.**

我不是存心要冒犯你；我不是要惹惱你。(請人諒解的話)

● "Hubert, I am not trying to offend you, but you were really a little too rude to her."

「Hubert, 我並不是想冒犯你，但你對她實在是太狠了一點。」

32. **I don't see why?**

不明瞭真正的原因何在

● "I can't go because I'm broke."

　「我不能去，因爲我一文不名。」

"I don't see why, you can write home for some money."

　「我看不出這有什麼關係，你可以寫信回家要錢啊！」

33. **I feel the same way**

我的想法與你的一樣；我有同感

● "I don't like this cake, it's too greasy."

　「我不喜歡這蛋糕，太膩了。」

"I feel the same way."

　「我有同感。」

34. **I get your point**

　　　　　　[pɔɪnt]

我懂你的意思

● "I get your point but I'm not sure I agree."

　「我懂你的意思，可是我並不見得同意。」

35. **I got (to) go**

我非走不可了；我該走了

● "It's getting late, I got to go now."

　「天色不早，我該走了。」

36. **I've got a big favor to ask of you. (=Could you do me a big favor?)**

有事想請你幫忙（你願意幫我一個大忙嗎？）

● "Jennifer, I've got a big favor to ask of you."

　「Jennifer, 請你幫個大忙。」

"Sure, what is it?"

　「當然（沒問題），什麼事？」

37. **I've got a feeling**

①我有預感（某事會發生）。②（在事情發生之後說）我早有預感會發生。

① ● "I've got a feeling, it's going to rain today."
「我有預感今天會下雨。」

② ● (After receiving a phone call) "Joy isn't coming tonight."
（接完電話）「Joy 今晚不來了。」

"I had a feeling she wouldn't make it."
「我早就是預感她來不了。」

38. I've got to run/go
我該走了（有急事待做）

● "It's nice talking to you, but I'm due at a meeting. I've got to run now, see you."
「很高興跟你聊天，但是我得參加一個會議，我該走了，再見。」

39. I've had enough.

[ə'nʌf]
①受夠了。②吃飽了。

① ● "I've had enough of your complaints."
「我受夠了你的抱怨。」

● "Stop nagging. I've had enough out of you."
「別再嘮叨，我已經受夠你了。」

② ● "I've had enough, I can't eat any more."
「我吃飽了，再也吃不下了。」

40. I've had it up to here with (someone or something)
我已受夠了（美國人講這話時，通常把手放在下巴下面喉嚨處，表示再多就要從嘴巴溢出來了。）

● "I've had it up to here with your nagging, I can't stand it any more."
「我已受夠了你的嘮叨，我不能再忍受了。」

41. I've heard a lot about you!

[hɝd]
久仰大名

● "It's nice to meet you, Miss Taylor, I've heard a lot about you."

「很高興認識你，Taylor 小姐，久仰大名了。」

"Same here."

「我也是。」

42. **I have no choice.**

[tʃɔɪs]

我別無其他選擇（請求別人諒解之意）

● "Why did you steal?"

「你為什麼要偷東西？」

"I had no choice. I need money badly."

「我急需要錢，我沒有別的路可走。」

43. **I have no idea.**

[aɪˈdɪə]

我不知道

● "Do you know how she did it?"

「你知道她是怎麼做的？」

"I don't have the slightest idea."

「我一點概念也沒有！」

● "Do you know where my sandals are?"

「你知道我的拖鞋在哪兒？」

"I have no idea."

「我不知道。」

44. **I have reached my limit!**

[ˈlɪmɪt]

我的忍耐已到了極限

● "Don't push me too hard. I have reached my limit."

「別逼人太甚，我已經忍耐到極限了。」

45. **I know it's not the (or a bad) time, ...**

我知道這不是談（某件事）的時候。（在某人家中遭受不幸
時，前去打擾詢問，商談一些急事。）

- "Mrs. Thomas, I know it's not the time to talk about this, but we have to find out who did it, so we need your help. I hope you understand."

「Thomas 太太，我知道這個時候談這件事很不恰當，但是我們必須查出是誰幹的，所以我們需要你的幫忙，我希望妳能諒解。」

46. **I mean what I said.**

我可是當真，不是說着玩的！

- "I don't want to see you anymore, and I mean what I said."

「我不想再見到你，我可是當真的。」

47. **I should have known**

我早該知道

- "I should have known she was just using me."
「我早該知道她只是在利用我。」

- "I should have known better."
「我早該知道得更清楚。」

48. **I suppose not.**

[sə'poz]

我想不會吧！（不是吧）

- "Does Jean want to go with us?"
「Jean 要跟我們一起去嗎？」

"I suppose not."
「我想不會吧？」

49. **I thought you'd (=would) never ask.**

（等了很久）我以爲你永遠不會開口。（邀請，徵求意見）

- "Would you like to marry me?"
「你願意嫁給我嗎？」

"Well, I thought you'd never ask."
「哦！我還以爲你永遠不會開口呢？」

50. **I too have my limit.**

          ['limɪt]

我的忍耐也是有限度的。

- "Don't push me to hard, I too have my limit."

「別欺人太甚，我的忍耐也是有限度的。」

51. **I'll be along later.**

我待一會兒就來

- "You go first; I'll be along later."

「你先去，我待會兒就來。」

52. **I'll be right with you.**

馬上就來

- "We are ready to order."

（在餐館中）「我們好了。（可以點菜了！）」

"I'll be right with you."

（侍者）：「我馬上就來。」

53. **I'll be there.**

我會準時赴約／到達

- "Judy, we have a meeting tomorrow morning at 10:00."

「Judy，明早十點我們有一個會議。」

"Don't worry, I'll be there."

「別擔心，我會準時到的。」

54. **I'll drink to that.**

我要爲…乾一杯（對人，對事）

- "Mary will buy us dinner, she said."

「Mary 說她要請我們吃飯。」

"I'll drink to that."

我要爲這件事乾一杯。」

55. **I'll get it.**

我來接電話；我來開門

● (Door bell) "I'll get it."

（門鈴）「我來開。」

● (Phone rings) "I'll get it. I think it's Bill."

（電話鈴）「我來接，我想是 Bill 打來的。」

56. I'll let you know.

到時我會讓你知道

● "I don't know when he will be back, but I'll let you know."

「我不知道他什麼時候會回來，但是（萬一他回來了）我會通知你。」

● "If you hear anything, let me know."

「假如你聽到任何消息，請讓我知道。」

57. I won't blame you.

[blem]

我不會怪你

● "Try your best, if you can't make it, I won't blame you."

「盡力而為，如果你做不到，我不會怪你的。」

58. I won't even take it as a gift.

白送我我也不要

● "Hey, do you want to buy my car?"

「嘿，你想買我的汽車嗎？」

"No thanks! I wouldn't take it even if it were a gift."

「不，謝了。免費送我我也不要。」

59. I'll say!

是啊！可不是嗎？就是嘛！

● "Boy, is it hot out!"

「乖乖，外面眞熱啊！」

"I'll say."

「就是嘛！」

60. **I'll see what I can do.**

我看看我能幫上什麼忙（表示樂意，但無絕對把握幫得上忙）

● "Mr. Jodash, I'm sorry to bother you again, but Billy (her husband) is out of a job again."

「Jodash 先生，很抱歉再一次打擾你，Billy（她的丈夫）又失業了。」

"O.K. Mrs. Baker, I'll see what I can do."

「好，Baker 太太，我看看我能幫得上什麼忙。」

61. **I'll take this/those/it/them.**

我買這件（買東西時，看中意時說：「要了；好」之意）

● "How much for this blue one?"

「這件藍色的要多少錢？」

"It's only $19.50."

「19塊半。」

"O.K. I'll take it."

「好，我就要這件。」

62. **I'll teach (someone) a lesson (he'll) never forget.**

我要給（他）一個終生難忘的教訓。

● "If I find out he really stole the money, I'll teach him a lesson he'll never forget."

「如果我證實他眞的偷了錢，我會給他一個永生難忘的教訓。」

63. **I wish there was something I could do.**

①我希望我能幫得上忙（在別人家中發生不幸時，表示你的關切，雖然不一定眞幫上忙）。

②我希望能做點什麼。（茫茫然不知做什麼好。）

① ● "Ivan, I'm sorry for the bad news; I wish there was something I could do."

「Ivan 我真為那個壞消息感到難過，我希望能為你做些什麼。」

② ● "I'm bored with sitting at home. I wish there was something I could do."

「我真煩透了，老坐在家裏，我真希望能有點事情做做。」

64. **I wish you all the luck in the world.**

祝你百事順心，萬事如意。

● "Congratulations, Leo. I wish you all the luck in the world."

「Leo，恭喜恭喜，祝你萬事如意。」

"Thank you, Mr. Kissinger."

「謝謝你，Kissinger 先生。」

65. **I wonder how low you can get.**

我不知你會墮落到什麼地步！我不知你會低賤到什麼地步！

● "You do that for money? How low you can get?"

「你那麼做是為了錢？你還能墮落到什麼地步？」

66. **I wouldn't give (someone) the time of day....**

不會為（某人）做任何的事。（如某人得罪了你）

● "I wouldn't give Bob the time of day after what he did at the last party we had."

「經過上次宴會他那樣對待我之後，我不會為 Bob 做任何的事。」

67. **If that's the way you want it.**

假如這就是你所希望（想要）的，想這麼做的（負氣，爭吵語）

● "You want to be alone? O.K. If that's the way you

want it, I will leave right now and never come back."

「你想要獨自一個人不受打擾？好，如果你眞的這麼想，
我馬上走，而且永遠不會回來（打擾你）。」

68. **If the shoe fits, wear it.**

如果是事實，就承認／小心吧！

● "Whoever's been taking money from the cash register
better stop. If the shoe fits, wear it."

「不管是誰拿了櫃子裏的錢，最好別再拿了。如果是你拿
的，就小心一點！」

69. **If you can't beat them, join them.**

　　　　　　　　[bit]　　　　[dʒɔɪn]

如果你打不贏他們，就加入他們好了！（不能同化對方，就
被對方同化吧！）

● "I hate fraternities."

「我討厭兄弟會。」

"So do I, but they're the only social life on campus,
and that's not going to change."

「我也是，但是他們是校園內唯一的社交活動，而且這情
形也不會改變。」

"I guess if you can't beat them, join them."

「我想，如果你鬥不過他們就加入他們吧。」

70. **Ignorance is bliss.**

無知就是福（知道的越少越好）

● "The more I read and watch the news, the more de-
pressed I get. I know why they say 'Ignorance is bliss.'"

「我看到及聽到的新聞越多，我就越感到沮喪，我明白爲
什麼人們說，「無知就是福」」

71. **imagine that**

[ɪˈmædʒɪn]

①想不到吧！②想想以後的情形……吧！

①②"I just won a thousand dollars in the lottery."

「我剛中了一千塊。」

"Imagine that!"

「想不到吧！」（想想以後的好日子吧！）

72. **impossible**

[ɪmˈpɑsəbl]

①不可理喻的；不講理的。②太難了。③做不成；去不成。

① ● "You are impossible."

「你真是不可理喻。」

② ● "That test was impossible."

「那考試真是太難了。」

③ ● "Kathy, I'm afraid dinner is impossible, I have to meet someone in the Ramada Inn. I'm sorry."

「Kathy，恐怕我不能跟你去吃晚飯了，我必須去Ramada 旅社見一個人，真是抱歉。」

"It's O.K. Don't worry. Maybe some other time."

「沒關係。別在意。改天再說。」

註：這裏的dinner也可改成party, meeting, shopping, trip等 等，意思也就小有改變。Physics, Chemistry, French is impossible 物理、化學……課程太難。

73. **Improving your mind?**

[ɪmˈpruvɪŋ]

在用功K書嗎？

● "What are you doing? Kim, Improving your mind?"

「Kim,你在幹啥？用功K書嗎？」

74. **(something is) in**

①上市；應市。②流行。

① ● "Cherries are in season now."

「櫻桃上市了。」

② ● "Mini-skirts are in again."
  「迷你裙又流行了。」

75. **in a jiffy**

    [ˈdʒɪfɪ]

  很快地

  ● "I'll be back in a jiffy. Don't go away."
    「我很快就回來。別走開。」

76. **in a row**

    [ro]

  一連；連續不斷

  ● "The Yankees defeated the Dodgers two years in a row."
    「洋基隊一連兩年打敗了道奇隊。」

77. **In a way, yes (or no).**

  從某一方面／某一觀點來說── 是的！/對！（表示還有其他
  的原因，角度）

  ● "You don't want Jimmy Carter to be reelected because
    you don't like him, right?"
    「你不想 Jimmy Carter 再度當選，因爲你不喜歡他，對
    吧？」
    "Well, ── In a way, yes."
    「嗯，從某一方面說來── 是的。」

78. **Into each life a little rain must fall.**

  每個人的一生中，總會遇到一些小挫折（別灰心之意！）

  ● "Hey, cheer up. Into each life a little rain must fall.
    Everything will be O.K. soon."
    「嗨！振作一點，每個人的一生中，總有不順的事！一切
    會很快轉好的！」

79. **in hot water (=in trouble)**

  惹上麻煩

● "I heard that Jimmy was in hot water again."

「我聽說 Jimmy 又惹上麻煩了。」

80. **(to be) in (one's) right mind**

精神正常

● "You want to live with him? You can't be in your right mind."

「你要跟他住在一起？你一定是瘋了。」

81. **(to do something) in style**

①一流的（享受）。②時髦。

① ● "We have plenty of money. Let's go in style and buy first class tickets."

「我們有很多錢，讓我們享受一下，買幾張頭等票。」

② ● "Mini skirts were in style during the 60's."

「在60年代迷你裙風行一時。」

82. **in that case**

[kes]

既然如此，我只好……（另作選擇；打算）

● "What would you like, sir?"

「先生，你要什麼？」

"I would like to have fried shrimp."

「我要炸蝦。」

"I'm sorry, Sir. We've run out of shrimp."

「對不起，先生，蝦已賣完了。」

"In that case, give me a sirloin steak."

「既然如此，給我一客沙龍牛排好了。」

83. **in the bag**

[ˈæg]

輕而易舉，如探囊取物

● "I think we can win the first prize."

「我想我們可以贏得第一獎。」

"Yeah, it's in the bag."

「是啊！一如探囊取物般。」

84. **in the first place**

①第一點。②壓根。

① ● "Why didn't he go to the bank?"

「他爲什麼不去銀行呢？」

"In the first place, he didn't know where the bank was. In the second place, he was too shy to ask directions."

「第一點，他不知銀行在哪兒？第二點，他不好意思問人。」

② ● "Why are you late?"

「你爲什麼遲到？」

"I didn't want to come in the first place."

「我壓根兒就不想來。」（迫不得已才來的！）

85. **in the hole**

[hol]

負債

● "His store went bankrupt, and now he's in the hole for $600,000."

「他的店倒了，現在負債六十萬。」

86. **in the same boat**

[bot]

同舟共濟；有難同當；處境相同

● "We're all in the same boat, so you might as well cooperate."

「我們現在都是在同一條船上（翻了大家一起淹死）所以你不妨合作一點。」

87. **in town**

本市；本鎭

● "This is the best Chinese restaurant in town."

「這是本市（鎭）最好的中國餐館。」

88. **in trouble**

[ˈtrʌbl]

①惹上麻煩。②懷孕（常指未婚懷孕）

① ● "Uh-oh, you're in trouble.'"

「嗷，你惹上麻煩了。」

② ● "Do you know what? She is in trouble."

「你知道嗎？她懷孕了。」

89. **incredible (=unbelieveable)**

[ɪnˈkrɛdəbl]

令人難以相信的（表示太好了！）

● "Tricia finished her test in 20 minutes and got an A."

「Tricia 在 20 分鐘內答完了，還得了個 " 甲 "。」

"Incredible."

「眞是叫人難以相信。」

90. **informer**

[ɪnˈfɔrmɚ]

告密者，線民

● "Tell your informer we need to know who did it before dawn."

「告訴你的線民，在天亮以前我們要知道是誰幹的。」

91. **intend to**

[ɪnˈtɛnd]

打算；意欲；存心

● "I did not intend to hurt him."

「我並不是有意要傷害他。」

92. **into (=nuts about, very interested in)**

喜歡；對…感興趣

● "Have you ever gotten into jazz?"

「你喜歡過爵士音樂嗎？」

"I used to be into jazz."

「我曾經喜歡過爵士音樂。」

● "I could really get into cutting school and going to the beach."

「如果翹課去海邊，我會很開心的。」

● "What are you interested in?"

「你喜歡什麼？」

"I'm into sports."

「我喜歡運動。」

93. **Is that clock right?**

那個鐘準嗎？

● "It's 2:30 now, Is that clock right?"

「兩點半了，那個鐘準嗎？」

"No. It's 10 minutes fast/slow."

「不，快（慢）了十分鐘。」

94. **Is that so? (=really)**

真的嗎？

● "I quit that job, because I don't like it."

「老子不幹了，因為我不喜歡那個工作。」

"Is that so? Are you sure you were not fired?"

「真的嗎？你確信你不是被解僱的？」（諷刺的問話）

95. **Is this seat taken/free?**

這位子有人坐嗎？

● "Excuse me, is this seat taken?"

「對不起，請問這位子有人坐嗎？」

"Yes it is. I'm sorry."

「抱歉，有人坐了！」

96. **It costs money!**

這是要花錢買的！

● "Who threw this half apple away? It costs money! You know."

「這半個蘋果是誰扔的？這蘋果可是要錢買的啊！知道嗎?」

97. it depends
[dɪ'pɛnds]

依情形而定（模稜兩可的雙關語，可好，可不好）

● "Would you like to work for us on a full time basis?"
「你願意在我們公司擔任專職嗎？」

"Well, it depends (on the salary / on who my boss is.)"
「（幹與不幹）要依（薪水的多少或誰是我的頂頭上司而定。）」

98. It destroyed me.
[dɪ'strɔɪd]

使我非常難過；不高興；悲痛

● "My brother smashed my brand new car last night. It destroyed me."
「我弟弟（哥哥）把我全新的車撞壞了，眞氣死我了。」

● "It destroyed Nancy when Greg told her he had no intention of marrying her."
「當 Greg 告訴 Nancy 他無意娶她時，Nancy 感到非常難過。」

99. It doesn't work.
行不通；不見效

● "Did you tell Mary you worked over time last night?"
「你是否已告訴 Mary，你昨晚加班？」

"Yes, but it didn't work. She knew I was lying."
「說啦！但沒有用，她知道我在撒謊。」

100. It happens.
也許意料不到，但可能發生，意即並非不可能發生的事

● "I can't believe he fell off the bridge."

「我不能相信，他會掉到橋下去。」

"It happens."

「這種事是可能發生的啊！」

101. **It has to be done.**

應該做的，這是我份內該做的事。

● "Thanks for your help."

「謝謝你的幫忙。」

"It had to be done."

「應該的。」

102. **It's a bargain, I assure you.**

　　　　['bɑrgɪn] [ə'ʃur]

我保證你絕對划算！

● "$250? It's too expensive."

「兩百五十塊？太貴了！」

"It's a bargain, I assure you."

「我敢保證，絕對划算！」

103. **It's a deal.**

　　　[dil]

一言為定

● "I'll babysit for you this evening, but you have to help me to do my homework tomorrow."

「今晚我幫你看小孩，但明天你要幫我做功課！」

"It's a deal."

「一言為定。」

104. **It's a free country** {you can't force me to do that/this.
　　　　　　　　　　　　{I'll do what I feel like.

這是一個自由國家，你不能逼我做它。（這是老美常愛掛在嘴上的一句話。）

● "I don't want to go college. It's a free country. You

can't force me to do that."

「這是一個自由國家。我不想上大學。你不能逼我去唸。」

"Yes, I can."

「我想‧，我可以。」

105. It's a long story.

說來話長

● "How did you get fired?"

「你怎麼會被炒魷魚了呢？」

"Well, it's a long story."

「唉，說來話長。」

106. It's a shame (=what a shame)

真可惜！

● "It's a shame you couldn't come last night. We really had a ball."

「真可惜，你昨晚不能來，我們玩的很開心。」

107. It's a small world.

這個世界真是太小了！世界真小啊！

● "You know Hubert too? It's really a small world."

「你也認識Hubert？這個世界真是太小了！」

108. It's a snap!

[snæp]

（某事）簡單得很！

● "Boy, English is murder."

「老天，英文真難啊！」

"It's a snap to me."

「對我說來簡單得很。」

109. It's about time.

是時候了

● "It's about time, let's go."

「是時候了，我們走吧！」

- "It's about time to say good night."
「該是說再見的時候了。」

- "Chrissie, I want to make a confession to you."
「Chrissie, 我要向你懺悔一件事。」

"Yeah, it's about time."
「是啊,該是時候了。」

110. It's an ill wind that blows no good.
時運不濟,人人倒霉。

- "Because of the oil crisis, I heard 20 companies were out of business."
「由於石油危機,聽說有二十家公司倒閉了。」

"Yeah, it's an ill wind that blows no good."
「是啊,時運不濟,人人倒霉。」

111. It's bad (or good) for public relations!
這樣社會大衆會對我們產生反感!

- "You want to cancel the order? It's bad for public relations."
「你要取消訂貨?這會影響我們外面的名聲。」

112. it's (someone's) fault
[fɔlt]
是(某人)的過錯

- "I'm sorry, it's my fault."
「我很抱歉,那是我的錯。」

"It's O.K."
「沒關係。」

113. It's for the birds!
沒意思!

- "This book is for the birds."
「這本書眞沒意思。」

114. It's getting late.
天色不早;時候不早

● "It's getting late. I better go now."
「天色不早，我該走了。」

"The night is still young. Stay a little longer."
「還早呢。多待一會兒嘛。」

115. It's Greek to me.

[grik]

我不知道，我不懂

● （中國人）A：「你踩到我的脚了。」
（美國人）B： "What did she say?"
「她說什麼？」
（美國人）C： "It's Greek to me."
「我不知道。」

● "Calculus is Greek to me. (I'm not good at it.)"
「我對計算一竅不通。」

116. It's in God's hands.

聽天由命

● "We've done everything we can to save him. Now it's in God's hands."
「我們已盡（一切）可能去挽救他的生命，現在一切都交給上帝了。」

117. It's just a matter of time.

遲早的問題

● "I know it will happen. It's just a matter of time."
「我知道會發生，只是遲早的問題。」

● "I'll go. It's just a matter of time."
「我會去的。只是遲早的問題。」

118. It's just your imagination!

[ɪmædʒəˈneʃən]

那只是你的幻覺罷了！

●"What's wrong?"
「怎麼了？」

"I think I heard something."
「我想我聽到了什麼。」

"I didn't hear anything. It's just your imagination."
「我啥也沒聽到，那只是你的幻覺罷了。」

119. **It's never too late to make amends.**

亡羊補牢，時猶未晚

●"Why don't you call her and say you're sorry. It's never too late to make amends."
「你為什麼不打電話給她，跟她說聲對不起，亡羊補牢，時猶未晚。」

120. **It's no laughing matter.**

那不是開玩笑的事情；正經一點；認眞一點。

●"You'd better be serious. This is no laughing matter."
「你最好正經一點。這可不是鬧着玩兒的。」

121. **It's no use**

沒有用的（無可奈何之語）

●"Let me talk to her. Maybe she will listen to me."
「讓我跟她談談，也許她會聽我的。」

"It's no use. She already made up her mind, I guess."
「沒有用的。我想她已經下定決心了。」

122. **It's none of your business.**

不關你的事（少管閑事之意）

●"It's none of your business. Butt out."
「不關你的事，滾開！」

●"It's none of your business. I'm not talking to you."
「不關你的事，我又不是跟你講話。」

123. **That isn't like you.**

這不像是你（的作風）

- "You let him go, just like that? That isn't like you."

  「你就這麼輕易地放了他一馬？這眞不像你。」

124. **It's not my day.**

  我今天眞倒霉。（從早到晚事事不順心，惡運連連）

  - "I missed my bus this morning. Then I lost my purse somewhere, and then I had a fight with Susan. Jesus, it's just not my day."

    「今早我先是沒趕上車。後來又不知把皮包搞丟到那裏！後來又跟 Susan 吵架，老天！我今天眞是倒霉透頂。」

125. **It's (That's) not nearly enough.**

  不夠；差得遠呢！

  - "Here is $1,500, take it."

    「哪，這裏是一千五，拿去。」

    "You owed me $5,000, remember? It's not nearly enough."

    「你欠我五千塊，記得嗎？這點錢哪夠？」

126. **It's not worth the effort.**

  得不償失；划不來。

  - "Why don't you give up? It's not worth the effort."

    「你爲什麼不放棄？這樣做是得不償失的。」

127. **It's now or never.**

  要不就現在，要不就算了。（要別人表明態度做決定）

  - "Do you want to marry me?"

    「你願意嫁給我嗎？」

    "Let me think. I'll tell you tomorrow."

    「讓我想一想。我明天告訴你。」

    "Nope. It's now or never."

    「不。現在就告訴我，否則算了。」

128. **It's (all) over.**

  一切都完了；都成爲過去了！

- "It's all over. I don't want to talk about it anymore."
  「一切已成過去，我不願再談它。」

129. It's over (one's) head.
超出（某人）的理解能力。

- "That math lecture was over my head. I couldn't understand a word."
  「那場有關數學的演講，遠超過我的理解能力。我是一個字也聽不懂。」

130. It's reported on reliable authority that. . .
[rɪˋlaɪ əbl] [əˋθɔrətɪ]
據可靠消息說……（報上常用）

- "It's reported on reliable authority that 5 Senators have received $200,000 from some Arab oil companies."
  「據可靠消息說，有五個參議員接受了阿拉伯石油公司二十萬元的賄賂。」

131. It's still on paper!
（紙上談兵）還早呢！

- "How are your plans for the new coffee shop coming along?"
  「你們新咖啡屋的計劃進行得如何？」
  "It's all still on paper."
  「仍然是紙上談兵，還早咧！」

132. It's up to you (=It rests with you) to decide.
需要你來決定

- "We've already picked some colors. It's up to you to decide which one to use."
  「我們已選了幾種顏色，由你決定用哪一種。」

133. It makes no difference.
沒有什麼不同。

● "Do you want to go to the movies or go shopping?"
「你想看電影還是逛街？」

"It makes no difference; whatever you want to do is fine."
「都可以，隨你便好了。」

134. It means nothing to me.
我一點也不在意

● "Joe says he hates you."
「Joe 說他恨你。」

"That means nothing to me."
「我才不在乎呢！」

135. It must be an inside job.
可能是內賊。（有內奸）

● "How could they know money was coming in at 10:15?
It must be an inside job."
「他們怎會知道錢是在10:15送來？一定有內奸。」

136. It mustn't happen again.
不可以再讓它發生！（可一不可二）

● "Sorry, I'm late. Mr. Seng."
「Seng 先生，對不起，我來遲了。」

"It mustn't happen again."
「這種情形一定不可以再發生。」

137. It never rains but it pours.
（事情）不發生則已，一發生則接二連三的來。（如你的朋友久無音訊，一下子全部都來約你出去玩。）

● "I hadn't had any visitors at my house for months and
suddenly last weekend all my relatives came by. It
never rains but it pours."
「幾個月來，我家裏一個訪客也沒有，上個週末突然間我的親戚全來了，真是不來則已，一來全部都來了。」

138. It sounds all right to me.

聽起來並無不妥之處。（贊成的意思）

- "Let's split it all fifty-fifty; how about that?"

  「我們對半分如何？」

  "That sounds all right to me."

  「好啊！」

139. It stands to reason.

道理顯而易見（不必多費口舌解釋）

- "It stands to reason. If you don't study, you don't pass."

  「你如果不唸書，考試就不會及格，這道理很明顯的。」

140. It won't be long.

不會太久

- "He will be right back. It won't be long."

  「他馬上會回來，不會太久的。」

- "Sir, Can I talk to you for a minute? It won't be long."

  「先生，我可以跟你談一下嗎？不會躭擱你太久的時間。」

- "It won't be long before I get my Master's degree."

  「距離我拿碩士學位的日子不會太久了。」

141. It won't do (you, me, him. . .) any good.

沒有好處；毫無幫助

- "Don't drink that much wine. It won't do you any good."

  「別喝那麼多酒，對你沒有好處。」

  "Don't bother talking to him; it won't do you any good."

  「不必跟他講，沒有用的。」

  註："It won't be anything good." 則是 " 準沒好事 "。(不是借錢，就是要債之類的！)

142. It won't take a minute.

不消一分鐘就行了。

●"I can fix it; it won't take a minute. You guys just sit inside and relax."
　「不消一分鐘，我就可以修好它，你們坐在車裏放寬心情（不必擔心也不必出來幫忙！）。」

143. It won't work.

行不通；沒用

●"Tell him I'm not home."
　「告訴他我不在家。」

"It won't work, he knows you are."
「沒用，他知道你在家。」

144. It would go ill with (someone)

（某人）會吃虧的

●"If she keeps fooling around with those guys, it will go ill with her sooner or later."
　「她如果繼續跟那些傢伙鬼混，遲早會吃虧的。」

1. **jail bait**

   [dʒel/bet]

   未成年（18歲以下）的女孩子們（萬一與她們發生關係可能被抓入獄中，故叫這些女孩子爲餌 bait ）

   - "Don't try to fool around with jail bait."

     「別想跟未成年的女孩鬼混。」

2. **jaunt**

   [dʒɔnt]

   遠足；旅行

   - "They went for a jaunt out in the country today."

     「他們今天到郊外去旅行。」

3. **No jaywalking**

   ['dʒe/wɔkɪŋ]

   行人請走行人穿越道（不可任意穿越馬路）

   - "Watch the signal; no jaywalking."

     「注意交通號誌，過街請走行人穿越道。」

4. **Jesus Christ**

   ['dʒizəs/kraɪst]

   老天！（驚嘆語）

   - "Julie landed in the hospital last night and she committed suicide."

     「Julie 昨晚被送進醫院，她自殺了。」

     "Jesus Christ, why?"

     「老天，爲什麼呢？」

5. **jinx**

   [dʒɪŋks]

   ①掃把（倒霉鬼）。②(v.)着了道；迷上了。

   ① ● "That guy is a real jinx. Every time he comes with us, it rains."

     「那個傢伙眞是個掃把星，每次他跟我們出去都會下雨。」

② ● "I can't stop, I think I've been jinxed."

　「我無法停止。我想我着了道。」

6. **jerk**

[dʒɝk]

沒用的東西；笨蛋；未經世故的人

● "You jerk!"

　「你這個笨蛋！」

7. **job**

汽車；機器

● "It's an American job."

　「這是一輛美國車。」

8. **jock**

[dʒɑk]

喜歡運動的人；運動迷

● "He's a real jock. He's always out on the athletic field or in the gym."

　「他是一個運動迷。他不是在田徑運動場上，就是在體育館裏。」

9. **jogging**

[ˈdʒɑgɪŋ]

慢跑

● "I love jogging."

　「我喜歡慢跑。」

註： push-up 是伏地挺身

　　 sit-up 是仰臥起坐

　　 pull-up 是拉單槓

10. **John**

[dʒɑn]

①嫖客的總稱。②厠所

① ● "Most hookers don't give a damn about their Johns. They just want to make money."

「絕大多數的妓女才不在乎她們的嫖客。她們一心想要的只是錢。」

② ● "Where is the John?"

「厠所在哪兒？」

11. Johnny on the spot

['dʒɑnɪ]   [spɑt]

及時雨（指適時出現的人）

● "You sure are Johnny on the spot. Can you give me a hand to change this tire?"

「你可真是及時雨啊！你能幫我換這輪胎嗎？」

註：John 是指厠所，在美國有許多可拖運的流動厠所，供工地、車站用，急着如厠時，John 適時而來，後來演變成「及時雨」。

12. joint

一根大蔴煙

● "Want to smoke a joint?"

「要不要來一根大蔴煙？」

13. joker

['dʒokɚ]

喜歡開別人玩笑的人

● "Who's that stupid joker?"

「那個愛開玩笑的笨蛋是誰？」

"He's my husband."

「他是我先生。」

14. juice (= electricity)

①電源；電力。②汽油。③醉。

① ● "Turn on the juice."

「打開電源。」

- "There's not enough juice to run the T.V. and the air conditioner."

「沒有足夠的電力同時供電視及冷氣機使用。」

② ● "We need to go to a gas station to get this car some more juice."

「我們得找個加油站，給這車加點油。」

③ ● "I got juiced last night."

「我昨晚喝醉了。」

15. **juicy**

[ˋdʒusɪ]

①多汁的。②精彩的，有意思的閑言（例如：某人有兩個太太之類的閑話）③性感（形容女子）。

① ● "I like juicy fruit."

「我喜歡多汁的水果。」

② ● "I heard some juicy gossip."

「我聽到了一些有趣的閑話。」

③ ● "She is a juicy piece of ass." （較粗野的說法）

　　　　(=She is very sexy.)

「她很性感。」

16. **jump on (=harass, hassle)**

[dʒʌmp] [ˋhærəs] [ˋhɑsl]

找麻煩；找碴兒

● "Don't jump on me. It's not my fault."

「別找我的麻煩。那不是我的錯。」

● "Where have you been? It's late. Do you know that?"

「你去哪兒啦？時間不早了，你知道嗎？」

"Oh, don't jump on me. It's only 10:30. I was with Lisa, we were studying for the final."

「哦，別找碴兒，才不過十點半，我跟 Lisa 在一起，我們在準備期末考。」

17. **jungle**

[dʒʌŋgl]

大都市中的黑暗地帶（弱肉強食）

● New York is a concrete jungle.
  紐約是一個堅固的黑暗地帶。

註：concrete jungle=big city. 有高大堅固的（水泥）房子，
    容易迷失。

18. **junk (=garbage)**

[dʒʌŋk] [ˈgɑrbɪdʒ]

①垃圾；便宜貨；破東西。②難吃的；不營養的。③毒品

① ● "Where did you get this junk?"
    「這個破東西你哪兒找來的？」

  ● "Take your car to the junk yard."
    「把你的車送到廢車場去。」

註：junk yard 是廢車場。

② ● "Soda, hamburgers, and TV dinners are all junk food."
    「汽水、漢堡、電視餐，都是沒有營養的食物。」

③ ● "He sells junk."
    「他販賣毒品。」

19. **junk dealer**

[dilɚ]

①舊貨店，估衣店。② (=drug dealer) 販賣毒品的人。

① ● "There are many junk dealers in the Wan-Hwa area."
    「在萬華一帶有許多舊貨店。」

② ● "He was arrested for dealing with junk."
    「他因為販賣毒品而被捕。」

20. **junk food**

[dʒʌŋk]

①沒有營養的食物。②零食；零嘴。

① ● "Let's go to McDonald's and have a Big Mac."
「我們去麥當樂，然後點個大漢堡。」

"Oh, I don't like that kind of junk food."
「哦，我不喜歡那種沒有營養的食物。」

② ● "Do you like to eat junk food?"
「你喜歡吃零食嗎？」

"Sure, especially ice cream and potato chips."
「當然，尤其是冰淇淋及炸馬鈴薯片。」

● "I'm a junk-food junkie."
「我是零食的癮君子。」（每天都要吃零食）

21. **junkie**

[ˈdʒʌŋkɪ]

注射海洛英上癮的人，有毒癮的人

● "Police caught two junkies in the Starlight Motel."
「警察在 Starlight 旅社抓了兩個注射海洛英的人。」

註：pusher 是賣毒品的人。

22. **Just as (or what) I thought (would happen)**
正如我所料，果然不出我所料

● "Joe won the first prize again which was just what I thought would happen."
「正如我所料，Joe 又得了第一。」

● "Just as I thought. While I'm sick, you go and find some other guys to play around with. I'm disgusted."
「正如我所料，當我生病時，你就跑出去跟別的傢伙鬼混，真叫人噁心！」

23. **Just look at you!**
瞧你那付德性

● "You have been drinking too much. Just look at you!"
「你喝得太多啦。瞧瞧你那付德性。」

24. **Just my luck.**

我的運氣就是這樣（通常指壞運，有自嘲的味道）

● "My only day off this month and it rains. Just my luck."

「（今天是）我這個月唯一的休假日，竟下起雨來，我的運氣就是這樣壞。」

25. **just out of curiosity**

[ˌkjurɪˈɑsətɪ]

只是出於好奇

● "Why are you sticking your nose in this?"

「你為什麼要管這閒事？」

"Just out of curiosity, you know."

「你知道的嘛，只是因為好奇而已。」

26. **Just what do you mean by this/that?**

你這是什麼意思？（對他人言行舉止不悅的問話）

● "Here's your money."

「這是你的錢。」

"Just what do you mean by this? This is only $50. You owe me $500."

「你這是什麼意思？這裏只有 50 塊，你欠我 500 塊。」

● "Just what do you mean by that remark?"

「你這樣說是什麼意思？」

27. **juvenile delinquent**

[ˈdʒuvənl] [dɪˈlɪŋkwənt]

太保、太妹

● "My sister says those juvenile delinquents pinched her on the ass as she walked by."

「我姊姊說，當她走過的時候，那些太保捏她的屁股。」

"What did she do?"

「她怎麼辦呢？」

"She hit them with her purse."
「她用她的皮包打他們。」

1. **keen on**
   喜歡；迷上
   - "She's very keen on singing."
     「她很喜歡唱歌。」

2. **keep**
   躭擱
   - "Don't let me keep you."
     「別讓我躭誤你的時間。」
   - "What kept you so long?"
     「你怎麼現在才來？」

3. **keep (someone) busy**
   讓（客人）忙於聊天、吃東西、跳舞…（以打發一段空白時間）。陪客人別冷落他們的意思。
   - "You keep them busy, I'll be right back."
     「你讓他們忙點，我馬上回來。」

4. **keep (you, me) company**
   ['kʌmpənɪ]
   與（人）爲伴；作伴
   - "Would you keep me company at the doctors? I'm sort of nervous."
     「你願意陪我去看醫生嗎？我有點緊張！」

5. **keep cool**
   [kul]
   ①保持冷靜。②保持涼爽。
   ① • "Keep your cool. Don't get so excited."
     「保持冷靜，別太激動。」
   ② • "The best way to keep cool in the summer is to swim."
     「在夏天裏保持涼爽的最好方法是游泳。」

6. **keep fit**
   保持健康；保重

- "Good-bye, and keep fit."
  「再見，多保重。」
  "O.K., I will "
  「好，我會的。」

7. **Keep (him, her) in (his, her) place.**
   使（他、她）安份點
   - "I don't want any trouble here. Why don't you keep your friend in his place?"
     （在酒吧中）「我不希望這裏發生任何的麻煩，你為什麼不叫你的朋友安份點？」

8. **keep in touch**
      [tʌtʃ]
   保持聯繫
   - "Bye, Janet. Keep in touch."
     「Janet 再見了。保持聯繫啊。」

9. **Keep off the lawn.**
   請勿踐踏草地
   Keep out.　(=Don't enter, Private property, etc.)
   閑人勿入！

10. **Keep out of this!**
    少管閑事！別管！
    - "Kim, you shouldn't yell at Linda. It wasn't her fault."
      「Kim，你不該對 Linda 大吼大叫，那又不是她的錯。」
      "Keep out of this, will you?"
      「少管閑事，行不行？」

11. **Keep stalling (someone).**
       [stɔlɪŋ]
    拖住；纏住（某人）。（拖延時間）
    - "Keep stalling him. I'll be right back."
      「拖住他。我馬上回來。」

12. **Keep the change.**

    [tʃendʒ]

    不必找了（零錢）

    ● "Here is $30, and keep the change."
    「這是三十塊，不必找了。」

    "Thank you, Sir."
    「謝謝你。」

13. **keep things from (someone)**

    （對誰）隱瞞（事情）

    ● "I keep nothing from you."
    「我對你毫無隱瞞。」

    ● "I know you kept a lot of things from me."
    「我知道你瞞了我許多事情。」

14. **keep up with the Joneses**

    [ˋdʒonzɪz]

    （Joneses 是指鄰居）（在物質生活上）與鄰居看齊，一較高下。

    ● "They're always buying new things just to keep up
    with the Joneses."
    「他們總是在買新的東西，以便跟鄰居一較高下。」

15. **Keep your hands to yourself.**

    不要亂摸

    ● "Keep your hands to yourself, or you'll be sorry."
    「別亂摸，否則你會後悔的。」

16. **Keep your nose out of this.**

    少管閑事

    ● "It's none of your business. Keep your nose out of
    this."
    「這不關你的事，少管閑事。」

17. **Keep your pants on. (=be patient)**

    不要緊張；忍耐點

● "Keep your pants on. She will come."
「忍耐點，她會來的。」

18. **Keep your sweaty hands off (me) ....**
　　　　　　　　['swɛtɪ]
少動手動腳；少毛手毛腳

● "Keep your sweaty hands off me, or you'll be sorry."
「少毛手毛腳，否則你會後悔。」

19. **kick**
[kɪk]
①挑剔；找碴兒。②討論。
① ● "He kicks about almost everything."
　　「他幾乎對每件事情都挑剔。」
② ● "Bring up your proposal at the next meeting and let them kick it around."
　　「下次開會把你的建議帶來，讓他們討論一下。」

20. **kick (something) around**
①考慮、考慮。②當靶子；欺侮；虐待。
① ● "Give me a couple days to kick it around."
　　「給我幾天時間考慮一下。」
② ● "You won't have Richard Nixon to kick around any more."
　　「你們再也無法把尼克森當靶子欺侮了。」

21. **kick the bucket (=die)**
死
● "He kicked the bucket three days ago."
　「他三天前死了。」

22. **kickback**
['kɪk͵bæk]
佣金

● "If he buys it, is there any kickback for me?"

「假如他買這個東西，你有佣金嗎？」

"Yeah, you can get a 10% commission."

「當然，你可以拿10%的佣金。」

註：commission 較公開，較光明正大。

23. **(It's) kid's stuff.**

[kɪd/stʌf]

這是小孩子的玩藝兒（大人不感興趣）

● "Would you like to read this?"

「你要看這（書）嗎？」

"No thanks. It's kid's stuff."

「不用，謝了！那是給小孩子看的。」

● "I don't smoke pot. It's kid's stuff."

「我不抽大麻。那是小孩抽的。」（表示自己抽些別的，比這要上道些。）

24. **kidding**

[ˈkɪdɪŋ]

①開玩笑。②當眞。

① ● "Don't get mad. I'm just kidding."

「別生氣。我只是開玩笑。」

● "Are you kidding?"

「眞的嗎？」（不是在開玩笑吧）

② ● "No kidding."

「我是說眞的。」（不是在開玩笑。）

25. **Kill (one's) eyes.**

受不了！

● "The small print in this book kills my eyes."

「這本書字體太小了，我的眼睛難受得要命。」

26. **(to) kill the goose that laid the golden egg**

斷了財源

● "I can't divorce him. I don't want to kill the goose that laid the golden egg."
「我不能跟他離婚，我可不願斷了財路。」

27. **kill with kindness**
愛之適以害之

● "You're spoiling her. You'll kill her with kindness."
「你過於溺愛她了，你會害了她。」

28. **(to) kiss ass, (= to brown nose)**
                              [noz]
拍馬屁

● "When he compliments the boss like that everyone knows he's just kissing ass."
「當他那樣恭維老闆時，大家都知道他是在拍馬屁。」

29. **knock (one's) block off**
打掉（人）的腦袋。（block 在此指腦袋瓜子）

● "If you stay out late again, your old man will knock your block off."
「如果你在外面再鬼混到這麼晚，你老頭會打掉你的腦袋。」

30. **knock it off (=stop it =cut it out.)**
不要這樣（停止做某件事）

● "Knock it off, will you? It looks so stupid."
「別再那麼做好嗎？看上去真驢。」

● "O.K. knock it off, you two."
（當你走進房間時，看到你弟弟們在打架，你可以說：）
「你們兩個給我住手。」

31. **knock off**
①免了；去掉；不計在內。②停止。

① ● "It's $3.05."
「三塊零五分。」

"Can you knock off the 5 cents?"
「你能不能少算那五分錢？」

② ● "It's 5:00, time to knock off from work."
「現在是五點鐘該是停止工作的時候了。」

32. **to knock on (someone's) door**
敲（某人）的門

● "Look! We've said all there is to say. Now go and don't come knocking on my door again!"
「喂，我們已經把該講的話都講完了，現在請出去，別再來敲我家的門了。」

33. **knock up**
[nɑk]
（未婚）懷孕；先上車（後補票）

● "Susan got knocked up, so she's getting an abortion."
「Susan 懷孕了，所以她要去墮胎。」

34. **know a thing or two**
①略知一、二。②知道不少。

① ● "What do you know about Jason Bush?"
「你對 Jason Bush 的瞭解有多少？」

"Well, I know a thing or two. He graduated from Harvard University, owns 2 banks, 5 motels, and 2 shopping centers. And he's handsome and still single."
「略知一二，他自哈佛大學畢業，擁有兩家銀行，五個（汽車）旅社，以及兩個購物中心。英俊瀟洒，而且仍然是單身。」

"I only know one thing, and that's that he drinks like a fish."
「我只知一件事，那就是他喝酒喝得很多。」

② ● "Do you have any idea why my car won't run?"
「你想為什麼我的車不動了？」

"No, but you should go ask David Hampton. He knows a thing or two about cars."

「我不清楚。但你可以去問 David Hampton, 他很懂車子。」

35. **know-it -all**

自以爲是萬事通的人

● "Why don't you ask Jimmy? He thinks he's a know-it-all."

「你爲什麼不去問問 Jimmy 呢？他自以爲是個萬事通。」

● "O.K. Mr. Know-it-all, what's the answer?" (sarcastic)

「好吧！萬事通先生，答案是什麼？（諷刺語）」

36. **know the score (=know the truth)**

[skor]

明白（瞭解；知道）事情的眞象

● "It took me three months to find out what the score was around here."

「花了我三個月的時間查明這件事的眞象。」

● "What happened to Nancy?"

「Nancy 怎麼了？」

"I don't know. You two are good friends; you should know the score."

「我不知道。你們兩個是好朋友，你該瞭解事情的眞象。」

1. **lack color (=boring)**
   不精彩

   ● "This show lacks color."
   這電影眞不精彩。」

2. **lady-killer**
   很得女孩歡心的男孩；使女孩子一見鍾情的男人

   ● "That George is really a lady killer. He has more girl-
   friends than he knows what to do with."
   「那個George眞是個很得女孩歡心的人。他的女朋友多
   得他無法應付。」

3. **land (a job) (=get)**
   找到（工作）

   ● "Let me tell you how to land a job—a real good one."
   「讓我來教教你怎麼找工作，一份好的工作。」

4. **last**
   ①維持；支持；保留；活。②最後。③牢固耐久（不會破；
   顏色不會變）。

   ① ● "How long will it last?"
   「它會維持多久。」

   "3 days."
   「3天。」

   ● "I won't last a day without you."
   「沒有你，我一天也活不下去。」

   ● "I had a headache."
   「我頭痛。」

   "Last long?"
   「有多久了？」

   "About 3 days."
   「大概三天吧！」

②● "He came in last in the Marathon."
　　「他是馬拉松比賽中最後一個到的。」

　● "This is my last clean shirt."
　　「這是我最後一件乾淨的襯衫。」

③● "Clothes made in Taiwan just don't last."
　　「台灣製的衣服不牢固。」

5. last call

最後一輪（在美國各州酒吧晚上酒禁的時間不同，停止賣酒前，最後一杯酒叫 last call ）

●"The bar is going to close in a minute. This is the last call for drinks."
　「酒吧馬上要打烊了，這是最後一次點酒了！」（還要喝什麼請快叫！）

6. late bloomer

　　['blumɚ]

大器晚成（多用於女孩身體發育晚）

●"I heard that David won the Nobel Prize."
　「我聽說David得了諾貝爾獎。」

"Yes, we went to the same junior high, but he was the last one in my class. I wonder how he made it after that."
　「是的，我們是初中同班同學，他那時考全班倒數第一名。我真不知道初中以後他是怎麼唸的。」

"May be he is just a late bloomer."
　「也許他是一個大器晚成的人吧！」

●"She's a late bloomer. When I knew her in high school she was skinny and shy. Now she's gorgeous."
　「她是遲開的花兒。當我在高中認識她時，她又瘦又害羞。現在她真是可人啊！」

7. **laugh at all the wrong places**

[læf]

表現不得時。（如看滑稽電影時，該笑不笑，全場不笑時，只聽他一個人的笑聲。）

● "I don't want to go to the movies with Alice."

「我不想跟Alice 去看電影。」

"Yeah. Alice laughs at all the wrong places."

「是啊，她老在不該笑的時候哈哈大笑。」

8. **lay your fingers (or hands) on (me, her)**

碰（我）

● "Don't lay your fingers on me."

「別碰我。」

9. **lazy bum (=lazy bone)**

[bʌm]

懶惰蟲；懶鬼；懶骨頭

● "You lazy bum, get working."

「你這懶蟲，快點工作。」

10. **(You have) to (learn to) live with it.**

學習去忍受（人、事）

● "My roommate is a real slob."

「我的室友真邋遢。」

"Mine, too, but you have to learn to live with it."

「我的室友也是一樣，但你要學習去適應。」

11. **leave**

①丟下別管。②別打擾；別管。③離開；走了。

① ● "Just leave it there."

「丟在那裏別管它。」

② ● "Leave me alone please."

「請別打擾我。」

③ ● "I'm leaving."

「我走了！」

12. **leave (me) alone**

①別理我；別管我。（讓我獨自靜一靜）。②別打擾。

① ● "You girls just go ahead, leave me alone."

「你們先走，別管我。（讓我一人靜一靜）。」

② ● "Leave your brother alone, will you, David?"

「David,別打擾你哥哥（弟弟），好嗎？」

13. **(to) leave (someone) cold**

[liv]

①使我對（某人）沒有好感。②（快刀斬亂麻的）離去；分手；不拖泥帶水。

① ● "I can't stand Martin. He leaves me cold."

「我不能忍受Martin, 我對他沒好感。」

② ● "Peter left Marilyn cold."

「Peter（乾淨俐落的）離開了Marilyn。」

14. **leave everything until the last minute**

凡事都拖到最後一分鐘。

● "Where's my tooth brush?"

「我的牙刷呢？」

"Why do you always leave everything until the last minute?"

「你爲什麼每件事都等到最後一分鐘呢？」

15. **leave a message**

[liv / ˈmɛsɪdʒ]

留話

● "Is Linda there?"

「Linda 在嗎？」

"Oh, I'm sorry, she is not in. Do you want to leave a message?"

「對不起，她不在。你想留話嗎？」

註：「我可以幫(你)記下留言嗎？」是 "Can I take a message?"

16. **leave (it) to (someone)**

由（人）來照料

● "You just go ahead and leave the baby to me."

「你去吧，把小寶寶留給我（照顧）。」

17. **leftovers**

['lɛft͵ovɚz]

剩菜

● "What do we get this evening?"

「今晚我們吃什麼？」

"Yesterday's leftovers."

「昨天的剩菜。」

18. **lefty (=southpaw)**

[lɛftɪ] ['saʊθ͵pɔ]

左撇子

● "Hi, lefty, what are you doing here?"

「嘿，左撇子，你在幹嘛？」

● "I'm a lefty."

「我是個左撇子。」

19. **lemon**

['lɛmən]

新車子外觀雖不錯但毛病百出

● "How much did you pay for this lemon?"

「這輛破車你花了多少錢買的？」

20. **let (someone) down**

使（人）失望

● "I'm counting on you; don't let me down."
「我全指望你了，別讓我失望。」

"I won't, Dad."
「我不會的，爹。」

21. **let go**
死心；放棄

●"She doesn't love you any more. Why don't you let go?"
「她已不再愛你了，你為什麼不死心呢？」

22. **Let me put it this way.**
讓我這樣說好了（換個方式；換句話說）·

● "O.K. Let me put it this way: 'If you don't give me the money before Friday, I'll take back all the equipment.'"
「好吧！讓我這樣說好了，『禮拜五以前如果你不把錢給我，我就收回所有的器材。』」

23. **(let me) take the wheel**
[hwil]
（讓我來）開車

● "You look tired. I'll take the wheel and you sleep in the back."
「你看來累了，讓我來開，你可以到後面去睡一下。」

24. **Let me through.**
讓我過去

● "Let me through. I want to talk to the mayor."
「讓我過去。我要跟市長講話。」

25. **Let sleeping dogs lie.**
不要過問；少惹事

● "What's wrong between Mabel and Roy."
「Mabel 跟 Roy 兩個人怎麼了？」

"I don't know. It's best just to let sleeping dogs lie."
「我不知道，你最好別管。」

26. **Let's call it quits.**

$\qquad$ [kwɪts]

①讓我們講和好嗎？（別再吵了！）　②停止。

① ● "Let's call it quits, O.K.?"

$\qquad$ 「讓我們講和好嗎？」

$\qquad$ "O.K."

$\qquad$ 「好。」

② ● "Let's call it quits at 8:30."

$\qquad$ 「八點半我們就停工。」

27. **Let's change the subject.**

$\qquad$ ['sʌbdʒɪkt]

我們換個話題吧！

● "I don't want to talk about him anymore; let's change the subject."

$\qquad$ 「我不想再談他，讓我們換個話題吧！」

28. **Let's flip for it (=I'll toss you for it.)**

$\qquad$ [flɪp] $\qquad$ [tɔs]

讓我們丟銅板決定

● "Let's flip for it."

$\qquad$ 「讓我們丟銅板決定。」

$\qquad$ "O.K. Tails."

$\qquad$ 「好，我要反面。」

註：heads 是正面。

29. **Let's get a bite (to eat).**

$\qquad$ [baɪt]

我們隨便吃點東西去吧。

● "I'm hungry. Let's get a bite to eat."

$\qquad$ 「我餓了。我們去吃點東西吧。」

● "Do you want a bite?"

$\qquad$ 「你要不要吃一口（蛋糕、麵包）？」

30. **Let's get down to business.**
讓我們言歸正傳。（談正事吧！）

- "It's late. Let's get down to business."
「時候不早了。我們談正事吧！」

31. **Let's go!**
走吧！動手吧！

- "It's late. Let's go."
「天色不早。走吧！（動手吧！）。」

32. **Let's go for a ride (=cruise, drive).**

                   [raɪd] [kruz]

讓我們兜風去。

- "It's such a lovely evening. Let's go for a ride."
「夜色眞棒。我們兜風去。」

註：go for a walk 則是散步去。

33. **Let's have it out!**
①大家把話說清楚！打開天窗說亮話。②來（打）吧！（一邊捲袖子，一邊說）。

① ● "What's bothering you? Let's have it out."
「什麼事困擾着你？讓我們把話說清楚。」

② ● "O.K. Let's have it out today."
「好吧！今天就讓我們把事情解決掉。」（打一架的意思）

34. **Let's leave it at that.**
①就讓它順其自然（保持原狀）。②就這麼辦。

① ● "I don't want to talk about it anymore. Let's leave it at that."
「我不想再談，就讓它順其自然吧！」

② ● "O.K. Let's leave it at that. You do the dishes, and I'll dust."
「好吧！就這麼辦，你洗碗，我來清理傢俱（拂去灰塵）。」

35. **Let's take a vote.**
   [vot]
   讓我們投票決定。

   ● "Janet wants to watch 'Three Is Company.' Lisa wants to watch 'Charlie's Angels'. Well, let's take a vote."
   「Janet 要看 " 三人行 "。Lisa 要看 " 霹靂嬌娃 "。那我們投票表決吧！」

36. **Let's talk business.**
   讓我們來談正事。

   ● "Let's talk business. I'm tired of beating around the bush."
   「我們談正事吧，我兜圈子兜煩了。」

37. **level-headed**
   ['lɛvl]
   腳踏實地

   ● "He is a level-headed young man. He will go very far."
   「他是一個腳踏實地的年輕人。他會有發展的。」

38. **(one's) life was hanging by a thread.**
   生命垂危。

   ● "His life was hanging by a thread."
   「他的生命垂危。」

39. **Like a hen with one chick. (=like ants on a hot griddle.)**
   像熱鍋上的螞蟻；焦急，（ 有小心保護的意思 ）

   ● "When he knew his wife was going to have a baby, he was like a hen with one chick."
   「當他知道他的太太快要生孩子了，他急得像熱鍋上的螞蟻。」

40. **Like father, like son.**
   有其父必有其子。

- "Leo is really a playboy."
「Leo 眞是個花花公子。」

"Of course, like father, like son."
「當然，有其父必有其子。」

註：沒有 "like mother, like daughter" 的說法。

41. Like hell I will.

[hɛl]

我才不會呢！

- "Will you call Nancy tonight?"
「今晚你會打電話給 Nancy 嗎？」

"Like hell I will."
「我才不會呢！」

42. Like what?

比方什麼？譬如什麼？

- "If he does that again. I'll do something serious."
「假如他再那麼做，我要給他一點顏色看看。」

"Like what?"
「譬如…？」

"Like kill him."
「譬如殺了他。」

43. line up

[laɪn]

①排隊。②安排好了。

① ● "Please line up."
「請排隊。」

② ● "I have my summer plans all lined up."
「我暑假的計劃已經全部安排好了。」

44. little gift

一點心意（微薄的禮物）不成敬意。

● "Here is a little gift from me and Marvin."
「這是我和Marvin 的一點心意，不成敬意。」
"Oh, how sweet of you! Thank you."
「哦，你真可愛，謝謝你。」

45. **Live and learn.**
活到老學到老。

● "I thought she liked ME all these years, but then she went off and married HIM. Live and learn."
「我以爲這些年來她喜歡的（人）一直是" 我 "，現在她却跟" 他 " 結婚了！這眞是活到老學到老！」

46. **loaded**
['lodɪd]
①喝醉了。②滿（壘、額）。③有錢。

① ● "He was pretty loaded last night."
「他昨晚喝得酩酊大醉。」

● "Don't get loaded."
「別喝醉了。」

② ● "The bases are loaded, so the Dodgers have to change the pitcher."
「滿壘，所以道奇隊必須更換投手。」

● "The gun is loaded."
「這槍裝滿了子彈。」

③ ● "How can you afford to buy it? You must be loaded."
「你怎麼負擔得起？你一定是很有錢。」

47. **loafer; loaf (v.)**
['lofɚ]
①混水摸魚的人；懶鬼。② " loafers "是不用鞋帶的鞋子。

① ● "He is really a loafer."
「他眞是一個會混水摸魚的人。」

- "He always loafs on the job."
  「他工作時總是摸魚。」
② - "He wears a pair of loafers."
  「他穿了一雙不用綁帶子的鞋子。」

48. **loan shark (n. v.)**
    [lon/ʃɑrk]
    放高利貸（的人）

    - "The Mafia is famous for loan sharking."
      「黑手黨以放高利貸聞名。」
    - "Don't borrow money from him. He's a loan shark."
      「別向他借錢，他是個放高利貸的人。」
    註： usury (v.) [ˈjuʒərɪ] 也是放高利貸。

49. **loan sharking**
    [lon/ʃɑrkɪŋ]
    放高利貸

    - "Loan sharking is a good way to make a lot of money, but it's dangerous."
      「放高利貸是賺錢的好方法，但是却十分危險。」

50. **loiter**
    [ˈlɔɪtə]
    作威作福

    - "We do not allow anybody to loiter around here."
      「我們不允許任何人在這附近作威作福。」

51. **Long absence, soon forgotten.**
    久別情疏

    - "I heard Linda has a new boyfriend now."
      「我聽說 Linda 有了新的男朋友。」
    "Yep. People say 'Long absence, soon forgotten.' and that's what happened to me."
    「是啊。俗話說『久別情疏』那正發生在我身上。」

52. **the long arm of the law**

法網恢恢，疏而不漏

- "He finally got caught, 500 miles from home. He could not escape the long arm of the law."

「他終於在離家五百哩的地方被捕了。真是法網恢恢，疏而不漏。」

53. **long face**

臭臉

- "John has a long face. He must have fought with his wife again. When you talk to him, be careful!"

「John 今天又擺了一張臭臉，他一定又跟他太太吵了，你跟他講話時，小心一點。」

- "What's that long face for?"

「幹嘛擺那張臭臉？」

54. **Long time no see.**

好久不見

- "Long time no see. Lucy, how have you been lately?"

「Lucy，好久不見。近來好嗎？」

"Not bad. How about you."

「還不錯。你呢？」

55. **look (=listen)**

嘿（瞧）；聽着

- "Look, I don't want to argue with you any more, I'm fed up with you."

「嘿，我不想再跟你爭論，我已經受夠你了。」

56. **Look before you leap.**

[lip]

三思而行（看清楚再跳）

- "If you want to marry Gary, fine. But I hope you will

look before you leap."

「如果你要嫁給Gary，沒問題，但我希望你三思而後行。」

57. **look casual**

['kæʒuəl]

(表情)自然一點(別太緊張等等)

● "Here comes Linda. Look casual."

「Linda 走過來了，放自然點！」

58. **Look what you did to (me, my car. . . .)**

瞧你幹的好事！

● "Look what you did to me."

「瞧你幹的好事！」（假如人家潑了你一臉牛奶，你可說此句。）

59. **Look with your eyes and not with your hands.**

(=look but don't touch)

請勿動手

● "Son, we're going into that glassware store. So, look with your eyes and not with your hands!"

「兒子，我們要進那家玻璃器皿店去，所以光看可別動手啊。」

60. **looney**

['lunɪ]

發瘋似的；奇怪的；莫明其妙的

● "He's looney. He drives everybody crazy."

「他真是莫明其妙，使得大家快發瘋了。」

註：loon 原是一種水鳥，叫聲很奇怪，現引申為莫明其妙的瘋子。

61. **loot (=money)**

[lut]

錢

- "Did you bring the loot?"
  「你帶錢來了嗎？」

62. **(to) lose (one's) touch**
    失去了神奇的技巧；失去神奇的手法；失去準頭

    - "What's wrong? It doesn't work. Have I lost my touch?"
      「怎麼回事？不靈了。難道我失去了神奇的技巧了嗎？」

    - "I was bowling great yesterday. I don't know what's wrong today."
      「我昨天打（保齡球）得很棒，我不知道今天怎麼搞的。」
      "You must have lost your touch."
      「也許是失去了準頭吧！」

63. **losing streak**
    [luzɪŋ / strik]
    一直輸下去

    - "This season the Red Sox won the very first game, and then had a long losing streak."
      「這一季，紅襪隊贏了第一場球之後就一直輸了下去。」

64. **lost (one's) shirt**
    [ʃɜt]
    輸慘了（中國人說，連褲子都輸掉了）

    - "I lost my shirt in Vegas."
      「我在拉斯維加輸慘了。」

65. **lost (one's) voice**
    [lɔst]   [vɔɪs]
    聲音沙啞

    - "After the Presidential campaign, he lost his voice for 3 weeks."
      「在奔走總統競選之後，他的聲音沙啞了三個星期。」
    - "I lost my voice because of the flu, so I can't talk now."
      「我因為感冒而聲音沙啞，現在無法講話。」

66. **loud mouth**

[laud]

大嗓門（的人）；大聲公（婆）

- "Flora is really a loud mouth."

「Flora 真是個大嗓門。」

67. **lousy**

['lauzi]

①差勁的；糟透了。②不順心的。③覺得身體不舒服。

① ● "Hey, Jerry, how was your final?"

「嗨，Jerry，你的期末考考得如何？」

"Lousy."

「糟透了。」

② ● "It's a lousy day."

「今天真不順心。」

③ ● "I'm feeling lousy. (I won't go to classes today.)"

「我覺得身體不舒服（今天不打算去上課了。）。」

68. **love child (bastard, illegitimate)**

[ɪlɪ'dʒɪtəmɪt]

私生子

- "He's a love child."

「他是一個私生子。」

69. **lucky devil**

幸運的傢伙

- "Olivia promised to go to the Senior Prom with you? You lucky devil."

「Olivia 答應跟你去參加畢業舞會？你這個幸運的傢伙。」

70. **lucky dog**

幸運的傢伙

- "You won the first prize, $5,000? You lucky dog."
  「你贏了五千塊？你這個幸運的傢伙。」

71. **lush (=alcoholic, drunkard.)**

  ['lʌʃ] [ˌælkəˈhɔlɪk]

  酒鬼

  - "Her husband is a lush."
    「她的先生是個酒鬼。」

1. **Mac (=buddy, pal, chap, fellow, cousin)**
   [mæk] ['bʌdɪ /pæl/tʃæp/ 'fɛlo /kʌzn]
   老兄

   ● "Thanks, Mac."
   「多謝了，老兄。」

2. **macho**
   ['matʃo]
   男性味十足的。（東西、人）

   ● "He's really into the macho image."
   「他表現得男性味十足。」（也許是充好漢。）

3. **(Are you) mad at me?**
   [mæd]
   你是在生我的氣嗎？

   ● "You mad at me?"
   「你在生我的氣？」

   "No, I'm mad at myself."
   「不，我在生我自己的氣。」

4. **madhouse (=looney bin; cuckoo's nest)**
   ['mæd,haʊs]
   瘋人院

   ● "You will go crazy too if you live in a madhouse."
   「如果你住在精神病院，你也會發瘋的。」

   ● "That's the worst dorm on campus. It's really a madhouse."
   「那是全校最糟的宿舍，簡直像瘋人院一樣。」

5. **(any) mail**
   有信嗎？（較少用 letter）

   ● "Hi, Mr. Johnson. Any mail?"
   「嗨，Johnson 先生（郵差）。有信嗎？」

● "Did the mail come yet?"

「信來了沒有？（郵差來過了嗎？）」

6. **make a deal**

　　[dil]

打商量；訂立協定

● "They made a deal: John will quit smoking if Linda stops biting her nails."

「他們立下一個協定：如果Linda 停止咬指甲的壞習慣，John 就戒煙。」

7. **(to) make a fast buck**

　　　　　　[bʌk]

①賺外快。②發橫財。（形容賺得快，而且容易）

① ● "Burt, do you want to make a fast buck?"

「Burt, 你想賺外快嗎？」

"Yeah!"

「當然。」

"O.K. Take this to Mr. Corwood of IBM and he'll give you $20."

「好，把這個拿給 IBM公司的 Corwood 先生，他會給你 20 塊。」

② ● "We're going to rob the University Bank. Do you want to make a fast buck?"

「我們要去搶University 銀行。你想發橫財嗎？」

"How?"

「怎麼發呢？」

"You can be our look-out."

「你可以替我們把風啊。」

8. **make a federal case**

　　　　　['fɛdərəl]

小題大作

- "That's not any big deal. Don't make a federal case out of it."

「那件事沒什麼大不了，可別小題大作。」

9. **make a fuss about (something)**

[fʌs]

小題大作；大驚小怪

- "Don't make such a fuss over it."

「別小題大作。」

- "It's not worth fussing about."

「那不值得大驚小怪。」

10. **make a pass at (someone)**

勾引（用言語）

- "He made a pass at me."

「他勾引我。」

註：Seduce 通常含有「達成目的」的意思。

11. **make a reservation**

[ˌrɛzəˈveʃən]

訂位（飛機、旅社，在美國上好的餐館也要先訂位）

- "If you want to go to a popular restaurant, you should make a reservation first."

「如果你想去一家好的餐館吃飯，你得事先訂座。」

12. **make a run to ....**

開小差；開溜。（短時間的，如 5 分鐘，一、二個小時）

- "I'm going to make a run to the liquor store. Do you want anything?"

「我要溜去酒店，你需要什麼嗎？」

註：take a French leave 是長時間的如一個星期。

13. **to make a scene**

[sin]

當眾（吵架、生氣、罵人、哭泣…）

● "Why didn't you tell your wife off at the party?"
　「你爲什麼不在宴會上罵你太太一頓？」

"I didn't want to make a scene in front of everyone."
　「我不想當衆出醜。」

● "Don't make a scene. Just send it back to the kitchen."
　（假如你是飯店老闆，發現客人菜裏有隻蟑螂，你叫來伙
　計說：）「別出聲，趕快端回厨房。」

14. **make the scene**
　參加；出現；露面

● "Are you going to make the scene over at Rick's party
　tonight?"
　「今晚你打算參加Rick的宴會嗎？」

"Yeah. You?"
　「是啊！你呢！」

"Yeah. I'll bring Joan, too."
　「我也會去，我還要帶Joan一起去呢！」

15. **(to) make (both) ends meet**
　使收支平衡

● "I'm trying to make ends meet this month."
　「我正試着使這個月收支平衡。」

● "It gets harder and harder to make ends meet."
　「要使收支平衡實在是越來越難了。」

16. **make (someone) feel cheap**
　使人覺得自己很低賤。（使人抬不起頭來）

● "You went out with Martin because of his money."
　「你跟Martin出去，是因爲他的錢。」

"Don't say that. You make me feel cheap. I'm not out for
his money. I went out with him because he's nice, not
like you."

「別那麼說。你讓我覺得自己很低賤，我不是衝着他的錢才出去。我跟他出去是因為他人很好，不像你。」

17. **make good**

①成功。②順利。③實現。

① ● "With your talent and my experience, I assure you we will make good in this business."

「以你的才幹與我的經驗，我相信我們幹這行一定會成功的。」

② ● "We made good time between Dallas and Houston."

「我們在 Dallas 到 Houston 之間一路都很順利。」

註：Dallas 在美國德州中部，Houston 在中南部。

③ ● "We had an agreement and he made good on his promise."

「我們有過協定，他實現了承諾。」

18. **make it easy**

說得更清楚點；更簡單點。（用更簡單、更容易的字去解說）

● "I'll make it easy. Catch the A bus downtown and get off at Arch Street. It's one block west of Arch on Walnut Street."

「我說得更簡單一點，你在市中心坐 A 車，在 Arch 街下車。（你要去的地方）在 Walnut 街上，是在 Arch 街西邊的一條街。」

19. **make it two**

來兩份（通常在點菜、叫東西時，例如你要的和先前朋友點的一樣，就可說 make it two）

● "I want a chef's salad with Thousand Island dressing and iced tea."

（對侍者說）：「我要主廚沙拉加 Thousand Island 沙拉醬和冰（紅）茶。」

"Make it two."

「來兩份。」

20. **(to) make no remark**

                [rɪˈmɑrk]

什麼也沒說

● "After you told her that, what did she say?"

「在你告訴她那些事之後，她怎麼說？」

"She made no remark."

「她啥也沒說。」

21. **make room**

①讓出位置。②借光（請讓個位子）

① ● "We can always make room for one more."

「我們可以再騰出一個空位來。」

② ● "Make room please."（進入電梯時，你滿手東西可說：）

「請讓一讓。」

22. **make sense**

                [sɛns]

①有道理（贊成對方說法）。②通；能理解；有道理。

① ● "That makes sense, but can you afford it?"

「有道理，但你負擔得起嗎？」

② ● "Can you read this letter for me? It doesn't make any sense to me."

「你能幫我看看這封信嗎？我一點也看不懂。」

● "Talking dollars makes sense."

（商人的口頭語）「價格若談不攏，其他的都是白談。」

（ sense 音與 cents 同）

23. **Make up (one's) mind.**

快拿定主意；下定決心

● "It's Jeff. Do you want to answer it or not? Make up your mind."

「Jeff（的電話），你到底要不要接？趕快決定。」

24. **man**

老兄；朋友

● "You've got to speak out, man."

「你得把話說出來啊，老兄！」

25. **man among men**

丈夫中之丈夫

● "I like Harold. He is a man among men."

「我喜歡Harold。他是個大丈夫。」

註：woman among woman　少用。

26. **man of the hour**

當今紅人（足球明星或宴會中及時帶來一大堆啤酒，受歡迎的人）

● "He's the man of the hour."

「他是當今紅人。」

註：mother／father (man/woman) of the year 則是模範母親／父親。

27. **Man proposes, God disposes.**

　　[prə'pozɪz]　　[dɪ'spozɪz]

謀事在人，成事在天（人算不如天算）

● "I heard your brother's company folded."

「聽說你哥哥的公司虧本了。」

"Yep. Man proposes, God disposes."

「是啊！人算不如天算。」

28. **man-to-man**

男人對男人的（通常指大人）

● "It's time we have a man-to-man talk, son."

「兒子，該是我們來個男人對男人談話的時候了。」

29. **many happy returns!**

（祝你）青春永駐，壽比南山！

- "Happy birthday and many happy returns."
「祝你生日快樂，青春永駐。」

30. **too many irons in the fire**
野心太大；好高騖遠

- "He will never succeed. He has too many irons in the fire."
「他永遠不會成功的，因為他太好高騖遠了。」

31. **Many men, many minds. (=too many cooks spoil the broth)** [kʊks] [spɔɪl]
[brɔθ]
十個人十條心（表意見紛歧不合作）

- "Did the committee decide on anything?"
「委員會決定了什麼了嗎？」

"No. Everybody had different opinions."
「沒有，每個人都有不同的意見。」

"Many men, many minds."
「十個人就有十個意見。」

32. **May God bless you.**
上帝保佑你

- "Good-bye, son. May God bless you."
「孩子，再見了。願上帝保佑你。」

33. **May I ask why?**
我能知道為什麼（要這樣做）嗎？

- "John, come over here right now!"
「John，趕快過來一下。」

"May I ask why? It's 3 o'clock in the morning."
「我能知道為什麼嗎？現在是凌晨三點哪。」

34. **May I have your name?**
請問尊姓大名

- "May I have your name?"

  「我可以知道你的大名嗎？」

  "Yes, Susan Summers."

  「我叫Susan Summers 。」

  註："Do you have a name?" 「你總有個名字吧？」是比較不客氣的問法。

35. **me and my big mouth.**

   我及我那張大嘴巴（表示自己多嘴，說了不該說的話，惹來麻煩。）

   - "What's wrong with Ida?"

     「Ida 怎麼了？」

     "It was me and my big mouth. I told her I saw Luke with Diana last night."

     「都是我跟我的大嘴巴惹的禍。我告訴她昨晚我看到Luke 跟Diana 在一起。」

36. **(to) mean business (=mean it)**

   認真的；當真的；說真的 （不是開玩笑的）

   - "He said he's going to ruin us and I think he means business."

     「他說他會毀了我們，我想他是當真的。」

37. **(I) mean it.**

   [min]

   （我是）當真的；（我是）講真的

   - "I don't want to see you again and I mean it."

     「我不想再見到你，我是講真的。」

38. **(something/someone) means no harm.**

   沒有惡意（不會傷害你）

   - "Don't be afraid of the dog's barking. He means no harm."

     「別怕那隻狗叫，牠沒有惡意。」

- "I meant no harm. I just wanted to look at the baby, and she jumped out of my arms onto the floor."

  「我沒有惡意，我只是想看看小寶寶，而她却跳出我的懷抱而跌在地上。」

  "No harm done, thank God."

  「感謝上帝，沒有受傷。」

39. **(something) means so much to me**

    （某事、某人）對我來說太重要了（意義重大）

    - "Lisa means so much to me. I can't live without her."

      「Lisa 對我的意義太重大了，我不能沒有她。」

    - "I never used to like money, but it means so much to me now."

      「我以前從未喜歡過錢，但現在它對我太重要了。」

40. **(someone or something) always means trouble (=a trouble maker)**

    ①（某人）總是礙事；惹事。②（某事）表示有麻煩；有問題。

    ① ● "Who did it?"

      「誰幹的？」

      "Bob."

      「Bob。」

      "Bob? He always means trouble."

      「Bob？他永遠就會惹麻煩。」

    ② ● "If he flys all the way from New York to see us instead of writing, it means trouble."

      「假如他大老遠從紐約飛來，而不寫信，那意味着我們有麻煩了。」

41. **measurements**

['mɛʒəmənts]

三圍 (指胸圍 bustline, 腰圍 waistline, 以及臀圍 hipline　)

- "What are her measurements?"

「她的三圍是多少？」

"36-24-36, I think."

「我想應該是 36-24-36 。」

42. **meat ball**

渾球

- "You're nothing but a meat ball."

「你除了是個渾球外啥也不是。」

43. **meet (someone) half way**

[mit]

妥協；各讓一步

- "Give him another chance. Meet him half way."

「再給他一次機會，雙方各退一步好嗎？」

"Well, O.K."

「好吧！」

44. **mess around**

[mɛs ə'raʊnd]

①胡搞；胡來。②來往；惹；沾染。③玩耍。④打擾；競爭。

①② ● "Don't mess around with her. She's no good."

「別跟她胡搞（來往），她不是個好東西。」

② ● "Don't mess around with drugs."

「別沾染上毒品。」

③ ● "I'm just going out to mess around."

「我正要出去玩。」

④ ● "Don't mess around with me, or you'll be sorry."

「別跟我爭，否則你會後悔的。」

45. **mess up**

   [mɛs]

   搞得亂七八糟的

   • "Did you see how bad he messed up when he tried to walk on stilts?"

   「你看到他試著穿上高蹺時那付糗樣子嗎？」

46. **Any message?**

   ['mɛsɪdʒ]

   有任何留言嗎？（從外返家時問）

   • "Any message, Ann?"

   「Ann, 有沒有留言？」

   "No."

   「沒有。」

47. **Might is right.**

   [maɪt]

   強權即公理

   • "That's not fair."

   「這不公平！」

   "Not fair? Might is right, remember?"

   「不公平？強權即公理，記得吧？」

48. **mighty (=very)**

   非常的；十分地

   • "That flick is mighty good."

   「那電影棒透了。」

   • "TNT is mighty powerful."

   「黃色炸藥威力很強。」

   • "This food is mighty tasty."

   「這東西（食物）真好吃！」

49. **made of the milk of human kindness**
   很有同情心的人

   ● "She is poor but still tries to help less fortunate people. She
   is really made of the milk of human kindness."
   「她雖然很窮，可是她仍然幫助比他更不幸的人。她頗有
   同情心。」

50. **Mind if I tag along?**
   不介意我跟着去吧？

   ● "Where are you going, Folks?"
   「各位，上哪兒啊？」
   "We're going to Hippie Creek, they said someone was
   swimming there, nude."
   「去 Hippie 溪，據說有人在那裡泳。」
   "Really? Mind if I tag along?"
   「真的嗎？不介意我一道去吧？」

51. **Mind your own business.**
   少管閒事（管你自己的事就好）

   ● "I'm not talking to you. Mind your own business, will you?"
   「我不是在跟你說話。只管你自己的事，好嗎？」

52. **not for minors**
   ['maɪnɚz]
   不是給未成年的（例如煙、酒不得售給未成年的人）

   ● "Are you over 18? This club is not for minors, you
   know."
   「你成年（超過18 歲）了嗎？你知道這個俱樂部可是不准
   小孩子來玩的！」

54. **miser (=cheap skate, skinflint, scrooge)**
   ['maɪzɚ]   ['skɪn,flɪnt] [skrudʒ]
   小氣鬼；吝嗇鬼

- "Mr. Rooper is such a miser. He never takes his wife out for dinner."

「Rooper 先生真是個小氣鬼。他從來不帶他的太太到外面吃飯。」

54. **(I sure) miss (you/him/her).**
我實在很想（你／他／她）

- "Mary, how are you? I sure miss you."
（電話或信上中）「Mary，妳好嗎？我實在很想妳。」

55. **miss the boat**
①坐失良機；沒當選。②遲到

① • "She missed the boat in the Miss U.S.A. pageant."
「她沒選上美國小姐。」

② • "If I miss the boat, please wait for me."
「如果我遲到了，請等我一下。」

56. **Mr. Innocence**
['ɪnəsns]
無辜先生（做錯了事，而裝着無辜的樣子）

- "Look at him. A whole six-pack of beer gone, and he's Mr. Innocence sitting on the sofa."
「瞧瞧他，半打的啤酒不見了，而那個無辜先生却坐在沙發上（一付無辜的樣子）。」

57. **(have) mixed feelings**
百感交集

- "When I heard Lily was going to marry James, I had mixed feelings."
「當我聽說 Lily 要嫁給 James 時，我真是百感交集。」

58. **Monday morning quarterbacking**
['kwɔrtɚ,bækɪŋ]
放馬後炮（就是事前不作聲，事後才發表高見）

- "If the Red Sox changed the pitcher in the 3rd inning, then
  they wouldn't have lost the game."
  「如果 Red Sox 在第三局換投手的話，他們就不會輸了。」
  "Yeah! Monday morning quarterbacking is easy."
  「是啊！放馬後炮當然容易。」
- "I know it must be the battery."
  「我就知道是電瓶出毛病。」
  "Yeah, why didn't you tell me earlier? Monday morning
  quarterback."
  「是啊，你爲什麼不早說呢？就只會放馬後炮。」

59. Money is no object

['abdʒɪkt]

錢不成問題（多少錢都沒關係）

- "I want you to find me another pearl like this one.
  Money is no object."
  「我要你幫我再找一顆相似的珍珠，錢不成問題。」

60. Money is the root of all evil.

['rut]

金錢是萬惡之源

- "Why do you need that much money? You know, money
  is the root of all evil."
  「你要那麼多錢做什麼？你該知道錢是萬惡之源。」

61. money talks (=money can buy everything)

錢能通神；有錢能使鬼推磨

- "He wouldn't help until I gave him a fifty."
  「他一直不肯幫忙，直到我給他一張 50 元大鈔。」
  "Money talks."
  「有錢能使鬼推磨嘛。」

62. **monkey business**

['mʌŋkɪ]

胡鬧；不正經之事

- "I've had enough of his monkey business. Tell him to act his age."

「我已受夠了他的胡鬧，叫他正經 點。」

63. **a monkey on (one's) back**

上癮

- "He should never have started smoking. It's like a monkey on his back. He just can't quit!"

「他真不該學抽煙的，上了癮，他就沒法戒掉了。」

64. **mood**

[mud]

心情

- "She is in a good (or bad, or terrible) mood now."

「她現在心情很好（不好；很不好）。」

- "Do you want to go to the beach?"

「你要不要去海邊？」

"I'm not in the mood."

「我沒有心情（去做某件事）。 」

65. **(someone) is more than a match for me.**

我敵不過（某人）；比不上（用在比賽上）

- "Jeff can run very fast. He is more than a match for me."

「Jeff 可以跑得很快。我跑不過他。」

66. **more than I can say**

①沒什麼好說的（沒有怨言的意思）。②表達不出。

① ● "At least he tried to help them out, which is more than I can say."

「至少他曾試著想替他們解圍，我實在沒什麼好再抱怨的了。」

② ● "I love you more than I can say."
「我愛你在心口難開。」

67. **moron**

['mɑrɑn]

低能兒；白痴

● "You moron! How can you lose your wallet on pay day?"
「你這個白痴，你怎麼會在發薪的日子丟了錢包呢？」

68. **motherfucker (=fuck)**

操！（比 fuck 更粗野）

● "You motherfucker! Get off my case."
「你操！少惹我。」

69. **move over**

挪開；讓開一點

● "I asked him to move over but he wouldn't budge."
「我請他挪開一點，但他動也不動。」

註："Make room, please." 是較客氣的說法 "budge" 是「動也不動」通常用在否定句中。

70. **move your ass.**

[æs]

走開（用於同輩朋友之間）

● "Move your ass, Jack."
「Jack, 走開！」

71. **Mr. Particular**

[pɚ'tıkjəlɚ]

挑剔先生（喜歡挑三挑四；難以取悅的）

● "Who's your English teacher?"
「誰是你的英文老師。」

"Derek Richman."
「Derek Richman. 」

"Oh, Mr. Particular."

「哦，挑剔先生。」

72. **muckraker**

['mʌk,rekɚ]

專門從事揭發壞人陰謀的人（尤指新聞記者有正派角的意思）

● "He's a muckraker."

「他專門揭發醜聞。」

● "The true story behind Watergate would never have come to light without the efforts of the muckraking journalists."

「如果沒有那些專門挖掘醜聞的新聞記者的努力，水門案件永遠不會公諸於世。」

73. **mud in your eye**

[mʌd]

乾杯（此俚語來自英國，老式說法）

● "Here's mud in your eye."

「乾杯！」

74. **to mug (v.), mugger (n.)**

[mʌg]　　[mʌgɚ]

搶劫；（在戶外）搶劫的人；強盜

● "His mother got mugged in front of her apartment. They never caught the mugger."

「他媽媽在公寓前被搶了，警察沒有捉到那個強盜。」

● "He was mugged in the Bronx."

「他在 Bronx 被搶了。」

註：Bronx 是 New York 最亂的一區。

75. **murder (=got killed)**

①難懂的。②要大命；要老命。

① ● "Boy, this history is murder."

「老天，這歷史真難懂。」

② ● "I got murdered on the final exam." (=got killed)
「期末考幾乎要了我的命。」

76. **must (reading) for men/women**
男性必讀（女性必讀）

● "This is a good book, a must for men."
「這是一本好書，男性必讀。」

● "This is must reading."
「這是必讀之物。」

77. **(something) must go**
（某樣東西）該戒了；除去

● "The doctor said drinking must go."
「醫生說不能再喝酒了。」

● "The husband told his wife that the cat must go."
「先生告訴太太說，一定要把貓送走。」

註：一般"wine"是指水果酒，white liquor 則是指酒精製成
的酒。

78. **(something) is my cup of tea**
（某件事）正合我的（喜好）胃口。

● "A nice dinner, a movie, and dancing afterwards. Now
that's my cup of tea."
「一頓豐盛的晚餐，一場電影，然後再去跳舞，這才真正
合我意。」

79. **My eyes are bigger than my stomach.**
['stʌmək]

眼大肚小（例如：在吃自助餐 buffet 時，拿得太多吃不完）。
（貪心不足蛇吞象）

● "I'm sorry, I can't finish my dinner. My eyes were bigger
than my stomach."
「對不起，我吃不下了，我的眼睛大過我的肚子。」

80. **My legs are going to sleep.**

    [l ɛgz]

    我的腿麻了。（例如坐得太久）

    ● "Oh, gosh, my legs went to sleep."

    「老天，我的腿麻了。」

81. **My lips are sealed.**

    [sild]

    我的嘴巴封住了。（表示自己口風很緊）

    ● "Don't tell Mary, I want to give her a surprise."

    「別告訴 Mary，我要給她一個驚喜。」

    "Don't worry, my lips are sealed."

    「別擔心，我的口風很緊。」

82. **my mouth is watering**

    流口水（聽到好吃的東西的時候）。

    ● "We have steak, lobster salad, and red wine for dinner tonight."

    「我們今晚有牛排、龍蝦沙拉、紅酒。」

    "It makes my mouth water just thinking about it."

    「光聽這些菜名，我就已經流口水了。」

83. **my nose is running; a runny nose**

    流鼻涕

    ● "My nose is running, I feel terrible today."

    「我流鼻涕，今天覺得很不舒服。」

    註："I got a runny nose today." 也是有相同之意。

84. **my treat**

    我請客

    ● "Waiter, check please."

    「先生，請算帳。」

    "(This is) my treat."

    「我請客。」

1. **name dropper**

    [drɑpɚ]

    會攀關係的人；狐假虎威的人

    ● "He is such a name dropper."

    「他眞是個會攀關係的人。」

2. **name it**

    說吧；儘管說吧

    ● "If you need anything, anything at all, just name it."

    「如果你需要幫忙，不管是什麼，儘管提出來。」

    ● "Whatever you like, you name it, you got it."

    「不管你喜歡什麼，只要你說出來，就可以得到。」

3. **nasty**

    [ˈnæstɪ]

    ①下流；低級。②討人厭。③突然翻臉。

    ① ● "Don't use that nasty word with me."

    　　「別對我說那些下流的話。」

    ② ● "Don't be so nasty."

    　　「別那麼討人厭。」

    ③ ● "After Brad spilled his beer on Anna-Lynn, her boyfriend

    　　got nasty and challenged him to a fight."

    　　「在Brad把啤酒打翻在Anna-Lynn 的身上之後，她的男

    　　朋友突然翻臉，並且單挑Brad 到外頭去。」

    註：在美國南部許多人習慣以兩個名字爲名(first name)

4. **(I/You) need a fix.**

    [fɪks]

    打海洛英，等等

    ● "I need a fix. It's been a couple of weeks since I got

    high."

    　　「我需要打一針（海洛英）。自從上次過癮以來，已經有

    　　一段日子了。」

註：fix 在此指打 heroin。

5. **needle** (=teasing, giving (someone) a hard time)

[nidl]

找麻煩；取笑

● "Everybody is needling me today. What's wrong?"

「今天每個人都在找我的麻煩，怎麼回事？」

● "Don't needle Jon about Heidi. Dave did and he regretted it."

「別取笑 Jon 有關 Heidi 的事。Dave 取笑過他，結果十分後悔。」（挨揍了！）

6. **never been better**

再好不過；從來沒這麼好過

● "How is business?"

「生意如何？」

"Never been better. Sales are up 125%."

「再好不過，銷售率升了 125%。」

7. **never give up**

永不死心（表示頑固）

● "I don't know what to do with Jack. He never gives up."

「我不知對 Jack 該怎麼辦。他永不死心。」

8. **never learn**

永遠學不乖（永遠不會從教訓中學乖）

● "You just never learn."

「你真是永遠學不乖。」

9. **nervous**

['nɝvəs]

①緊張。②擔心。

① ● "Don't be nervous."

「別緊張。」

② ● "I'm nervous about Gordon."
　　「我爲 Gordon 擔心。」

10. **nice going** (=good work/well done)
幹得好！

　● "Nice going, boys. I'm proud of you."
　　「幹得好，孩子們。我爲你們感到驕傲。」

11. **night coach**
夜間班機

　● "If you want to save some money, you should take the night coach. You can get at least a 20% discount."
　　「假如你想省錢的話，你該坐夜間班機，至少可以省上 20% 的錢。」

12. **night owl** (=night hawk)
　　　[aʊl]　　　[hɔk]
夜貓子

　● "I'm a night owl."
　　「我是個夜貓子。」

13. **no backbone**
　　['bæk'bon]
沒骨氣

　● "Peter has no backbone. That football player insulted him and he just stood there."
　　「Peter 一點骨氣都沒有。那個足球球員羞辱他，他只是站在那兒。」

14. **no hard feelings**
不要介意；不傷及感情

　● "I'm too busy to help you study tonight. No hard feelings, I hope?"
　　「今晚我太忙了，不能幫你溫習功課，希望你不會介意？」

● "No hard feelings, O.K.?"
　「不要記掛在心，好嗎？」

　"O.K."
　「好！」

註：在爭論過後（不是爭吵），希望對方不會記掛在心上而
　　不愉快，就可用這句。

15. **(There's) no need.**
不必了；不需要；不必費神

● "Should we call John up and invite him?"
　「我們是不是該去拜訪一下 John 順便邀請他？」

　"No need. He went to the movies tonight."
　「不必，他今晚去看電影了。」

16. **a No No**
不可以做的（小孩子吸手指頭、拿剪刀，媽媽就會說 No , No ,
表示不可以。）

● "Judy, smoking is a No No."
　「 Judy , 不可以抽煙。」

● "Asking a woman's age is a No No."
　「問婦女的年齡是不可以的。」

17. **No one raised his voice.**
無一人出聲；講話

● "How was the meeting?"
　「會議如何？」

　"Very quiet. No one raised his voice."
　「很安靜，沒人發言。」

18. **no soap (=No way)**
　　[sop]
不可能；不行

● "Can you lend me $20.00?"
　「你能借我 20 塊嗎？」

"No soap."

「不行。」

19. no strings attached

[strɪŋz] [əˈtæʃt]

沒有交換條件；沒有責任要負

● "You can try our new vacuum cleaner for two weeks and
if you don't want to buy it, just return it. There's no
strings attached."

「你可以試用這吸塵器兩個星期，你如果不想買就退回，
不必負任何責任。」

● "Hey Tim, will you let me use your car?"

「嘿，Tim, 你願意讓我借用你的車嗎？」

"O.K."

「沒問題。」

"You mean it? No strings attached?"

「真的？沒有任何條件？」

20. no way

休想；作夢；不可能

● "Could I borrow your girl for a night?"

「你的女朋友可不可以借我一晚？」

"No way."

「休想。」

21. no wonder

[ˈwʌndɚ]

難怪

● "Mary has a date tonight."

「Mary 今晚有約會。」

"No wonder she can't go to the movies with us."

「難怪她不能跟我們一起去看電影。」

22. **nobody**

    [ˈnoˌbɑdɪ]

    小人物；無名小卒

    ● "Who are you?"
      「你是誰？」

      "I'm a nobody."
      「我是個無名小卒。」

    ● "What's a nobody like you doing in a place like this."
      「像你這樣的無名小卒到這種地方來幹嘛？」

23. **Nobody is perfect.**

              [ˈpɝfɪkt]

    沒有人是完美無缺的；那個人不犯錯呢？

    ● "How can you forget to bring charcoal when you go out for a Bar-B-Q picnic?"
      「出外烤肉，你怎可能忘記帶木炭呢？」

      "Well, nobody is perfect, right?"
      「沒有人是完美無缺的，對不對？」

24. **None of your games.**

    不要耍花樣（表示不會上當）

    ● "Where were you last night? I tried to call about 20 times."
      「你昨晚到哪兒去了？我打了將近二十次的電話。」

      "I was bowling with Rudy."
      「我跟Rudy打保齡球去了。」

      "None of your games, please. Rudy was with Kathy at the movies. Now, just what were you doing?"
      「別耍花樣，Rudy昨晚跟Kathy看電影去了。現在告訴我，你做什麼去了？」

25. **None of your lip. (=shut up)**

    別回嘴！（非常強烈的命令語句）

● "Now look, Mike! I told you not to go there! So I don't want to hear any of your lip."

「Mike, 聽着！我叫你不要去那個地方，別回嘴。」

26. nosy

好管閑事的

● "You know what? You're really nosy."

「你知道嗎？你眞愛管閑事。」

27. **Not a voice was raised in opposition.**

一聲反對都沒有。

● "What was Congress' reaction?"

「國會的反應如何？」

"Not a voice was raised in opposition."

「一點反對都沒有。」

28. **not bad**

還不賴，還不錯（有好的意思）

● "How's school /business?"

「近來功課／生意如何？」

"Not bad."

「還不賴。」

29. **not give (or care) a hoot (=not give two bits)**

                [hut]   [bɪts]

毫不在乎

● "She kept singing and didn't give a hoot about others."

「她一直不停地唱歌，毫不在乎別人（的反應）。」

30. **not half bad**

一點也不壞；好

● "Felix? He's not half bad."

「Felix? 他一點也不壞。」

31. **Not in this life!**

這輩子休想！

- "If you step out of this room, don't ever try to come back, not in this life."

  「如果你走出這房間，這輩子別想再回來。」

- "Grace, would you marry me?"

  「 Grace, 妳願意嫁給我嗎？」

  "Maybe, but not in this life."

  「也許，但不是這輩子（下輩子再說吧！）」

32. not necessarily

[nɛsə'sɛrəlɪ]

不一定要…；不見得要…（如何如何）（具備某種條件）

- "I want to marry someone who is handsome, but not necessarily rich."

  「我要嫁一個英俊的，但不一定要有錢。」

33. not necessary

['nɛsə,sɛrɪ]

不必

- "Do I have to bring my I.D. with me?"

  「我要不要帶着證件（身份證、學生證…）？」

  "It's not necessary."

  「不必。」

34. not really

①並不是十分的，眞的（喜歡、討厭…）。②不盡然；不見得（表示相反的意見）。

① ● "Do you like this shirt?"

  「你喜歡這件襯衫嗎？」

  "Not really."

  「並不十分喜歡。」

② ● "Peter is really a good guy."

  「 Peter 眞是個好人。」

"Not really."

「不見得。」

35. **(That's/It's) not true.**

那不是實話；沒這回事

- "Who started the fight?"

「是誰先引起這場爭吵的？（或是打架）」

"Janet."

「是 Janet 。」

"That's not true. I didn't start the fight."

「那不是眞的，不是我。」

36. **nothing but the best**

最好的；最考究的

- "She wears nothing but the best."

「她只穿最考究的衣服。」

- "We sell nothing but the best."

「我們只賣最好的貨品。」

37. **nothing in (someone)**

一無可取

- "Why should I marry you? There's nothing in you."

「我爲什麼要嫁給你？你一無可取。」

38. **Nothing works.**

一籌莫展；諸事不順

- "Have you found out the way to solve the problem?"

「你找到解決（問題）的辦法了嗎？」

"Nothing works."

「一籌莫展。」

39. **(a) nuisance**

[ˋnjusəns]

討厭鬼；討人厭的人

● "He is a nuisance."

「他是一個討厭鬼。」

● "Don't be a nuisance! Let's go."

「走吧！別做討厭鬼。」

40. **nuts**

[nʌts]

①瘋子。 nuts —adj. (=nutty)/ 瘋的；狂的。 ②睪丸。

①   ● "You are really nuts."

「你眞是瘋了。」

  ● "What a nut."

「眞是一個瘋子。」

② ● "He kicked him in the nuts."

「他踢了他的下體一脚。」

1. **no obligation**

   [ˌɑblə'geʃən]

   沒有義務那樣做

   ● "Jane and I broke up last month. I've got no obligation to
   ask her out to the big dance."

   「Jane跟我上個月就吹了，我沒有義務要邀請她去那個盛
   大的舞會！」

2. **O.D. (=overdose)**

   服用過量的痲醉劑（安眠藥）

   ● "She died of on overdose."

   「她因服（痲醉）藥過量而死。」

   ● "She O.D. ed."

   「她服藥過量。」

3. **(that's) odd (=that's strange=that's funny)**

   [ɑd]

   眞奇怪啊！

   ● "Joe hasn't shown up yet? That's odd."

   「Joe 還沒來嗎？奇怪！」

4. **off**

   失常（因爲累，或心不在焉）

   ● "He's a little off today!"

   「他（投手）今天有點失常。」

5. **off base**

   大錯特錯

   ● "You are off base this time. I didn't go out with Jack. I
   went out with my aunt."

   「你這次可大錯特錯了，我不是跟Jack出去，我是跟我姑
   姑出去。」

6. **off the bench**

[bɛntʃ]

（球員）披掛上陣

- "Magic Johnson came off the bench to score 24 points."

  「Magic Johnson　披掛上陣得了二十四分。」

7. **off the wall**

[ɔf]　[wɔl]

奇怪的

- "He's off the wall. Don't listen to him."

  「別聽他的，他精神不正常。」

- "He made some off the wall remark when I asked him about him and Sue."

  「當我問起他跟Sue 的事的時候，他胡說了一大堆話。」

註：drive (someone) up the wall　是逼人發瘋，如 "You're driving me up the wall." 「你逼得我快發瘋了。」

8. **Oh brother!**

啊；老天啊！

- "Oh, brother, I blew it again."

  「啊，老天，我又搞砸了。」

9. **Oh dear, (oh) man; (oh) boy; brother; (oh) gosh; (oh) my goodness**

（均爲驚嘆語）老天！

- "Oh dear, I've done it again. What's wrong with me?"

  「老天，我又做了。我到底是怎麼回事？」

10. **old bag**

[bæg]

老雞婆；老巫婆

- "That old bag is bitching about everything again."

  「那個老雞婆又再對每樣事情囉嗦了。」

11. **old hen**

[hɛn]

老雞婆

- "Who told you this?"
  「誰告訴你的？」

  "Mrs. Lamb."
  「Lamb 太太。」

  "Oh, that old hen."
  「哦，那個老雞婆。」

12. **old man**

老頭（爸爸）；丈夫；同居的（男的）；老闆。

- "I have to talk to my old man first."
  「我必須先跟我老頭談一談。」

註：old lady 是老娘，老媽。

13. **on a diet**

[daɪət]

節食

- "Sorry, I can't eat cake. I'm on a diet."
  「對不起，我不能吃蛋糕，我正在節食。」

14. **on a friendly footing with (someone)**

與（某人）交情很好

- "Do you know Smith family?"
  「你認識 Smith 家人嗎？」

  "Sure, we're on a friendly footing with the Smiths."
  「當然，我們跟 Smith 家交情很好。」

15. **on and on**

不斷地；不停地

- "He talked on and on until I fell asleep."
  「他說了又說，直到我睡着了。」

16. **on (one's) back**
    找麻煩

    ● "My mother is always on my back about my homework."
    「我媽媽總是找我功課上的麻煩。」

    註：如果有人on your back 你可說 "Get off my back." 意指：
    　　「別煩我。」(=Leave me alone.)

17. **on (one's) high horse**
    道貌岸然（自己認為道德很高總是訓人）

    ● "I don't want to talk to her; she's always on her high horse
    (=she won't get off her high horse.)."
    「我不想跟她講話，她總是道貌岸然的。」

18. **on my list**
    　　　[lɪst]
    在預定要做的事之中

    ● "Don't forget to buy bread and eggs."
    　「別忘了買麵包及蛋。」
    　"Yeah. They're on my list."
    　「好，都在（採購）單子上。」

    ●"Are you going to study for the test tomorrow?"
    　「你是否打算準備明天的考試啊？」
    　"Yeah. It's on my list."
    　「對，已經在我的（計劃）單上。」

19. **on the beam**
    　　　[bim]
    完全正確；對了

    ● "Don't tell me you won the first prize again?"
    　「你是不是又得了第一名？」
    　"You're on the beam as usual."
    　「像往常一樣，你又對了。」

"No. You are. You won, not me."

「不，（我可不是像往常一樣的又對了）你才是，你贏了
第一，不是我。」

（ No 是針對 as usual 的一個玩笑語 ）

20. **on the button**

恰到好處；完全正確

● "The governor is a great speaker. What he said was right on
the button."

「州長是個大演說家，他的話恰到好處。」

● "How old do you think I am?"

「你猜我幾歲？」

"30"

「30。」

"You got it right on the button."

「完全正確。」

21. **on the dole (=on unemployment)**

[dol]

失業

● "He has been on the dole for three months."

「他已經失業三個月了。」

22. **on the double**

['dʌbl]

快一點

● "Now, move it! On the double!"

「現在，開始（行動）！快點！」

23. **on the house**

由餐館或酒店請客；本店請客

● "This drink is on the house."

「這杯酒由本店請客。」

24. **on the line (=on the phone)**

   電話

   ● "Bob's on the line. He wants to talk to you."

   「Bob 打來的，他要跟你講話。」

25. **on the edge**

   充滿刺激

   ● "He liked adventure and living dangerously. He lived his life on the edge."

   「他喜歡冒險的生活，他喜歡生命充滿刺激。」

26. **on the right track**

   [træk]

   遵循的方向正確

   ● "We haven't caught the criminal yet, but I think we're on the right track."

   「我們還沒抓到那個罪犯，但我想我們的方向是對的。」

   ● "He hasn't figured out the problem yet, but he's on the right track."

   「他還沒找個解決問題的方法，但他遵循的方向是對的。」

27. **(to be) on the right train but the wrong track**

   辦的事情對，但方向錯了。

   ● "I can't understand why we failed."

   「我不懂我們怎麼會失敗。」

   "Maybe we were on the right train but the wrong track."

   「也許我們做的事情對，只是方向錯了。」

28. **on the rocks**

   [raks]

   加冰塊（喝酒時不習慣喝純酒 straight，加點冰塊以沖淡一下。）

   ● "I want a Martini on the rocks."

   「我要一杯馬丁尼加冰塊。」

29. **on the run**

①發動猛攻。②逃跑；躲避。

① ● "The New York Yankees know they are far behind, so they are on the run now."

「紐約洋基隊知道他們自己遙遙落後，現正在發動猛攻。」

② ● "The terrorists are on the run from the FBI."

「恐怖份子現正逃避 FBI 的搜捕。」

30. **on the tip of (one's) tongue**

話在舌尖（但一時又想不起怎麼說）

● "I can't think of his name. It's right on the tip of my tongue but I can't quite remember it."

「我記不起他的名字了，他的名字就在我的嘴邊，但我一下想不起來。」

31. **on top of the world**

①真是稱心滿意。②飄飄欲仙（吸毒之後）

① ● "I have everything I want, I'm on top of the world now."

「我想要的我都有了，我現在真是稱心如意。」

② ● "After taking the drug, he felt like he was on top of the world."

「在吸食毒品之後，他覺得飄飄欲仙。」

32. **(to be) on the wagon**

戒酒（也許是暫時性的）

● "Would you like a drink, Sam?"

「Sam，你要來一杯嗎？」

"No thanks. I'm on the wagon."

「不，謝了！我最近在戒酒。」

● "I'm on the wagon this week."

「我這一星期不喝酒。」

33. **on your feet**

站起來（多半用於軍隊中的命令語）

- "On your feet and get moving."

「站起來，走！」

34. **once and for all**

一勞永逸

- "Let's get rid of this once and for all."

「讓我們一次把這事解決了。」

35. **Once is too often.**

一次都嫌多

- "I never cheated before. . . ."

「我以前沒說過謊…」

"Once is too often."

「一次都嫌多。」

36. **One man's meat is another man's poison.**

一樣東西，對甲有益，未必對乙也有益；一個人的食物，可能是另一個人的毒物；你喜歡，別人未必喜歡。

- "I don't understand why he hates parties. I always have such a good time."

「我不明白他為什麼討厭宴會，我每次都玩得很開心。」

"One man's meat is another man's poison."

「你喜歡，別人未必喜歡。」

37. **One misfortune rides upon another's back.**

[mɪsˈfɔrtʃən]

禍不單行

- "I lost my job yesterday, and I got hit by a car this morning. Oh, shit, one misfortune rides upon another's back."

「我昨天被解僱了，今早又被車撞，噢，他媽的，真是禍不單行。」

38. **one night stand**
短暫的；一夜風流

* "I met her at a bar. We had a one night stand."
   「我在酒吧認識她，我們有了一夜的露水姻緣。」
   註：原為在夜總會只表演一夜，後被引用為 " 短暫之一切 "
   如性關係等等。

39. **one price**
不二價

* "Can you come down a little?"
   「能便宜一點嗎？」

   "Sorry, it's one price for all."
   「對不起，不二價。」

40. **one thing at a time**
一件一件按次序來

* "Hey, I'm not a superman. I can only handle one thing
   at a time, O.K.?"
   「嘿，我又不是超人，一次一件慢慢來，好嗎？」

41. **onesided (game, deal, argument)**
['wʌn'saɪdɪd]
一面倒的（球賽、生意、爭吵…）

* "How was the game?"
   「球賽如何？」

   "Terrible, it was a onesided game, and of course we
   were the losers."
   「糟透了，那是一場一面倒的比賽，當然我們是輸家。」

42. **or else what?**
要不然怎樣？（當別人威脅你：「做，不然我…」你反問：
「不然怎樣？…」。）

- "Give me $25,000, or else I'll. . ."

  「給我二萬五千塊，不然我就…」

  "Or else what?"

  「就怎樣？」

43. **organization (=family)**

    [ˌɔrgənaɪˈzeʃən]

    幫會

    - "He belongs to the Chicago organization."

      「他屬於芝加哥幫的。」

44. **orgy**

    [ˈɔrdʒɪ]

    ①無遮瘋狂舞會（通常指美國的裸體舞會）。②酒菜很豐盛的宴會。

    ①② ● "Have you ever been to an orgy?"

      「你參加過無遮瘋狂舞會嗎？」（或，你參加過酒菜
       很豐盛的宴會嗎？）

      "Never."

      「從來沒參加過。」

45. **other way around**

    相反的方法或方式

    - "Why do we say 'He put on his shoes and socks' and not the other way around?"

      「爲什麼我們說，『他穿上鞋子、襪子』，而不是『他穿
       上襪子、鞋子』？」

      "I don't know."

      「我不知道。」

46. **out-a-sight (or out-of-sight)**

    很棒；很美

    - "This movie is really out of sight."

      「這電影真棒。」

47. **(He's) out in left field.**
　（他是個）局外人！（他）完全不知道！

- "What does he know? He's out in left field."
　「他知道什麼？他是個局外人。」

註：left field 原自棒球術語 " 左外野 "。

48. **out of (one's) range.**
　　　　　　['rendʒ]
　超出能力之外

- "You want me to lend you $10,000? That's out of my range."
　「你要我借你一萬塊？那是超出我能力之外的。」

49. **out of shape**
　健康欠佳

- "He is out of shape."
　「他身體健康欠佳。」

- "He's in good shape."
　「他身體很健康。」

註："in shape" 則是 " 身體健康 "。

50. **over my dead body**
　休想（除非我死了）

- "Dad, I want to marry Marisa."
　「爸，我要娶Marisa。」
　"Over my dead body."
　「休想。」

- "Can I borrow your car?"
　「我能借你的車嗎？」
　"Over my dead body."
　「休想。」

51. **over the hill**

①過氣。②日漸老邁。

① ● "How do you like Barbara Streisand?"

「你覺得芭芭拉史翠珊如何？」

"She's over the hill."

「她已過氣了。」

② ● "She is over the hill."

「她日漸老邁。」

52. **over the hump**

[hʌmp]

已度過那難過的日子（通常指星期三）

● "It's Thursday. We're over the hump for this week."

「今天是星期四，我們又過了星期三（週末快到了）。」

● "If you pass the College Entrance Examination, you're over the hump."

「如果你通過大學入學考試，你就度過那難過的日子了。」

● "Wednesday is hump day."

「星期三是一小關。」

53. **overtime**

[ˈovɚˌtaɪm]

①加班。②加班費。

①"Dear, I have to work overtime tonight. I won't be home for dinner."

「親愛的，今晚我得加班，我不會回來吃晚飯了。」

②"I get lots of overtime on my new job."

「在這份新工作上，我領了很多加班費。」

1. **pack**

   [pæk]

   ①收拾；整理行李（準備離去）。②擁擠。③背袋。

   ① ● "What are you doing?"

   「你在幹嗎？」

   "What do you think? I'm packing, of course."

   「你認爲呢？當然是在收拾行李啊！」（也許是打算離家出走）

   ② ● "This restaurant is usually very packed during these hours."

   「這家餐館在這個時候通常是很擠的。」

   ③ ● "Have you seen my pack?"

   「你看到我的背包了嗎？」

2. **packed like (=as close as) sardines**

   [sɑr'dinz]

   擠得像沙丁魚一樣

   ● "Oh, boy, this bus is packed like sardines in a can."

   「噢，老天，這輛公車眞是擠得跟沙丁魚罐頭一樣。」

3. **pack away**

   吃得很多

   ● "Two eggs, two orders of French toast, three pieces of bacon, and one big glass of orange juice. You sure do pack it away, don't you?"

   「兩個蛋，兩份烤麵包，三片培根（火腿肉）和一大杯橘子汁，你吃得眞多啊！」

   ● "Boy, he can really pack it away."

   「乖乖，他吃得眞多。」

4. **packy (=liquor store, state store, package store)**

   賣酒的地方（在美國有"酒店"專門賣一瓶瓶，一箱箱的酒，

像麵包店一樣）

● "Let's go down to the packy and get a case of beer."
「我們去酒店買一箱啤酒回來吧。」

5. **page**
[pedʒ]
尋找（餐廳中侍者舉著一個牌子找人）

● "Kent, someone is paging you."
「Kent, 有人找你。」

6. **a pain in the ass/neck**
[pen]
麻煩人物；頭痛人物

● "He is a pain in the ass."
「他是一個令人頭痛的人物。」

7. **(to) paint oneself into a corner**
陷自己於困境（因爲事先沒好好計劃過）

● "Don't make too many promises this early. You'll paint yourself into a corner."
「別這麼早許下太多的承諾，你會把自己陷入困境。」

8. **a pair**
[pɛr]
一對佳偶或一對活寶

● "Here comes Jack and Janet."
「Jack 跟 Janet 走來了。」
"They are really a pair."
「他們眞是一對。」

9. **pal**
[pæl]
朋友

● "I met a guy yesterday. I think he's your pal."
「我昨天遇到一個傢伙，我想他是你的朋友。」

10. **panties**

['pæntɪz]

女性的內褲（男性的則是 shorts ）

- "What are you doing, wearing my panties."
  「你幹嘛穿着我的內褲？」

11. **(too much) paper work**

公文太多；工作繁重；太多的公文（填表）手續

- "I have to work overtime again, because there's much paper work that has to be done."
  「我又得再加班了，因爲太多的公文等着完成。」
- "You can get some free books if you fill out these forms, but I think there's too much paper work."
  「如果你填完這些表格，你可以得到一些免費的書刊，但我想這些公文手續實在是太繁複了。」

12. **party-crasher**

['kræʃə]

不速之客（不請自來的人）

- "We don't want any party crashers, so be careful about who you let in."
  「我們可不歡迎任何的不速之客，所以當你讓客人進來時小心一點。」

13. **the party is over**

快樂的時光過去了

- "The party is over. From now on we have to study hard."
  「歡樂的時光過去了。從現在開始，我們得好好唸書。」

14. **party pooper**

掃興的人（例如，宴會中遲到或早退的人）

- "Oh, don't be such a party pooper. It's still early."
  「哦，別做掃興的人，天色還早呢！」

15. pass $\left\{\begin{array}{ll}\text{out} & \text{昏過去} \\ \text{away/on} & \text{死了} \\ \text{over} & \text{沒有提升（第一副手）而選用了別人}\end{array}\right.$

● "After hearing the bad news, she passed out."

「聽到那壞消息後，她昏了過去。」

●"She passed away three weeks ago."

「三個禮拜前她過世了。」

● "My mother recently passed on."

「我媽媽最近過世了。」

● "They passed me over, and picked John to be the new president

「他們沒有提升我，而選了 John 成爲新的校長。」（ 沒 提升原來的副校長當新校長，而選用了別人。 ）

16. (to) pass the buck

推卸責任

● "No one will accept responsibility for the news leak. Everyone is passing the buck."

「沒有人願意爲走漏消息的事負責，大家都在推卸責任。」

17. (someone is) past praying for

（某人）無藥可救

● "She's been drunk for ten years now."

「她酗酒至今整整有十年了。」

"She's really past praying for."

「她眞是無可救藥。」

18. pay for

①付（ 賬 ）。②付出代價

① ● "How are you going to pay for this?"

「你打算怎麼去付這筆費用呢？」

"I'm going to ask my father for the money."

「我打算問我爸爸要錢。」

② ● "I swear. You are going to pay for this someday."

「我發誓，總有一天你要償還這筆（仇）債。」

19. **pay (someone) off**

收買（一個人）；賄賂

● "I'm going to pay her off. She knows too much, and I want to make sure she's on our side."

「我要收買她，她知道得太多，我要確定她是站在我們這邊。」

20. **Peace be with you./God be with you.**

祝你一路平安。　　上帝與你同在。

● "Go, my boy. Peace be with you."

「去吧！孩子。祝你一路平安！」

21. **peach**

[pitʃ]

漂亮；風度優雅（尤指女的）

● "What a peach!"

「多漂亮的一個女人！」

● "She is really a peach."

「她真是一個漂亮的女孩。」

22. **peanuts**

['pi,nʌts]

很少（的錢）

● "He's willing to work for peanuts because he is poor."

「因為他窮，他願意做待遇很低的工作。」

23. **peeping Tom**

[pipɪŋ] [tɑm]

偷看者；窺伺者

● "You are a peeping Tom."

「你是一個窺伺者。」

24. **(a) penny pincher**

   [ˋpɛnɪ] [ˋpɪntʃɚ]

   小氣鬼

   ● "He's a real penny-pincher."
      「他是一個小氣鬼。」

25. **penny wise and pound foolish.**

   [paʊnd]

   斤斤計較；心胸狹窄；目光短視

   ● "He's penny wise and pound foolish."
      「他真是斤斤計較，目光短視。」

26. **pep talk**

   [pɛp]

   精神講話（如教練鼓勵球員）

   ● "The coach gave his baseball team a pep talk before the game."
      「那個棒球隊教練在賽前對他的隊員精神講話。」

27. **period/monthly**

   [ˋpɪrɪəd] [ˋmʌnθlɪ]

   （女孩的）例假

   ● "She is worried because she missed her period."
      「她十分擔心（懷孕了！）因為例假沒來。」

28. **(something, nothing) personal**

   [ˋpɝsnl]

   涉及個人恩怨，喜好，私事

   ● "It's nothing personal, I just don't like the way she talks."
      「沒有什麼個人的恩怨，我只是不喜歡她說話的方式罷了。」

   ● "I want to talk to him. It's something personal."
      「我想要單獨跟他談一談，是有關私人的事。」

●"Don't get too personal."

「別問及個人隱私的問題。」

29. **pest**

[pɛst]

電灯泡（指人）

●"Pearl, do you want to go to movies with us?"

「Pearl, 你要不要跟我們去看電影？」

"No, thanks. I don't want to be a pest."

「不，謝了！我可不想當電灯泡。」

30. **petty cash**

小數額的金錢

●"My house was robbed but I was lucky. All the robber got was some petty cash."

「我家昨天遭竊，幸好，小偷偷走的只是一點點錢而已。」

31. **phoney**

['fonɪ]

冒牌貨；假的，虛假的人

●"He is such a phoney. (=He's phoney.)"

「他是個冒牌貨。」

●"This watch is phoney. It looks like a real Rolex, but it only costs me $20."

「這個錶是冒牌的，它看上去像勞力士錶，事實上只花了我20塊。」

32. **phooey on (you/name)**

['fui]

去他的；管你去死；哼…

●"Phooey on you. I don't give a damn."

「管你去死，我才不在乎呢。」

33. **pick a quarrel/fight with (someone)**

向（某人）挑釁

● "She picked a quarrel with me last night."
「她昨晚找我吵架。」

34. pick on

[pɪk]

找碴；找麻煩

● "Why is everybody picking on me today? Did I do anything wrong?"
「爲什麼今天每個人都找我的麻煩？我做錯了什麼嗎？」

35. pick up

①把上；吊上（馬子、凱子）。②取貨（錢、海洛英之類的）③漸有起色；漸漸好轉。④車子換擋起步快。⑤小型輕便貨車。

① ● "He picked her up at the local bar, and they got married within the month."
「他在當地的一家酒吧把上了她，不消一個月兩人就結婚了。」

② ● "Where do we make the pick-up?"
「我們在那兒取貨（錢）？」

③ ● "His business picked up after he changed his policy."
「在他改變方針之後，公司漸有起色。」

④ ● "This car can pick up really fast."
「這輛車換擋很快。」

⑤ ● "He owns a 1980 Ford pick-up truck."
「他擁有一輛1980年福特的小型貨車。」

36. pickled

[ˈpɪkld]

①浸泡；醃。②喝醉。

① ● "Pickled vegetables keep longer."
「醃過的菜可以保存長久些。」

② ● "Every Friday he drinks until he gets pickled and goes to sleep."

「每個星期五，他喝酒直到大醉然後上床睡覺。」

37. **picky**

[pɪkɪ]

挑剔

● "You're really picky."

「你真挑剔！」

38. **picture**

①想像。②（懂；明白；瞭解）情形。

① ● "Can you picture how we'll look 50 years from now?"

「你能想像50年後我們會是什麼樣子嗎？」

② ● "Yes, I get the picture."

「是的，我懂了（明白了）。」

39. **pin-up-girl**

海報女郎

● "She is the pin-up-girl of July's Playboy."

「她是花花公子雜誌七月份的海報女郎。」

註：cover girl 是封面女郎。

40. **pink slip**

[pɪŋk/slɪp]

解僱或失敗的意思。（因為在美國解僱及一般警告信函都是用粉紅色）

● "Jennifer got a pink slip in her last pay envelope, so she's looking for a new job."

「Jennifer 在她最後一次薪水袋中收到了解僱通知，所以她現在正在找新的工作。」

41. **pipe down**

[paɪp]

說話小聲點

- "Hey! Pipe down? I'm on the phone."
  「嘿，小聲點，我正在打電話。」
- "Pipe down. I'm trying to get some sleep."
  「安靜一點，我想睡一會兒。」

註：pipe up 正好相反。

42. **piss (someone) off**

[pɪs]

氣死（人）了。（此種說法較粗俗）

- "That bitch really pissed me off."
  「那個賤人眞是氣死我了。」

  "So what? There are plenty of fish in the sea."
  「是又怎樣？（想開點）天涯何處無芳草。」

43. **pisser**

['pɪsɚ]

開心；眞棒；眞好

- "What a pisser."
  「眞棒。」
- "He's a pisser."
  「他是個開心果。」

44. **pitch black**

[pɪtʃ] [blæk]

黑漆漆

- "It's pitch black here."
  「這裏眞黑！」

45. **pitch in (litter)**

把廢物丟入垃圾筒

- "Pitch in, and help us to keep our city clean."
  「請合作（把廢物丟入垃圾筒）使我們的市容永保清潔。」

46. **(a) plain Jane**

平凡；普通的女孩（不出色）

● "She's a plain Jane."

「她是一個平凡的女孩。」

47. **platform · shoes**

['plæt,fɔrm]

厚底鞋（身材矮小女仕之恩物）

● "She likes to wear platform shoes, because they make her look taller."

「她喜歡穿厚底鞋，因爲它們可以使她看上去高些。」

48. **play games**

耍花招；玩花樣

● "Don't play games with me."

「別跟我玩花樣。」

49. **play hooky**

['hʊkɪ]

逃學；曉班

● "Why do you play hooky?"

「你爲什麼逃學？」

"I hate school."

「（因爲）我討厭學校。」

50. **(to) play it by ear**

到時再說（現在不必太早擔心！表示行動重於計劃）隨興之所至

● "Where do you think we should stop and eat tonight?"

「你認爲我們今晚該停在哪兒吃飯？」

"I don't know. Let's just play it by ear."

「我不知道，到時再說。」

51. **(to) play one person (off) against another**

挑撥離間（以坐收漁翁之利）

●"He's jealous of our friendship, so he's trying to play

us off against each other."

「他妒嫉我們的友誼，所以他想挑撥我們。」

52. **play possum**

['pɑsəm]

裝死

● "Get up Stanley, I want to talk to you, I know you're not sleeping. Don't play possum."

「 Stanley 起來，我有話要跟你說，我知道你還沒睡着。別裝死。」

註：opossum [ə'pɑsəm] 是一種鼠，遇到強敵會裝死。

53. **play with (someone)**

玩弄（某人）

● "Can't you see? He's just playing with you."

「你難道看不出來？他只是在玩弄你。」

54. **plumb nonsense**

['plʌm]

無稽之談；胡說八道

● "I'm going to marry Alex? That's plumb nonsense."

「我要嫁給Alex？胡說八道。」

55. **pluses and minuses**

優點與缺點；長處與短處

● "Let's talk about his pluses and minuses."

「我們來談他的優點與缺點。」

"O.K. On one hand, he's honest and hard working; on the other hand, he's too young and inexperienced."

「好！他一方面很誠實，努力工作；另一方面則是太年青且缺乏經驗。」

56. **no point**

沒有必要

- "There's no point in inviting Stuart; he'll say he's too busy."

「沒有必要邀請 Stuart, 他會說他很忙。」

57. **poker face**

['pokɚ]

撲克牌面孔（沒有表情，你猜不出他心中想什麼）

- "Just look at that poker face!"

「瞧瞧那張撲克牌臉。」

58. **POST NO BILLS!**

[post / no / bɪlz]

禁止張貼

59. **(to) pound (=to eat fast)**

[paʊnd]

吃得很快

- "That girl pounded down 4 bowls of rice with her dinner."

「晚餐時那個女孩一口氣吃了四碗飯。」

60. **pound the pavement**

['pevmənt]

沿門挨戶的找工作

- "He's been pounding the pavement since he got here, but he can't find a job."

「他打從到這裏來就沿門挨戶的在找工作，不過還沒找到。」

61. **pour cold water on (someone's plans, ideas, . . .)**

潑冷水

- "I was anxious to start until he poured cold water on my plans with a lot of criticism and no praise."

「在他對我的計劃大肆批評（沒有讚美），猛潑冷水之前，我本來很急切的要動手去做的。」

62. **pour it on**

[por]

不斷地做某事（加油拼到底）

- "The American hockey team really poured it on in the third period and beat the Russians by three goals."
  「美國曲棍球隊在第三節拼命努力，最後以三球贏了蘇俄。」

63. **preach to deaf ears**

[pritʃ]

白費口舌（對方心意已定，無法說服）

- "You're preaching to deaf ears. He won't listen to you."
  「你在白費口舌。他不會聽你的。」

64. **Not precisely**

[prɪˈsaɪslɪ]

不盡然；不完全是這樣；不完全正確（precisely 則為完全正確）

- "You mean if you have money you will go with us?"
  「你是說假如你有錢的話，你會跟我們一起去？」

  "Not precisely. If I have money and time, I'll go with you."
  「不完全對。（我是說）假如我有錢以及時間，我會跟你們一起去。」

65. **prime time**

[praɪm]

黃金時間（係指電視晚上 6 － 9 點收視率最高的時間）

- "The Carol Burnett Show has been taken off of Wednesday night prime time."
  「女丑劇場從星期三的黃金時間換下來了。」

66. **private-eye (=detective)**

[ˈpraɪvɪt]

私家偵探

- "What do you do for a living?"

「你是幹什麼的？」

"I'm a. private-eye."

「我是個私家偵探。」

67. **pro (=professional)**

[pro]

職業性的

- "He is the No. 1 pro football player. He scored three touchdowns in the last game."

「他是最佳的足球球員，他在上次比賽中攻進了三球。」

註：美式足球一個touchdown 得六分。

68. **No problem**

[ˋprɑbləm]

沒問題

- "Norma, can you help me to clean my house? I've got guests coming over tonight."

「Norma, 你能幫我清理一下房子嗎？今晚我有客人要來。」

"No problem."

「沒問題。」

69. **propose a toast (to someone)**

[prəˋpoz] [tost]

敬酒

- "Let's propose a toast to Dr. Sung."

「我們敬 Sung 博士一杯。」

- "I propose a toast to you."

「我敬你。」

70. **prove it**

[pruv]

拿出證據來

● "You took my money."

「你拿了我的錢。」

"Prove it."

「拿出證據來。」

71. **pub (=bar)**

[pʌb]

酒吧

● "Would you like to go to that pub again tonight?"

「今晚你願意再去那間酒吧嗎？」

註：pub 比一般 bar 要 homey（舒適）一點。

72. **puffed up**

[pʌft]

擺架子

● "He's puffed up with self-importance."

「他自以為了不起的擺架子。」

73. **(to) pull (something)**

耍花樣

● "I wonder which of our thoughtless neighbors pulled that one."

「我不知道是哪一個缺德（差勁）的鄰居幹的好事。」

74. **(Someone tried to) pull a fast one on us but we outsmarted him.** [aut'smɑrtɪd]

（某人）想騙我們，還早呢！（我們比他聰明之意）

● "That son of bitch, he tried to pull a fast one on us but we outsmarted him."

「那個混蛋，他想騙我們，還早得很哩！」

75. **pull a stunt**

[stʌnt]

耍花樣；騙人

● "This isn't the first time you've pulled that stunt on someone."

「這不是你第一次騙人。」

註：stunt man 是大明星的替身（代其拍攝危險動作的戲）

76. **pull an all-nighter**

[pʊl]　　[naɪtɚ]

開夜車

● "I had so much homework I had to pull three all-nighters last week."

「上星期我有那麼多的功課，我必須開三天的夜車才趕得完。」

77. **(to) pull (one's, someone's) leg (=joking; kidding)**

開玩笑

● "Don't take him seriously. He's just pulling your leg."

「別把他當真，他只是在開你的玩笑。」

78. **pull (something) out of the fire**

轉敗為勝

● "He pulled it out of the fire in the 5th round."

「在（拳賽）第五回合中他轉敗為勝。」

79. **pull over**

靠邊停下來

● "Hey, mister pull over and show me your driver's license."

「嘿，老兄，靠邊停下來，讓我看看你的駕照。」

80. **punk**

[ˋpʌnk]

地痞流氓

● "He's a punk."

「他是一個地痞流氓。」

81. **push a pen; pencil-pusher**

    文抄工作。文書員

    - "I don't want to get a job where all I do is push a pen."

      「我不願意找一份只是抄抄寫寫的工作。」

    - "I don't want to be a pencil-pusher."

      「我不願意當文書員。」

82. **push the panic button**

    ['pænɪk/'bʌtn]

    緊張

    - "I still had 2 chapters to read so I pushed the panic button and got it done by 1 o'clock."

      「我還有兩章要唸,所以我加緊唸書,結果在一點以前看完了。」

    - "If Greg calls, don't push the panic button. Tell him I'll be back in an hour from the library."

      「假如Greg打電話來,別緊張,告訴他我一個小時內會從圖書館回來。」

83. **push too far/hard**

    [puʃ]

    欺人太甚

    - "Don't push me too hard!"

      「別欺人太甚。」

    - "You've just pushed me too far."

      「你真是欺人太甚了。」

84. **(a) pushover**

    容易做的事;容易解決的事;容易打發的人

    - "That creep is a pushover."

      「那個討厭鬼很容易打發的。」

85. **put aside**

①暫放一邊。②存 (錢)。

① ● "He put aside his personal problems and got the job done."

「他把他個人的困擾撇開，專心地把工作完成了。」

② ● "You should put aside some money for an emergency."

「你該存點錢以備不時之需。」

86. **put down**

①責備；責怪。②出醜 (拆穿別人的隱私或糗事)。③放下。

① ● "My old man always puts me down."

「我老頭總是責怪我。」

② ● "Did you hear Shirley put down Theresa? I never heard anything so funny in all my life."

「你有沒有聽到 Shirley 出 Theresa 的醜事？這輩子我從沒聽過那麼好笑的事。」

③ ● "Put down that newspaper and talk to me."

「把報紙放下來，跟我聊一聊。」(通常是太太對先生抱怨的話。)

87. **put in a word for (someone)**

替 (人) 說好話

● "When you see Senator Carson, don't forget to put in a word for me."

「見到 Carson 參議員時，別忘了替我說幾句好話。」

88. **put (someone) in his place**

當面糾正一個人，使他不要太過份。

● "If I see him, I'll put him in his place."

「假如我見到他，我會教訓他一頓。」

89. **put my finger on (something)**

明白指出 (通常用在否定句，表示心中知道，但又無法明白指出。）

● "There's something different about him but I just can't put my finger on it."
「他有點不太一樣，但我又說不出來。」

90. **put (someone's) nose out of joint**
使（某人）丟臉

● "Mary put his nose out of joint when she said she wouldn't go to the prom with him."
「當Mary 說她不會跟他去參加舞會時，眞是讓他大大的丟臉。」

91. **put (someone) on**
①請將對方接過來（通電話時）= put (someone) through。
②欺騙；開玩笑。③穿上（衣服）化粧。④製作。⑤裝出來的（動作、行爲⋯）。

① ● "Mr. Smith, here is a call from Mr. John Williams."
「 Smith 先生，Williams 先生打電話來。」
"Put him on, please."
「請接過來。」

② ● "You are putting me on."
「你在開我玩笑吧？」（表懷疑的說法）

③ ● "Put on your clothes."
「穿上你的衣服。」

④ ● "This school is putting on a play."
「這所學校正在製作一齣戲。」

⑤ ● "Her smile was a put on."
「她的笑容是裝出來的。」

● "She puts on so many acts, you know."
「她那些都是裝出來的，你知道嗎？」

92. **(to) put (something) on ice**

暫時放一邊不做

- "Let's put the plan for the new building on ice until we have the money to finance it."

「在我們得到金錢支助之前，讓我們先把建築這棟新大樓的工程計劃暫放一邊。」

93. **put on some tunes**

[tjunz]

放點音樂

- "Let's put on some tunes and dance."

「讓我們放點音樂跳跳舞。」

94. **put (someone) on the payroll**

['pe,rol]

給（人）一份差事

- "Roland, please put him on the payroll. I think we need some extra help here."

「Roland，請找點事讓他做做，我想我們這兒需要額外的幫手。」

"Yes, Mr. Ford."

「好的，Ford 先生。」

95. **put (someone) on the spot**

逼得（某人）走頭無路

- "I'll put her on the spot."

「我會逼得她走頭無路。」

96. **P.X.**

福利社（軍中免稅的商店）。（這字在美國本土很少用）

- "Where did you get this?"

「你哪兒買來的？」

"I bought it from the P.X. the day before yesterday."

「前天我從福利社買來的。」

1. **quack**

   [kwæk]

   密醫

   - "He's a quack."

     「他是個密醫。」

2. **quarterback**

   ['kwɔrtɚ,bæk]

   首腦人物或主持人（quarterback 本指美式足球中的靈魂人物
   ，指揮全隊進攻的。）

   - "He's the quarterback of this big sales operation."

     「他是這次大拍賣計劃的主腦。」

1. **racist**
   ['resɪst]
   有種族偏見的人
   - "He's a racist. He always makes crude remarks about blacks."
   「他是個有種族偏見的人,他總是對黑人做很粗野的批評。」

2. **rack (one's) brains**
   絞盡腦汁;苦苦思索
   - "I racked my brains, but I still couldn't think of the answer."
   「我絞盡了腦汁仍然想不出問題的答案。」

3. **rack up**
   [ræk]
   累積
   - "He racked up a lot of points playing space invaders."
   「他玩電動玩具積下不少分。」

4. **racket**
   ['rækɪt]
   ①非法的行為(如勒索,欺詐等)②爭吵聲。
   ① - "He's new at this racket."
   「他幹這一行還是新手。」
   ② - "What's all that racket about?"
   「那邊在吵些什麼?」
   - "Stop making such a racket, kids."
   「別吵了,小鬼。」

5. **rainy day**
   ['renɪ]
   苦難的日子
   - "Save some money for a rainy day."
   「存點錢以備萬一。」

6. **raise**

   [rez]

   要求加薪

   - "It's very difficult to ask for a raise."

     「要求加薪很難。」

   - "Ellen got a raise and two more days-off."

     「Ellen 得到了加薪而且多了兩天的假。」

7. **raise (one's) voice**

   提高嗓門；大聲

   - "Don't raise your voice. I'm not trying to argue with you."

     「別那麼大聲。我不是要跟你爭吵。」

8. **rats**

   [ræts]

   糟糕

   - "Rats! I missed my plane."

     「糟糕，我誤了飛機。」

9. **razz**

   [ræz]

   喝倒采（=boo ）轟下台來（有冷嘲熱諷之意）

   - "The audience razzed him off the stage."

     「觀衆把他噓下台來。」

10. **razzle-dazzle**

    ['ræzl/'dæzl]

    ①（運動會；球賽）正常地順利進行。② (=fancy) 特別裝飾；花式別緻的；高級的。

    ① - "It was a razzle-dazzle football game."

      「那場足球賽進行得很順利。」

    ② - "That's a razzle-dazzle looking car."

      「那是一輛外觀別緻的車子。」

11. **reach**

[ritʃ]

聯絡

- "I tried to reach you all morning, but your phone was busy."

  「今早我一直想跟你聯絡，可是你的電話老是佔綫。」

- "How can I reach you?"

  「我怎能跟你聯絡？」

  "Call 331-3333. I'm there every morning."

  「打 331‐3333 。每天早上我都在那裏。」

12. **read (one's) mind**

[rid]　　　　[maɪnd]

看穿對方心思

- "What would you like for dinner? How about Cantonese food?"

  「今晚你想吃什麼？廣東菜怎麼樣？」

  "You must have read my mind."

  「你一定是看穿了我的心思。」

13. **ready to drop**

[drɑp]

快要倒下來了！（累壞了！）

- "This is my first night working in a restaurant. I'm ready to drop."

  「這是我第一晚在餐館工作，我累得快要倒下來了。」

14. **ready to risk (one's) life**

準備好了，隨時可以拼命（表示願意犧牲。)

- "Are you sure you really want to go?"

  「你確定你真的要去嗎？」

  "Yes, I'm ready to risk my life."

  「確定，我已準備好隨時犧牲。」

- "I'd risk my life to protect my family."
  「我願意為保護我的家庭而犧牲。」

15. **(be) reasonable**
   講理點（別胡鬧）

   - "You want me pay you $800 for the damage? Be reasonable, man. That car wasn't even worth that much."
     「你要我賠你八百塊？老兄，講講理啊！你的車還值不了那麼多錢呢？」

16. **red light district**
         ['dɪstrɪkt]
   風化區；綠灯戶

   - "Does Taipei have a red light district?"
     「台北有風化區嗎？」

17. **red tape**
   公事程序；官樣文章

   - "I hate dealing with government offices. There's always so much red tape."
     「我討厭跟公家機關打交道，公事程序太麻煩了。」

18. **red-handed**
   當場；現場（犯）

   - "The thieves were caught red-handed."
     「那個小偷當場被捉到了。」

19. **(a) red-letter day**
         ['rɛd 'lɛtə]
   快樂的日子；值得慶祝的日子（因為喜事或慶典）

   - "I just won the lottery. This is indeed a red-letter day."
     「我剛中了獎，這的確是個值得慶祝的日子。」

20. **refuse to recognize (someone) any longer**
   拒絕再理某人

● "I refuse to recognize him any longer."
「我拒絕再理他。」

21. **regular**

['rɛgjələ]

老主顧

● "He is a regular here."
「他是本店的老主顧。」

22. **Rest assured that I'll do my best.**

[ə'ʃurd]

我一定盡力，請放心。

● "Hugh, you got to help me."
「Hugh, 你一定要幫我。」

"Don't worry, rest assured that I'll do my best."
「放心，我一定會盡全力幫你。」

23. **return kindness with ingratitude**

[ɪn'grætə,tjud]

恩將仇報

● "After all these years, you return kindness with ingratitude."
「這麼多年後，你竟然恩將仇報。」

24. **ride (=lift)**

[raɪd]

搭便車

● "Would you give me a ride? I want to go downtown."
「我要去市中心，你能讓我搭個便車嗎？」

● "Do you need a ride?"
「你需要人（開車）送你去嗎？」

25. **riding on the crest of the wave**

[krɛst]   [wev]

得意至極

● "Just look at Billy!"

「瞧瞧 Billy（的德性）！」

"Yeah, he got what he wanted; he's riding on the crest of the wave."

「是呀！他得到一切他所要的，他眞是得意極了。」

26. **right of way**
先行權

● "The pedestrian always has the right of way."

「行人永遠有先行權。」

27. **right on time**
準時

● "Hello, Mr. Smith, you're right on time. Come in please."

「嗨，Smith 先生，你眞準時啊！請進，請進。」

28. **ring a bell**
喚起一點記憶；提示

● "Does it ring a bell?"

「（這）有沒有喚起你一點記憶啊？」

● "It doesn't ring a bell."

「一點提示作用也沒有。」

29. **rip off joint**
[rɪp / dʒɔɪnt]
黑店

● "NT$300 for breakfast?! What a rip-off joint."

「一客早點 300 塊（台幣）？眞是黑店。」

30. **rip (something) off (something) in broad daylight**
光天化日下順手牽羊

● "Why was Judy caught by the cops?"

「Judy 爲什麼被抓了？」

"Because she ripped off a fur coat in broad daylight."

「因爲她公然偷了一件毛皮大衣。」

31. **road hog**

    [hɑg]

    把車開在中間綫，霸佔車道的人

    - "That road hog won't pull over and let me pass."
      「那個霸佔車道的人不肯把車開到路邊讓我先過。」

32. **roll (=hit the road=let's bolt)**

    [rol]

    ①開車吧。②走吧。③開始吧！

    - "Let's roll!"
      「我們去吧！」

33. **roll in the hay (=make love)**

    做愛（較舊的說法）

    - "They went for a roll in the hay."
      「他們親熱去了。」

34. **rook**

    [rʊk]

    （被）敲竹槓；上當；受騙

    - "$500 for a pair of sunglasses? You got rooked."
      「五百塊一副太陽眼鏡？你上當了。」

35. **rotten luck**

    ['rɑtn]

    倒霉

    - "What rotten luck! I was hit by a ball."
      「我被球打中了，眞倒霉。」

    註：rotten 是爛了；壞了，如 "This juice is rotten." "This
       meat smells rotten."

36. **rough**

    [rʌf]

    日子不好過

● "I'll be on your side when times are rough."
「當日子不順時，我會在你旁邊的。（幫助你）」

37. **(one more) round**
①（再來）一巡酒（每人再來一杯）。②（還有）一回合（拳擊）

① ● "Bartender, let's have one more round of beer."
「酒保，（每人）再來一杯啤酒。」

② ● "He was knocked out in the 7th round."
「他在第七局被打昏了。」

38. **rub (him, her) out**
[rʌb]
殺害；宰了

● "John, rub him out."
「John，把他做了。」

● "They rubbed him out before he could call the cops."
「他們在他報警之前幹掉了他。」

39. **rubber check**
空頭支票

● "Mr. Nicholl, here is another rubber check."
「Nicholl 先生，這裏又有一張空頭支票。」

40. **ruin (one's) day**
['ruɪn]
破壞（某個人）一天平靜的好心情

● "I had a fight with my wife this morning, and it ruined my day."
「今早我跟我太太吵了一架，（那場架）破壞了我的好心情。」

● "I'm not going to let anything ruin my day."
「我不會讓任何事破壞我平靜的日子。」

41. **run**
①經營。②競選。③管理；負責。

① ● "He is running 3 restaurants and 2 motels in L.A."
「在洛杉磯他經營三家餐館，二家汽車旅館。」

② ● "Ronald Reagan ran again in the 1984 Presidential campaign."
「雷根 (Ronald Reagan) 再次為 1984 年的（美國）總統競選。」

③ ● "I'm the one who runs this place, you know."
「你要明白，這裏是我在負責（你少發號司令）。」

42. **run off at the mouth (=talk too much)**
說得太多了

● "Don't run off at the mouth about this to anyone."
「這件事不要對別人說得太多。」

43. **run out of (money, time, idea....)**
用盡；用完了；賣完了

● "I'm afraid we ran out of gas."
「恐怕（汽）油用完了。」

● "I'm sorry we ran out of eggs."
「對不起蛋賣完（用光）了。」

● "We ran out of time (or ideas)."
「我們的時間到了。」（用盡了主意）

44. **runaround**
推三推四的（不願做或不願去）

● "Are you going or not? Don't give me the runaround."
「你到底去不去？別推三推四的。」

1. **(something, someone) is safe with me**
   跟我在一起保證安全，不會有問題

   - "Don't tell this to anybody."
     「別告訴任何人哦！」
     "Don't worry, I won't. Your secret is safe with me."
     「放心！我不會的，你的秘密絕不會洩出去的。」

   - "Don't worry, your sister is safe with me."
     「別擔心，我會好好兒照顧你的妹妹的。」

2. **(I'm no) saint**
   [sent]
   我又不是聖人（怎會不犯錯）

   - "How can I turn down that kind of offer? I'm no saint."
     「我怎能拒絕那種出價（賄賂）呢？我又不是聖人。」

3. **same here (=me too)**
   我也一樣（對事情有相同看法）

   - "Waiter, I want a banana split."
     「先生，來一個香蕉船。」
     "Same here. (=Me too.=Make that two.)"
     「我也一樣。」

4. **same old story**
   舊戲重演；老掉牙的故事

   - "Don't tell me that same old story."
     「別告訴我那個老掉牙的故事。」

5. **Saturday night special**
   廉價的手槍（品質不好）

   - "Where did you get that Saturday night special?"
     「你那支廉價手槍打哪兒來的？」

6. **Save your breath!**
   [sev]　　[brɛθ]
   省點力氣吧！別浪費口舌！

- "I won't go to that party with you, why don't you save your breath?"

「我不會跟你去參加那個宴會的，你省點力氣吧！」

7. **say something**

說話啊（別呆在那裏）；動動腦筋啊

- "Don't just stand there, say something."

「別光是站着，說話呀！」

8. **Say when.**

到時告訴我一下（例如人家給你添加酒、咖啡，到了你滿意的份量時告知對方一下。）

- "Would you like some more coffee?"

「你願意再來點咖啡嗎？」

"Yes, please."

「好的。」

"Say when."

「夠了就告訴我。」

"When, thank you."

「好，夠了，謝謝你。」

註：當人家說 "Tell me when." 時你的回答可以是 "now", "when", "O.K."

9. **scare the daylight(s)/shit out of (someone)**

[skɛr]

嚇人

- "I scared the daylights out of them last night."

「我昨晚把他們嚇得半死。」

10. **scram**

[skræm]

滾

- "Scram, before I change my mind and decide to teach you a lesson."

「在我改變心意決定要修理你之前快滾。」

11. **scrape up the money**

[skrep]

積攢（錢）

- "We scraped up the money and paid the bill."

「我們存夠了錢，並且把賬單付清了。」

12. **scratch (that)**

[skrætʃ]

去掉

- "Scratch that idea, it won't work."

「別動那個腦筋，行不通的。」

13. **as a screen**

[skrin]

用來做掩飾（用在比較抽象的地方）

- "He used his respectability as a screen for his illegal dealings with organized crime."

「他利用他的聲望做爲他與黑社會罪犯非法交易的掩飾。」

14. **screw**

[skru]

①敲詐；騙。②操（＝fuck）（粗話）。

① ● "He tried to screw me out of $50."

「他想敲詐我50塊。」

② ● "Screw you."

「去你的／幹！」

- "Did you screw her last night."

「你昨晚動了她嗎？」

15. **see**

①明白；知道。②視情形而定。

① ● "Can you show me how to use this can opener?"

「你能示範一下怎麼用這個開罐器嗎？」

"Of course, it's very easy, just twist here, see?"

「當然，很簡單，就這麼轉，明白吧？」

② ● "I'll see what I can do for you."

「我會看看我能幫上什麼忙。」

16. **see (someone) out/home/to the door**

送出門／送回家／送到門口

● "Let me see you out."

「我送你出去吧！」

17. **see (something) through**

親眼看一件事徹底完成，做好

● "It's going to be hell getting him to apologize to her, but I'm going to see it through."

「要他向她道歉，簡直不可能，但我要親眼看他這麼做。」

18. **see through (someone)**

看穿（某人）

● "You can see through me."

「你可以看穿我。」

● "I can see right through her excuse."

「我可以看穿她的藉口。」

19. **see you around**

再見

● "Well, it's nice talking to you Kim, but I have to go to class now, see you around."

「哦，Kim 真高興跟你聊，現在我該去上課了。再見！」

20. **sell (someone) down the river**

[sɛl]

出賣

● "He sold us down the river."

「他出賣了我們。」

21. **sell (someone) short**

①打折扣；不兌現。②對（我）沒有信心。③出賣我。

● "I'm your friend, don't sell me short."

「我是你的朋友，別對我沒信心（或別出賣我）。」

22. **Send (him/her) in.**

叫／請（他／她）進來！

● "Sir, Mr. Larson wants to see you."

「先生，Larson 先生想見你。」

"Mr. Larson? Oh! Send him in."

「Larson 先生？哦！請他進來。」

23. **sensational**

[sɛn'seʃənl]

棒透了

● "How do you feel about my speech?"

「你覺得我的演講如何？」

"Sensational!"

「棒透了。」

24. **serious**

['sɪrɪəs]

①嚴重。②正經的；說真的。

① ● "Elvis was sick."

「Elvis 病了。」

"Is it serious?"

「嚴重嗎？」

② ● "Let's be serious."

「讓我們認真一點。」

● "I'm going to kill him, I'm dead serious."

「我要殺他，我可是當真的。」

25. **set**

①決定了；就這麼辦。②辦好了。

① ● "So, you'll take care of the food, and I'll take care of the rest. Set?"

「好，你負責食物，我負責其他的東西。好吧？」

"Set."

「就這麼說定了。」

② ● "Mary, how's everything?"

「Mary，一切好吧？」

"It's all set, Mr. Jackson."

「Jackson 先生，一切都準備好了。」

26. **set up**

①建立；訂立。②陷害。

① ● "That program was set up months ago."

「那個節目幾個月前就訂好了。」

② ● "How was he arrested?"

「他怎麼被捕的？」

"It was a set-up."

「被人陷害。」

● "He sets me up."

「他陷害我。」

27. **setback**

挫折

● "This was a major setback in the Allies campaign for world peace."

「這是民主國家尋求世界自由中的一項重大挫敗。」

● "How's your research going?"

「你的研究進展的如何？」

"Not good. Just one setback after another."

「不好，挫敗一個接一個的來。」

28. **shadow (v.)**
跟踪

- "He shadowed the suspect for 3 days and then was killed by a speeding taxi."
「他跟踪了那個嫌疑犯三天，而後被一輛超速的計程車撞死了。」

29. **shake (someone) off**
[ʃek]
擺脫

- "Let's shake him off at the next turn."
「下一個轉彎，讓我們擺脫他。」

30. **shame on you**
[ʃem]
真丟臉（責罵人家做錯事，例如小孩偷吃東西；小小年紀學做扒手！）

- "Mom, tell Jack I'm not home. I don't want to see him."
「媽，告訴 Jack 我不在，我不想見他。」
"How can you treat your old friend like this, shame on you!"
「你怎麼能這樣對待你的老朋友！真丟臉。」

31. **sharp**
①漂亮；時髦；英挺（指東西，或男人）。②刺眼（有諷刺味）。③聰明；伶俐 (=smart; bright) 。
① • "This car is real sharp."
「這部車真漂亮。」
①② "He looks (really) sharp in his tux."
「他穿上晚禮服看上去真漂亮。」
③ • "He's really sharp. He understood right away."

「他眞聰明，馬上就明白了。」

註：tux=tuxedo [tʌk 'sido]

32. SHARP CURVE AHEAD!

[ʃɑrp] [kɝv] [ə'hɛd]

前有彎路

● "Be careful. Sharp curve ahead."

「小心點，前有彎路。」

33. shiner (=black eye)

['ʃaɪnɚ]

眼睛給打紫了。

● "John got a shiner in the fight yesterday."

「 John 的眼睛在昨天的打鬪中被打紫了。」

34. shit/hell

[hɛl]

他媽的

● "Oh, shit, I just blew it."

「他媽的，我把它搞砸了。」

35. shoot

[ʃut]

①有話快講，有屁快放。（用於同輩朋友之間 ）②（ shit 較
弱的說法 ）他媽的；狗屎。（女孩子常用，如：懊悔時。）

① ● "Can I ask you a question?"

「我能不能問你一個問題？」

"Shoot."

「講吧！」

② ● "Aw, shoot."

「噢，眞他媽的。」

36. shoot the breeze (=have a chat)

擺龍門陣；閑聊；瞎扯

● "What are you guys doing?"
　「你們在幹啥？」

　"Shooting the breeze. What else?"
　「當然是在瞎聊。否則還能做些什麼？」

37. **short cut**
　①捷徑。②投機的方法。

● "This is a short cut to the library."
　「這是去圖書舘的捷徑。」

● "I know a short cut to make money."
　「我知道一個賺錢的捷徑。」

38. **short fuse**
　　　[fjuz]
　易於動怒

● "He's got a short fuse; he gets angry easily."
　「他是一個衝動的人，他很容易動怒。」
註：short out　是指電線短路。The electricity shorted out.

39. **shot**
　[ʃɑt]
　①試試看。②姑且一試。③很快地離去。

① ● "Give it a shot."
　　　「讓我們試試看。」

② ● "A shot in the dark."
　　　「姑且一試。」

③ ● "He was gone like (or in) a shot."
　　　「他很快地離去。」

40. **shove off**
　[ʃʌv]
　走；滾開

● "I've got to shove off now." (=I have to run now.)
　「我該走了。」

● "Shove off, you creep."

「滾開，討厭鬼。」

41. **show off** (n. v.)

①愛出風頭的人。②炫耀；現○'

① ● "I don't like her; she's a show-off."

「我不喜歡她，她是個愛出風頭的人。」

② ● "He's showing off his new car again."

「他又在炫耀他的新車。」

42. **Show (someone) the back door!**

叫（人）滾！送客（不禮貌的）

● "I don't want to talk to you any more. Billy!"

「我不想再跟你談了。Billy（叫人送客）。」

"Yes, Mr. Scotch."

「什麼事，Scotch 先生。」

"Show Mr. Lee the back door."

「送 Lee 先生出去。」

43. **shower**

①淋浴。② shower party 美國女孩在結婚前由所有女性朋友為她開的慶祝會。③小雨。

① ● "A lot of Americans like to take a shower in the morning."

「很多老美喜歡在早上（睡醒後）淋浴。」

② ● "We're going to hold a shower party for Linda this weekend."

「這個週末，我們要爲 Linda 舉行一個慶祝會。」

③ ● "If it rains tonight it won't be more than a shower."

「如果今晚會下雨，也不過是小雨罷了。」

44. **Now showing**

['ʃoɪŋ]

正在上映

* "Deep Throat is next week's attraction. Now showing is The Devil in Miss Jones."

「Deep Throat 是下星期的巨獻，現在上映的片子是 The Devil in Miss Jones. 」

45. **shrug (one's) shoulders**

[ʃrʌg]

聳聳肩（表示不知道或無可奈何）

* "Don't just shrug your shoulders. I know you can do more than that."

「別只是聳你的肩膀，我知道你能盡更多的力。」

46. **a shut out (n.); shut out (v.)**

掛零（沒得分）

* "We shut them out."

「我們使對方掛零。」

* "What was the score of yesterday's game?"

「昨天比賽的分數如何？」

"It was a shut out. We beat them—seventeen to nothing."

「有一隊吃鴨蛋。我們以十七比零打敗了他們。」

47. **shut up**

[ʃʌt]

閉嘴

* "Shut up, creep!"

「閉上你的嘴，討厭鬼！」

* "Why don't you shut up?"

「你為什麼不閉上你的嘴？」

48. **shyster**

['ʃaɪstɚ]

下流律師

* "You don't want to go to that lawyer? He's nothing

but a shyster.''

「你不會想去找那個律師吧？他啥也不是，只是一個下流的律師。」

49. **sick**

[sɪk]

①噁心。②厭惡透頂。③病態（心理不正常）。④生病。⑤討人厭。

① ● ''You make me sick.''

「你令我作噁。」

② ● ''I'm sick and tired of you.''

「我對你厭惡透了。」

④⑤ ''He is sick.''

「他有毛病。（他討人厭）。」

④ ● ''I have been sick for a month.''

「我病了一個月。」

50. **sidekick (=help=assistant)**

['saɪd,kɪk]

助手（非正式的；半開玩笑地說）

● ''He's my sidekick.''

「他是我的助手。」

51. **sidewalk**

['saɪd,wɔk]

人行道

● ''There are a lot of noodle stands on the sidewalk.''

「在人行道上有許多麵攤。」

52. **sing the same song/tone**

①志同道合。②處境相同；同病相憐。

① ● ''What do you want to drink?''

「你想喝什麼？」

"Whiskey on the rocks."
「威士忌加冰塊。」

"We're singing the same song."
「我們倒是有志一同。」

② ● "What are you doing here?"
「你在這兒幹嘛？」（在酒吧中）

"I had a fight with Gloria."
「我跟 Gloria 吵架了。」

"In this case, we're singing the same song."
「看這情形，我們倒是同病相憐。」

53. **single handedly**
[ˋhændɪdlɪ]

單槍匹馬

● "I did it single handedly."
「這件事是我一個人做的。」

54. **sis (=sister)**
[sɪs]

①小妹（親切之稱呼，如：少男想向小女搭訕時用）

● "Hi sis. Where are you going?"
「嗨，小妹，你去哪兒啊？」

55. **sissy**
[ˋsɪsɪ]

娘娘腔的男人

● "He's such a sissy; he doesn't like to go out with the boys."
「他真娘娘腔，他不喜歡跟男性朋友一起玩。」

56. **sit in**
靜坐示威

● "This is the 56th day of the sit-in in City Hall to

protest Proposition 13."

「這是第５６天靜坐在市政廳中抗議１３號提議。」

57. **sitting duck**

[dʌk]

①冤大頭（容易被騙；上當）②甕中鼈。

① ● "Forget it. I'm no sitting duck."

「休想，我又不是冤大頭。」

● "What do you think I am? A sitting duck."

「你以爲我是什麼？冤大頭啊？」

② ● "We're sitting ducks out here in the open. Let's find some cover."

「這地方沒東西掩護，我們成了甕中鼈。讓我們找個地方躲起來。」

58. **(a) six-pack**

[sɪks/pæk]

半打裝

● "Buy a couple of six-packs of beer."

「買一些啤酒。」

59. **sizzler**

[ˈsɪzl ɚ]

①特別（驚喜、危險）之事。②炎熱的日子。

① ● "This novel is a real sizzler."

「這本小說眞特別。」

② ● "Today is a real sizzler. It's 100°F."

「今天眞熱，氣溫高達華氏一百度。」

60. **skid row (=slum)**

[skɪd/ro]

酒鬼窟（例如便宜的旅館、公寓）

● "He was brought up on a skid row. No wonder he

won't touch alcohol."

「他是在酒鬼窟中長大的，難怪他滴酒不沾。」

註：ghetto 貧民窟（多半是黑人區，或南美人區。）

61. skin magazine

有裸體照片的雜誌

● "Throw that skin magazine away."

「把那本有裸體照片的雜誌丟掉。」

62. skinny

[skɪnɪ]

瘦骨嶙峋；皮包骨

● "You're skinny."

「你真瘦得可以啊。」

63. skirt-chaser

['tʃesɚ]

登徒子；花心蘿蔔；花蝴蝶（現較少用到）

● "Charles? He is a skirt-chaser."

「Charles? 他是個花心蘿蔔。」

64. sky high

物價高漲

● "The price of gasoline jumped sky high."

「油價漲得天般高。」

65. slave-driver

[slev]

①工頭；不受歡迎的老闆（逼你拼命工作的人）

① ● "We called him slave-driver because he worked us too hard."

「我們叫他魔頭，因為他驅使我們工作。」

66. slip (one's) mind

忘了

● "Where are the tickets?"

「票呢？」

"Oh my God. I'm sorry. It slipped my mind; I forgot to bring them with me."

「哦，老天，對不起，我忘了帶來了。」

67. **slob**

[slɑb]

髒鬼

● "Move, slob."

「滾一邊去，髒鬼。」

68. **sloppy**

[slɑpɪ]

邋遢（穿衣邋遢；或吃飯時飯粒四散！」

● "Mary is pretty, but she's a sloppy dresser."

「Mary 長得很漂亮，但她的穿着眞邋遢。」

69. **slow**

（生意）清淡

● "Good evening, Mr. Williams. How's business?"

「Williams 先生，晚安，生意如何？」

"Oh, pretty slow I guess."

「哦，我想很清淡吧！」

70. **slow poke**

[pok]

慢蝸牛（開慢車的人，如蝸牛在爬行）

● "Get out of my way, slow poke!"

「滾開，別擋路，慢蝸牛！」

71. **(a) small potato**

無足輕重的人

● "He's just a small potato."

「他只是一個無足輕重的人。」

72. **be/get smart**

[smɑrt]

放聰明點；識相點

- "Be smart! Nobody can save you now. Talk...."
  「放聰明點，現在沒人能救你了，說…」

73. **smart aleck**

[ˋælɪk]

自負而令人討厭的人；自作聰明的人

- "Who's the smart aleck that did it?"
  「是哪個自作聰明的人幹的？」

74. **smash**

[smæʃ]

①粉碎。②很好。③醉。

① • "He was drunk, drove into a supermarket, and smashed the front window."
  「他喝醉酒了，開車衝進一家超級市場，撞碎了前面的窗戶。」

② • "Your party was a smash."
  「你的宴會很棒。」

③ • "I really got smashed last night."
  「我昨晚真是喝得酩酊大醉。」

75. **smirking at**

[smɝkɪŋ]

嘲笑

- "Stop smirking at me."
  「別嘲笑我。」

76. **smut (=erotic novel)**

[smʌt] [ɪˋrɑtɪk]

黃色小說

- "Are you reading smut?"

  「你在看黃色小說嗎？」

77. **snack**

    [snæk]

    零食；點心（midnight snack 即宵夜）

    - "Excuse me, can you tell me where the snack bar is?"

      「對不起，請問你販賣部／福利社在哪兒？」

    - "Would you like to have a snack?"

      「你要不要來點零食？」

      "No, thank you."

      「不用，謝謝你。」

78. **Snap to it! (=make it snappy)**

    [snæp]

    動作快一點！

    - "Snap to it, we have to finish it before 12."

      「動作快一點，我們必須在12點前做完它。」

79. **snitch**

    [snɪtʃ]

    奸細；愛打小報告的小人；告密的人

    - "Ivy is such a snitch; she told Mr. Bond about our plan."

      「Ivy 是個愛打小報告的小人，她告訴了 Bond 先生我們的計劃。」

80. **snob!**

    [snɑb]

    勢利鬼；自以為了不起的人

    - "Don't be such a snob, Rudy."

      「Rudy，別那麼勢利。」

    - "Rudy refuses to listen to anything besides classical music. What a snob!"

「 Rudy 拒絕聽古典音樂以外的音樂，眞是一個自以爲了不起的人。」

81. **snow**

①假意恭維；挖苦。② (cocaine)古柯鹼（鎮靜劑）。③ 敷衍。

① ● "You're very pretty."

「你眞漂亮。」

"Don't try to snow me, I know how I look."

「別挖苦我，我知道自己的長相。」

② ● "My roommate bought a gram of snow and turned me on to a couple of lines."

「我的室友帶回一公克的古柯鹼，並且給了我兩三劑。」

③ ● "Don't try to snow me."

「別敷衍我。」

82. **snow job (n.) (=beat around the bush)**

敷衍

● "He tried to give me a snow job but I knew better not to listen to him for too long."

「他想敷衍我，可是我知道不必跟他浪費太多時間。」

83. **snow white**

純潔無瑕疵的女孩。

● "Miss Ronstand is a hooker? No kidding! We always thought she was snow white."

「 Ronstand 小姐是個妓女？不是說笑吧！我們一直以爲她是個純潔的女孩。」

84. **so far**

①到目前爲止。②到此爲止；以此爲界。

① ● "How's everything?"

「一切如何？」

"So far so good."

「到目前一切尙好。」

② ● "I can go only so far; I'm sorry."
「我只能到此爲止，對不起。」

● "She's a nice girl. She only goes so far."
「她是個好女孩，她只肯到某一步爲止。」（在此指行爲有限度，不跟別人上床之意。）

85. **so help me God**
我發誓是眞的；的的確確的（發誓時用）

● "Did you really see Helen with Dick last night?"
「昨晚你眞的看到 Helen 跟 Dick 在一起嗎？」
"Yes, I did, so help me God."
「是的，我發誓我眞的看到了。」

86. **So long, I'll be seeing you.**
再見；後會有期

● "So long, Christine. I'll be seeing you."
「再見了，Christine, 後會有期。」

87. **so-so**
馬馬虎虎；還不賴

● "How's everything?"
「一切如何？」
"Well, so-so."
「馬馬虎虎。」

88. **So that's how it's done!**
原來如此！原來是這麼一回事

● "So that's how it's done. I can do it now."
「原來如此，現在我會做了。」

89. **so what?**
是又怎樣？是又如何？

● "O.K. O.K. I lost my watch again; so what?"
「好，好，我是又丟了手錶，怎麼樣呢？」

90. **So what else is new?**

    還有什麼新鮮事？（諷刺語，表示所說的已不新鮮。）

    ● "You say you won the lottery? So what else is new?"

    「你說你中了彩券？還有什麼新鮮事？」

    ● "John had a fight with his wife last night."

    「John 昨天跟他太太吵了一架。」

    "So what else is new?"

    「還有其他新鮮點的消息嗎？」

    註：他們常常吵，所以吵架對他們說來已不是新鮮事。

91.

some { friend / movie / dinner / businessman / students / boss

與眾不同的（或好或壞）

    ● "He's some teacher."

    「他真是一個（好、壞）老師。」

    ● "This is some food."

    「這種食物真不一樣。」

92. **Some day (my/your) prince will come (or ship will come in).**

    總有一天（我／你）會找到如意郎君的。（財運到來！）

    ● "The boys around here aren't to your taste? Don't worry, some day your prince will come."

    「這周圍的男孩不合你的胃口？沒關係，總有一天你的白馬王子會來到。」

    ● "I may be poor now, but one day my ship will come in, and things will be different around here."

    「我現在也許很窮，但等到有一天，我財運來了，一切就會不同了。」

註：prince 是指白馬王子，意中人，也有人用 Mr. Right。
早年英美等國靠航運做生意，ship 即表示鈔票來了。

93. **Some do, some don't.**

有的是，有的不是。有的有，有的沒有

● "Do all Americans have guns?"

「是不是所有的美國人都有槍？」

"Some do, some don't."

「有的有，有的沒有。」

94. **some other time**

改天

● "Hey, July, would you like to go shopping with us
this afternoon?"

「嘿，July, 今天下午你願意跟我們去買東西嗎？」

"I'm sorry, I'm busy this afternoon. Maybe some other
time. O.K.?"

「對不起，今天下午我很忙。改天好嗎？」

95. **(someone) is not (oneself) today.**

（某人）今天很反常，很失常

● "I don't know why I'm not myself today."

「我不知道我今天為什麼這麼失常。」

● "What's wrong with you? You're not yourself today."

「你今天怎麼搞的？你很反常。」

96. **something**

了不起

● "He is really something."

「他真了不起。」

● "Is that something?"

「棒吧？」

97. **Something is burning. . .**

   ['bɜˋnɪ ŋ]

   ①有東西燒焦了（如咖啡，牛肉…）。②有東西在燃燒（如愛情）

   ① ● "Something is burning."

   「有東西燒着了。」

   "Let me go and take a look."

   「我去看看。」

   ② ● "Something is burning inside, no one can deny that."

   「我們心中有東西在燃燒，沒有人能否認這件事。」

98. **Something you should know.**

   有件事你該知道（但你還不知道。常用在指一些不幸，不好的消息。）

   ● "Lily, I don't know how to say this, but there's something you should know. Allen got married yesterday."

   「Lily，我不知該怎麼說，但有件事你應該知道。Allen昨天結婚了。」

99. **Sometimes you win, sometimes you lose.**

   勝敗乃兵家常事

   ● "Take it easy , John. You know, life is not always full of fun. Sometimes you win, sometimes you lose."

   「別太難過，John。你是知道的，人生不是一直都是快樂的，勝敗乃兵家常事。」

100. **bitch**

   [bɪtʃ]

   ①討厭鬼；賤人；母狗（常用來罵女人）。②抱怨。

   ① ● "She's a real bitch."

   「她真是一個討厭鬼／賤人。」

   ② ● "She likes to bitch. (=She's bitchy.)"

   「她喜歡抱怨事情。」

101. son of a bitch（常以 S.O.B. 代之）

狗養的

●"You son of a bitch, how can you do that to me?"

「你這狗養的，你怎能這樣對我？」

102. bitchy

①心情不好。②尖酸刻薄。

① ● "She's in a bitchy mood."

「她今天心情不好。」

② ● "She is really bitchy."

「那女人很刻薄。」

103. sonny

小子；小鬼（暱稱）

● "Hey, sonny, where is the post office?"

「嘿，小鬼，郵局在哪兒？」

104. sore (=angry, mad)

生氣

● "I was really sore when I heard the news."

「當我聽到那個消息，我感到非常的生氣。」

105. Sorry is never good enough.

對不起有個屁用；對不起有什麼用？

● "I'm sorry."

「對不起！」

"Sorry? Sorry is never good enough."

「對不起？對不起有個屁用！」

106. (It) sounds great!

（主意）聽起來不錯！

● "Let's go shopping first, then we can dine out, how about that?"

「讓我們先去買東西，然後在外面吃飯，如何？」

"Sounds great!"

「聽起來不錯！」

107. space cadet

[kə'dεt]

心不在焉的人；做白日夢的人（發呆）

- "Did you see him getting into the wrong car? What a space cadet!"

  「你看到他上錯了車吧？他真是個心不在焉的人。」

108. (I) spaced it again. (=spaced it out)

（我）又忘了

- "Where's the key?"

  「鑰匙呢？」

  "Oh, gosh, I spaced it again."

  「哦，老天，我又忘了！」

- "What were you saying?"

  「你說什麼？」

  "I don't know, I spaced it out."

  「我不知道，我忘了。」

109. spare

[spεr]

①饒了（某人）。②備胎。③備用油（刻度 0 以下的）。④借。

① ● "This time I'll spare you, but don't let me catch you doing it again."

  「這次我饒了你，可別再犯。」

- "Spare me the gory details."

  「饒了我（拜託），別告訴我那些殘酷的細節。」

② ● "Is there a spare in the trunk?"

  「後面行李廂裏有備胎嗎？」

③ ● "I'm driving on the spare already. Let me know if you see a gas station."

「我已經在用備用油了，假如你看到加油站時請告訴我。」

④ ● "Can you spare me $5.00?"

「你能借我五塊錢嗎？」

110. spare time; spare room

空閑的時候；空房間

● "What do you usually do in your spare time?"

「你平常空閑時做些什麼？」

● "We've got a spare room, you can stay here tonight."

「我們有間空房間，你今晚可以住在那兒。」

111. spare tire

①備用車胎。②腰部肥胖。

① ● "I'm afraid we got a flat tire. Do we have a spare tire in the trunk?"

「恐怕爆胎了，我們後面車廂內有沒有備胎？」

② ● "What size belt does your father wear?"

「你爸爸繫幾號的皮帶？」

"I don't know exactly, but he's got a spare tire so he must use a pretty large size belt."

「我不太清楚，但他的腰很粗，可能要用相當大號的皮帶。」

112. speak for yourself

光說你自己就好（別把我們也牽扯進去）

● "You know, students are lazy."

「你是知道的，學生都是懶惰蟲。」

"Hey, speak for yourself."

「嘿，光說你自己就好了。」

113. **speak of the devil (and the devil comes)**

['dɛvl]

說到曹操，曹操就到！

- "Speak of the devil. . . . Hi, John."

「說到曹操（曹操就到）。嗨，John。」

114. **speak out**

說出來

- "What's on your mind? Why don't you speak out?"

「你心裏有什麼事？爲什麼不說出來？」

115. **speak to (someone) alone**

單獨談談

- "Good morning, Mr. Bush. Could I speak to you alone?"

「Bush 先生，早，我能跟你單獨談談嗎？」

116. **speak up (=speak out)**

①說大聲點。②爲自己辯護。③說出來（別憋在肚子裏）。④從實招來。

① ● "Hi, man, you got to speak up. I can't hear you."

「嘿，老兄，說話大聲一點。我聽不見。」

② ● "Speak up for your rights."

「要爲自己的權益辯護。」

● "Speak up for someone."

「爲別人辯護。」

③ ● "What's on your mind? Speak up!"

「你心裏在想些什麼？說出來聽聽！」

● "You got to speak up, man."

「有話你得說出來啊！」

④ ● "You better speak up. Where did you go? Why are you so late coming home?"

「你最好從實招來。你去哪兒了？爲什麼那麼晚回家?」

117. speed trap

[spid] [træp]

埋伏的交通警察（抓超速車）

- "Here comes a speed trap. Drive carefully."
  「來了一個公路警察，小心點開。」

118. speeding

[spidɪŋ]

①超速。② speed 也可當「興奮劑」解。speed 是吃了興奮劑。

① ● "I got a speeding ticket this morning."
  「今早我被開了一張超速罰單。」

  ● "Slow down. You are speeding."
  「慢一點，你超速了。」

② ● "He talks so fast, I think he's speeding."
  「他講話講得那麼快，我想他吃了興奮劑了。」

119. spicy

[spaɪsɪ]

①味道很濃（調味品放得多）。②辣 (=hot)。③黃色的。

①② "Do you like Mexican food?"
  「你喜歡墨西哥菜嗎？」

  "Yes, I like it. It's very spicy."
  「不錯，我喜歡。墨西哥菜很辣。」

③ ● "I want to hear all the spicy details about the scandal."
  「我要聽聽有關醜聞全部的精彩內容。」

  ● "They like to tell spicy jokes."
  「他們喜歡說黃色笑話。」

120. spit it out (=shoot)

（坦白）說出來

● "What's on your mind? Spit it out!"

「你心裏到底在想什麼？說出來！」

121. split

[splɪt]

①蹺頭（溜；跑）。②分（帳）。③分手（常與 up 連用）。

① ● "Hey, the cops are coming. Let's split."

「嘿，條子來了，蹺頭吧！」

② ● "Let's split the bill."

「讓我們對半分帳。」

"Let's split a bowl of noodles."

「讓我們分吃這碗麵。」

③ ● "David and Linda split up last week."

「David 跟 Linda 在上個星期分手了。」

122. split (three, four, five. . . .) ways

分（三、四、五）等份

● "What are you going to do with this money?"

「你將怎處理這筆錢？」

"Let's split it 5 ways."

「把它分成五份。」

123. sponge

[spʌndʒ]

①(n)海量（千杯不醉）。②(v)敲竹槓；揩油。

① ● "He can drink 12 bottles at one sitting. He drinks like a sponge."

「他一次能喝 12 瓶，他真是海量。」

② ● "Are you trying to sponge money from me again?"

「你又想向我搾錢了？」

● "He's such a sponge when he visits, always taking and never giving."

「每次他來，他老揩油，總是取而不予。」

124. spring chicken

①生手（什麼都不懂的笨蛋）；菜鳥。②年青。

① ● "Don't lie to me. I'm no spring chicken."

「別騙我，我可不是菜鳥。」

② ● "I'm no spring chicken. On my next birthday, I'll be 27."

「我可不年青。我馬上 27 歲了。」

125. spring fever

['fivɚ]

思春（春天來了，動物，人，對異性又展開追求。）

● "I just can't seem to concentrate on my work."

「我似乎無法集中精神在工作上。」

"You probably just have a case of spring fever."

「你也許染上思春病了。」

126. square

[skwɛr]

①古板。②豐富；豐盛。

① ● "My old man is a square."

「我老頭是個老古板。」

② ● "You still can have three square meals every day. Just leave out the bread, potatoes, and sweets."

「你每天仍然可以有豐盛的三餐。只是別去碰麵包，馬鈴薯，及甜點。」

127. square 1

從頭開始（像大富翁這一類的遊戲，第一步就叫 square 1，所以引申為從頭開始）

● "After that setback, we had to start over from square 1."

「在那次挫敗之後，我們必須從頭再開始。」

128. stall

[stɔl]

①拖延。②避免回答問題

① ●"Why are you stalling on the report? The deadline is next week."

「你爲什麼還不交報告？下星期就截止了。」

② ●"Quit stalling and tell me the answer."

「別顧左右而言他，告訴我答案。」

129. (to) stall for time

拖時間（可能別有企圖）

●"Why haven't they voted on this issue yet?"

「他們對這件事爲何還不表決呢？」

"I think they're stalling for time."

「我想他們是想拖時間吧！」

130. stall out

熄火（汽車拋錨）

●"My car stalled out downtown."

「我的車在市中心拋錨了。」

131. stand

忍受

●"I can't stand the way he talks."

「我無法忍受他說話的樣子。」

●"How can you stand him?"

「你怎麼能忍受他呢？」

132. start all over again

[start]

重新再來過；重新開始

●"Let bygones be bygones; let's start all over again."

「讓過去的成爲過去，讓我們重頭再來。」

133. starting line-up

（最重要）最有把握的事，所以先做（球賽中，一開始教練大多先排上最佳陣容，以便有把握獲勝，所以引申最先做。)

- "In next week's Chicago campaign I'm going to use crime control, inflation, and unemployment as my starting line-up."

  「在下週芝加哥的競選中，我將以防治罪犯，通貨膨脹，及失業問題當我演講的開場白。」

- "It will be hard to win the ball game without our best player in the starting line-up."

  「開賽時不排上我們的最佳陣容是很難贏球的。」

134. stay out of (my way)

滾開；別擋路；少管閒事

- "I want to fix the window. Stay out of my way."

  「我要修理窗戶了，別擋我的路。」

- "After what he said to me, if he knows what's good for him, he'll stay out of my way."

  「在他對我說了那些話之後，假如他識趣的話，他會滾得遠遠的。」

- "It's none of your business, so stay out of it."

  「不關你的事，少管。」

135. stay put (=don't move)

別動

- "Stay put; I'll be right back."

  「別動，我馬上回來。」

136. stay up all night (=stay up late)

熬夜

- "I had to stay up all night to get this paper finished. I hope the teacher likes it."

  「我必須熬夜趕完這份報告，我希望老師會喜歡它。」

137. stay where you are (=don't move)

留在原地；別動

●"Stay where you are, I'll go call for help. I'll be right back."

「別動，我去求救，我馬上就會回來。」

138. steal the whole show

[stil]

搶盡風頭（此字來自電影、電視、舞台表演，現引申到一般的宴會，舞會中。）

●"She stole the whole show at last night's party."

「昨晚的宴會上，她搶盡了風頭。」

●"Don't try to steal the whole show, Mary. You're over-acting."

「Mary，別想搶出風頭。你表現得有點過火。」

139. step aside

滾到一邊；閃開

●"Step aside, kid. You're in my way."

「小鬼，閃開。你擋住我的路了。」

140. stick around

[stɪk]

再待一會兒；別走開

●"Please stick around, I want to tell you something."

「再留一下，我有事要告訴你。」

●"We'll be right back after the commercial, so stick around (=stay tuned)."

「廣告後再見，別走開哦！」

141. Stick'em up! (=Hands up!)

舉起手來

●"Stick 'em up, and don't make a move."

「舉起手來！別動！」

142. still up?

還沒睡嗎？

- "Still up? It's 2 in the morning."

「還沒睡嗎？（凌晨）兩點了！」

"Yes, I'm working on my paper."

「是啊，我還在趕報告。」

143. Still water runs deep.

大智若愚

- "I would never have expected Jenny to win the prize."

「我從未料到 Jenny 會得獎。」

"Remember! Still water runs deep."

「記住！大智若愚。」

144. stingy

[ˈstɪndʒɪ]

小氣

- "Don't be so stingy, give me ten more dollars."

「別那麼小氣，再給我十塊。」

145. stood up

爽約；被放鴿子（通常用在男女一對一的約會中）

- "We got stood up."

「（兩男約兩女沒來）我們被放鴿子了。」

- "She stood me up for the last time."

「這是她最後一次放我的鴿子。」

- "I hate being stood up."

「我討厭被人放鴿子。」

146. Stop all this foolishness!

[ˈfulɪʃnɪs]

別講廢話／傻話

- "I don't know why I'm so stupid...."

「我不知道我為什麼會那麼笨。」

"Oh, stop all this foolishness. It's not all your fault."

「哦，別講傻話。那不全是你的錯。」

147. **straight**

①喝酒時，酒中不加冰塊。②正直；誠實。③非同性戀的（
人，酒吧…）。④直接。⑤老實說。

① ● "I want a Martini. Make it straight."
　　「我要一杯馬丁尼，不要加冰塊。」

② ● "He's very straight."
　　「他很正直。」

③ ● "This is a straight club."
　　「這是一個非同性戀的酒吧！」

④ ● "Go straight home; do you hear me?"
　　「直接回家去，聽到了嗎？」

　 ● "Please go straight ahead about three blocks, then you'll
　　find it."
　　「往前直走大約三條街，你會找到它的的。」

⑤ ● "I'll tell it to you straight. . . ."
　　「我老實地告訴你…」

148. **(a) street price**

價格公道

　 ● "$500, it's too expensive, can you come down a little?"
　　「500塊太貴了，你能便宜一點嗎？」

　　"I'm sorry, we can't, as a matter of fact, $500 is the
　　street price."
　　「對不起，不行，事實上，500塊的價格是十分公道的。」

149. **street smart**

　　　[smɑrt]

識途老馬；老（台北）。（對該地方的一切瞭如指掌，本來
是指壞事瞭如指掌，現也用在好事上）

　 ● "After living in New York for a month, he finally got
　　street smart, and didn't worry about being mugged."

　　「在紐約住了一個月後，他終於變成老紐約了，不再擔心

被騙。」

150. stretch my leg/back

[strɛtʃ]

伸懶腰

● "I have been sitting on this desk whole day; I have to go stretch my leg/back."

「我坐了一天的辦公桌；我要去伸伸懶腰。」

151. strike an attitude

[straɪk] [ˈætəˌtjud]

擺架子

● "Don't try to strike an attitude with me."

「別想跟我擺架子。」

152. strike back

[straɪk]

還擊

● "I'm not a born loser; I'll strike back someday."

「我不是個天生的失敗者，總有一天我會還擊。」

153. strike out

失敗了（原為三振出局）

● "Did you ask her for a date?"

「你約她了嗎？」

"Yes."

「約了。」

"What happened?"

「結果呢？」

"I struck out."

「她不肯出來。」

● "I went to the embassy to get a visa and then went to buy tickets for the football game."

「我去大使館辦簽證，然後又去買足球賽的票。」

"Any luck?"

「運氣好嗎？」

"Nope. I struck out at both places. They wouldn't give me a visa and the tickets were sold out."

「不好，兩件事都沒辦成。他們不肯給我簽證，球賽票又賣完了。」

154. stuck

[stʌk]

①陷住；進退不得。②卡住了。③工作不順利；難倒。④陷害人；整人。

① ● "My car got stuck on Main St."

　　「我的車子在Main街上被堵了。」

② ● "It's stuck. I can't move it."

　　「（門、車）卡住了，我推不動它。」

③ ● "Can you help me with this math problem? I'm stuck."

　　「你能幫我解決這數學難題嗎？我被難倒了。」

④ ● "You stuck me with your little sister for a date?? You'll get yours someday."

　　（你們有四張音樂會的票，你沒有女伴，要你室友代找，他却找來他十二歲的妹妹）。「你幫我約了（陷害也！）你小妹一起去聽音樂？？？你總有一天也會嚐到同樣的苦頭。」

155. stuff (=thing)

東西

● "I don't like this stuff."

　　「我不喜歡這種東西。」

● "What's this stuff?"

　　「這到底是什麼玩藝兒。」

"Chicken feet."

「雞脚。」

156. stuffed (=full=bloated)

吃得好脹；好飽

- "What a delicious dinner. I'm stuffed now."

「這頓晚飯眞好吃，我吃得好撐。」

註：stuffed (bell) pepper　靑椒鑲肉。

157. stuffed shirt

[stʌft/ʃɝt]

勢利鬼

- "What a stuffed shirt!"

「眞是一個勢利鬼！」

158. stuffy

['stʌfɪ]

①很悶（空氣不流通，或氣氛不佳）②驕傲。

① ● "Let's go. It's very stuffy in here."

「我們走吧！這裏好悶哦。」

② ● "I don't like that store. All the clerks are real
stuffy."

「我不喜歡那家商店，所有的店員都很驕傲。」

159. style

[staɪl]

風格；格調

- "I like your style."

「我喜歡你的風格。」

- "Jim has no style. That's why he can't find a girlfriend."

「Jim 沒有自己的風格，所以他找不到女朋友。」

160. suck

[sʌk]

①糟糕。②眞討厭。

① ● "I just failed the test. That sucks."

「我剛考砸了。眞糟糕！」

② ● "He sucks."

　「他眞討厭。」

　● "That sucks."

　「那事（或東西）眞討人厭。」

161. sucker

[sʌkɚ]

①容易上當或受騙的笨蛋；凱子。②抗拒不了（某人，某事）的人。

① ● "He is a sucker."

　「他是個笨蛋。」

　● "I'm not a sucker."

　「我可不是凱子！」

② ● "He's a sucker for blondes."

　「他容易被金髮女子迷倒。」

162. sugar daddy

老凱子

● "Don't try to get anything from me. I'm not your sugar daddy."

　「別想敲我，我可不是老凱子。」

163. super (=superintendent)

['supɚ]

公寓管理員

● "He was hired as the super of an apartment complex."

　「他被僱爲公寓的管理員。」

164. sure is

當然是

● "Hey Buzzy. Is Vivian your sister?"

　「嗨，Buzzy, Vivian 是你姊姊（妹妹）嗎？」

　"Sure is."

　「當然。」

165. a sure thing

一定的；毫無疑問的事

● "We buy these shirts below factory price, sell them at market value and make a killing. It's a sure thing."

「我們以低價買進，若以市價賣出，毫無疑問一定會賺大錢。」

166. survive

[sə`vaɪv]

熬得過；活得下去的；保住小命

● "I don't know how I'll pass those tests."

「我不知怎麼捱過那些考試。」

"Well, you'll survive anyway."

「你會熬得過的，絕對死不了。」

167. no sweat

[swɛt]

沒問題

● "Can you help me fix my car?"

「你能幫我修一下車嗎？」

"No sweat."

「沒問題。」

168. sweet talk

灌迷湯；說好話

● "Don't give me that kind of sweet talk; I'm not a kid."

「別給我灌迷湯；我又不是小孩子。」

169. swell

[swɛl]

棒透了；漂亮極了

● "How was your vacation?"

「你的假渡得如何？」

"It was swell."

「棒透了。」

1. **(Someone's) table manners are atrocious**
   [ə'troʃəs]

   吃東西的樣子真是難看！（嘖嘖有聲，把菜翻上翻下，骨頭滿地丟。）

   ● "Your table manners are atrocious.　You talk with your mouth full, eat with your hands, and put your elbows on the table."

   「你吃飯的樣子真難看。講話時嘴裏塞滿食物，用手抓東西，又把兩個手肘支在桌上。」

   "So what else is new?"

   「還有呢？」

2. **tacky**
   ['tækɪ]

   （穿衣）俗不可耐的（例如，穿上咖啡色長褲配上藍上衣、綠外套。）

   ● "Don't be tacky when you're attending a formal party."

   「當你參加一個正式的宴會時別穿得太俗氣。」

   ● "The decor in that new coffee shop is real tacky.　Everything is made of plastic."

   「那家新的咖啡店的裝潢真是粗俗，每樣東西都是塑膠做的。」

3. **(to) tail**
   [tel]

   （被）釘梢；跟踪

   ● "We've been tailed by the cops."

   「我們被警察釘上了。」

   ● "I want you to tail my husband, and see what he does everyday between 7:00 and 10:00 P.M."

   「我要你跟踪我的先生，看他每天晚上七點到十點間都做些什麼。」

4. **tailgate**

['telget]

緊跟着前車

- "That truck was tailgating, so I let him pass me."

  「那輛卡車一直緊跟在我後面，所以我讓他超過去。」

- "Don't tailgate."

  「請保持距離。」

5. **take a short cut**

抄捷徑；走捷徑

- "I know some short cuts for making money."

  「我知道一些賺錢的捷徑。」

- "Can we take a short cut?"

  「我們能走捷徑嗎？」

6. **take for a ride**

剝削利用；欺騙

- "It's very obvious he's taking you for a ride."

  「那是一件很明顯的事，他在剝削利用你。」

7. **take off**

①起飛。②離去。

① ● "Ladies and Gentlemen, now we're going to take off. Please fasten your seat belts and observe the no smoking sign. Thank you."

  「各位先生，各位女士，我們現在準備起飛。請繫緊安全帶，注意不要抽煙的訊號灯，謝謝。」

② ● "He took off to (=for) Mexico the night before his wedding day."

  「他在結婚前一晚溜到墨西哥去了。」

8. **talk back**

回嘴

- "Don't you talk back to me or I'll hit you."
  「你別回嘴，否則我揍你。」

9. **talk behind someone's back (=gossip)**
   嚼舌根

   - "Don't talk behind people's backs."
     「別在別人背後說別人的閑話。」

10. **talk (someone's) ears off (=nagging)**
    嘮叨個沒完（聽的人耳朵都聽麻了。）

    - "Whenever I run into her, she talks my ears off. She's really a blabbermouth."
      「每次我碰到她，她嘮叨個沒完。她真是個大嘴巴。」

11. **take a break**
    休息一下（美國人上班有 coffee break 休息個 5 分，10 分的，以便恢復一下精神，好再接再勵。）

    - "O.K. let's take a break now." the teacher said.
      老師說：「好，現在我們休息一下。」

12. **to take (a) French leave**
    開小差

    - "He took a French leave again."
      「他又開小差了。」

13. **take a good look**
    仔細看清楚點

    - "I want you to take a good look. Is this the guy who robbed you?"
      「我要你仔細的看一看，是不是這個傢伙搶了你？」

14. **take a leak**
    [lik]
    上 1 號小便的意思（不夠文雅，只能用於同輩近友。平常講 I have to wash my hands 就好了！）

● "Excuse me, I have to take a leak."

「對不起，我要去上 1 號。」

15. **take a powder (=get lost!)**

滾開！

● "I don't want you around. Take a powder."

「我不需要你在這裏，滾開。」

註：這種用法較舊。

16. **take a rain-check**

（延期）改天

● "Mary, would you like to go to the movies with me tonight?"

「Mary, 今晚你願意跟我去看電影嗎？」

"I'm sorry, I'm busy tonight. Can I take a rain-check?"

「對不起，今晚我很忙。能不能改天？」

17. **take care**

①保重。②照顧。③對付；解決。

① ● "Take care, Earl."

「Earl 保重了。」

② ● "Take good care of my baby sister."

「小心照顧我的小妹妹。」

"I will."

「我會的。」

③ ● "Leave it to me, I'll take care of him."

「讓我來，我會對付他的。」

18. **take cover**

躲一下；掩護一下

● "Here come the Germans, take cover."

「德軍來了，掩護一下。」

● (Door bell):

（門鈴響了）：

"It's May, you better take cover."

「是May, 你最好躲一下。」

19. **(to) take five/ten (=to take 5/10 minutes to rest)**
休息（五／十分鐘）
- "Let's take five."

「我們休息五分鐘吧。」

20. **take good care of yourself**
請善自珍重！（臨別叮嚀話）
- "Take good care of yourself, O.K.?"

「好好照顧自己，好嗎？」

21. **take it easy**
別急；別生氣慢慢來
- "Don't get mad, take it easy."

「別生氣，慢慢來。」

22. **take it or leave it**
　　　　　[liv]
要就拿，不要就拉倒。
- "Here is $5000, take it or leave it."

「這裏有五千塊，要就拿，不要就拉倒。」

23. **take it out on (person)**
出氣
- "Just because you're unhappy doesn't mean you can take it out on me."

「你心裏不舒服，並不表示你可以拿我出氣。」

24. **take sides**
袒護
- "I'm not taking sides, Fred, but you shouldn't take that from Paul."

「我並不是在袒護誰，Fred, 但是你不該容忍Paul。」

25. **take that**

    看招

    ● "Take that, you bum."

    「看招，你這無賴。」

26. **take the cake**

    第一名；超過他人；無人能出其右；無人能勝過…(諷刺語)

    ● "I've heard a lot of silly excuses but this one really takes the cake."

    「我聽過很多可笑的藉口，但這個却是可笑得再也找不出一個能出其右的了。」

27. **take the pill (=on the pill)**

    常指女孩吃避孕丸（一般吃藥最好用 take medicine ）。

    ● "Don't worry, I'm on the pill."

    「別擔心，我已吃過（避孕）藥了。」

28. **take (someone's) word**

    相信（某人）

    ● "She will come. Take my word for it."

    「相信我。她會來的。」

    ● "O.K. I'll take your word this time, but don't let me catch you next time."

    「好，這次我相信你，下次別再讓我逮到。」

29. **take your choice**

    [tʃɔɪs]

    選一個你喜歡的（如：要人選蘋果，或在酒吧中看到兩個漂亮的小妞，你要對方先選。）

    ● "Take your choice, the blonde or the brunette?"

    「選一個吧！金髮的還是棕髮的？」

    "I'll take the blond."

    「我要那個金髮的（女郎）。」

30. **Take (or Get) your hands off me.**

把你的手拿開；別碰我！（女孩厭惡男友時可用，比較不客氣）

- "Take your hands off me, and leave me alone."

「把你的手拿開，別惹我。」

31. **take your position**

[pə'zɪʃən]

各就各位

- "Actors, take your positions. Lights. ...camera. . .action!"

「各位演員請就位，灯光（準備）…攝影…開始！」

32. **take your time**

不必急；慢慢來

- "It's no rush, just take your time."

「不急，慢慢來。」

- "John? Is that you? I'm fixing this window, I'll be right with you."

「John，是你嗎？我正在修窗戶，我馬上過來陪你。」

"Oh, don't worry, take your time."

「哦，別擔心，慢慢來。」

33. **taken in**

被騙；上當

- "You got taken in by that book salesman? How much did he take you for?"

「你上了那個書籍推銷員的當了？他騙了你多少錢？」

"$20 down, and $5 a month for a year."

「20元首款，以及（分期付款）每個月5元，要付上一年。」

34. **taking the wrong attitude**

['ætə,tjud]

態度不對

- "What you said was right, but you were taking the wrong attitude."

  「你說的話很對，但你的態度不對。」

35. **taking without giving**

    光受不予；老佔便宜（常用於男女之間感情）

    - "You're always taking without giving."

      「你（對感情）永遠是光接受不付出。」

36. **talk over**

    ①說服。②商量。③內容太高深的閑談，超過一個人的理解能力（如談高等物理等等）。

    ① ● "Did she talk you over to her side?"

       「她說服你了嗎？」

    ② ● "I want to talk it over with Ingrid before I decide."

       「在我決定之前，我要跟 Ingrid 商量一下。」

    ③ ● "Don't talk over my head, O.K.?"

       「別談太高深的東西，好嗎？」

37. **talking off the top of (one's) head**

    不經大腦而信口胡言

    - "Don't pay any attention to him. He's always talking off the top of his head."

      「別理他。他整天只會信口胡說。」

38. **tease**

    [tiz]

    ①揶揄；嘲弄；尋人開心；開人玩笑；逗笑。②刮鬆頭髮使其高（如做鳥巢頭）。

    ① ● "I'm just teasing."

       「我只是在開玩笑。」

       ● "Don't tease me."

          「別尋我開心。」

- "She flirts with guys all the time, but when someone gets interested, she gives them the cold shoulder. What a teaser."

  「她一天到晚賣弄風騷，但一旦有人對她發生興趣，她又冷落對方。就會尋人開心。」

② ● "She teases her hair to get it that way."

  「她把她的頭髮刮成那個樣子。」

39. **tearing one's hair out**

['tɛrɪŋ]

氣得要命

- "Was she mad? She was (almost) tearing her hair out."

  「她生氣了嗎？她氣得要命哦！」

40. **tell**

分別；區分；分清楚

- "Can you tell the twins apart?"

  「你能分得出那兩個雙胞胎嗎？」

- "You must learn how to tell right from wrong."

  「你一定要學習怎麼去分辨善惡好壞！」

- "I can't tell which is mine. They're all alike."

  「我分不清那個是我的。他們都是一個樣子。」

41. **to tell (someone) off**

臭罵一頓

- "She told me off, because she caught me with Judy one night."

  「她罵了我一頓，因為有一晚，她抓到我跟 Judy 在一起。」

42. **terrific**

[tə'rɪfɪk]

太棒了！很棒！

- "How was the game."

  「那場比賽如何？」

  "Terrific!"

  「棒透了！」

- "Gee, your hair smells terrific!"

  「乖乖，你的頭髮真香！」

43. **text (=text book)**

  [tɛkst]

  教科書；課本

- "How many texts do you have to buy for this semester?"

  「這學期你要買幾本課本？」

- "What kind of texts are you using now?"

  「你們現在用的是那種教科書？」

44. **T. G. I. F. (=Thank God It's Friday)**

  感謝上帝週末又到了。（感謝上帝，禮拜五總算到了！——
  美國人禮拜六不必上班）

45. **Thank Heaven**

  ['hɛvən]

  感謝上天；謝天謝地

- "Thank Heaven; Johnny is safe now."

  「感謝老天，Johnny 安全了（脫險了）。」

46. **Thanks for telling me (letting me know)**

  謝謝你告訴我（這件事、消息、情報）

- "Luke? This is Joyce. Do you know that we don't have class tomorrow? Dr. Landcaster has to go to a conference."

  「Luke 嗎？我是 Joyce. 你知道明天不上課嗎？Landcaster
  博士要去參加一個會議。」

  "Really? Thanks for telling me."

  「真的嗎？謝謝你告訴我。」

47. **That's about it.**
  就這麼多了

  ● "Is that all?"
  「就這麼多了嗎？」

  "Yes, that's about it."
  「是的，就這麼多了！」

48. **That's (much) better.**
  好多了（改善以後比以前好多了！）

  ● "Try it again now."
  「再試一下。」

  "Well! That's much better."
  「嗯，好多了。」

49. **That's close**
  差不多（所猜雖不中，亦不遠矣）

  ● "I guess you're 24 years old."
  「我猜你今年24歲。」

  "That's close. I'm 23."
  「差不多，我23。」

  ● "Ruth, guess what?"
  「Ruth，猜猜看發生了什麼事?」

  "You won the lottery?"
  「你中獎了？」

  "Close, but no, I passed the exam."
  「差不多，但不是這個，我考試及格了。」

50. **That's final.**
  ['faɪnl]
  話到此爲止（接不接受隨你）不必再談了。

  ● "I'll pay $350 for it, and that's final."
  「我願意出350元，並且這是最後的出價。」

51. That's/It's for me.

①是我的（如電話鈴響了，你說：「是我的。」）。②正是我喜歡的（如端上你喜歡的菜時，或音樂點放機響起一曲你喜歡的歌時，你可說：「哦，那是爲我而放的。」）

① ● (Phone rings)

"I'll get it. I think it's for me."

（電話鈴響）「我來接。我想是找我的。」

② ● (Music)

"Oh, great. That's for me."

（音樂）「哇！眞棒，正是我喜歡的。」

52. That's for sure.

絕對正確的事；當然；擔保（表示斬釘截鐵的心意）

● "If I hear him saying that, I'll punch him out, that's for sure."

「假如我聽到他那麼說，我絕對會揍他。」

● "I'll be back someday. That's for sure."

「我總有一天會回來。這是可以確定的事。」

● "Junk food is great."

「零食眞好吃。」

"That's for sure."

「當然。」

53. That's funny!

①（簡直是）開玩笑！（聽起來）眞可笑！②奇怪。

① ● "John said I am the one who is going to get fired? That's funny!"

「John 說我要被解僱了？眞是好笑！」

② ● "That's funny. I thought I already put that away. What's it doing on the table?"

「眞奇怪！我以爲我已經把它拿開了。它怎麼又在桌子上？」

54. **That's it!**
  對了。

  ● "Where is my check?"
  「我的支票呢？」

  "Is this your check?"
  「這張是你的支票嗎？」

  "That's it!"
  「嗯！」

55. **That's more like it.**
  那還差不多（較前滿意）

  ● "Let's split it fifty fifty, how about it?"
  「我們對半分如何？」

  "Yeah, that's more like it."
  「唔，那還差不多。」

56. **That's my specialty.**
  　　　　　['spɛʃəltɪ]
  那是我的看家本領

  ● "You need your hair cut? That's my specialty."
  「你要理髮？那是我的看家本領。」

57. **That's news to me.**
  真是新聞啊！（表示訝異！）

  ● "Where is Michael?"
  「Michael 在哪裏？」

  "He's taking a girl out."
  「他跟一個女孩出去了。」

  "Taking a girl out? That's news to me. I thought he was
  afraid of women."
  「跟一個女孩出去了？那真是新聞啊！我以為他怕女人。」

"It's his sister."

「那女孩是他的姊姊（妹妹）。」

58. **That's no excuse.**

[ɪkˈskjuz]

那不是理由；那不是藉口

● "Sir, I was late this morning, because I overslept."

「先生，今天早上我因為睡過頭了，所以遲到。」

"That's no excuse."

「那不是理由。」

59. **That's not fair.**

[fɛr]

這不公平；那是不公平的

● "I got two tickets, so Chris and I are going to the rock concert tonight."

「我有兩張票，所以Chris 和我今天晚上要去參加一個音樂會。」

"That's not fair. I want to go too."

「那不公平，我也要去。」

60. **That's really something.**

真要得；真是與眾不同；真棒

● "This is my new car."

「這是我的新車。」

"Boy, that's really something."

「乖乖，真棒啊！」

61. **That's that!**

①不必再談下去。②做完了。

① ● "You can't go to the movies tonight. And that's that."

「你今晚不能去看電影，就是這樣。」

② ● "Well, that's that! Now I can go home and eat."

「好了，做完了！現在我可以回家吃飯了。」

62. **That's the best excuse you can come up with?**
   那是你所能想出來的最好的藉口嗎？（表示不能令人信服）

   ● "Can I have $100, Dad?"
   「爹，我可不可以拿100塊。」
   "$100? I just gave you $100 last week."
   「100塊？我上星期才給你100塊。」
   "Yes, but I was robbed this morning."
   「是啊，但是今天早上我被搶了。」
   "Is that the best excuse you can come up with? Are you on drugs, or what?"
   「那是你所能想到的最好的藉口嗎？你是吃了大麻還是怎麼了？」（真會胡說八道）

63. **That's my boy!**
   好孩子！乖孩子（真聽話）
   ● "Give me the knife. . . that's my boy."
   「把刀給我…乖孩子。」

64. **That's the way it goes.**
   事情往往就是這樣子的。
   ● "He lost all his money gambling."
   「他賭輸了所有的錢。」
   "Well, that's the way it goes."
   「事情往往就是這樣子的。」

65. **That joke's pretty old! (=That's an old one.)**
   老掉牙的笑話
   ● "Why don't you laugh?"
   「你為什麼不笑呢？」
   "That joke's pretty old."
   「那個笑話老掉牙了。」

66. **That news will keep.**

以後再說吧！待會再說！（事情不急，拖一下也無妨）

● "I want to go home and tell Mom about the scholarship."

「我要回家告訴媽有關獎學金的事。」

"That news will keep for a while. We have to do some errands first."

「這事待會兒再說，我們得先跑腿幹點活。」

67. **That will be all.**

就這麼多（沒有了）；就這些（東西）

● "Do you need anything else?"

「你還要（買）其他的東西嗎？」

"No, that will be all."

「不，就這些（東西）。」

68. **That'll do.**

這就行了；可充數；也可以。

● "Could I have a Martini?"

「我可不可以要一杯馬丁尼？」

"I'm sorry, we only serve beer here."

「對不起，我們這兒只賣啤酒。」

"Well, that'll do."

「也可以。」

69. **The best defense is a good offense.**

        [dɪˈfɛns]   [əˈfɛns]

最好的防禦是攻擊（先下手為強）

● "I don't know what to do with John. He's always picking on me."

「我真不知該如何對付 John，他總是找我的麻煩。」

"Remember, the best defense is a good offense."

「記得嗎？最好的防禦是攻擊。」

70. **the Big Apple (=New York City)**

    專指紐約市

    ● "Where do you come from?"

    「你從那來？」

    "The Big Apple. And you?"

    「紐約市。你呢？」

71. **The bill is on me. (=This is my treat.) (=Be my guest.)**
    (=It's on me)

    ● "The bill is on me; you pay next time."

    「這次我付，下次你付。」

72. **The die is cast.**

    　　　　　[kæst]

    事已成定局（不可反悔）

    ● "If you don't like law school, why don't you drop
    out?"

    「如果你不喜歡唸法律，你為什麼不退學呢？」

    "The die is cast. I'm in debt up to my ears, and I'll
    have to become a lawyer to get out of debt."

    「事已成定局。我現在債台高築，我必須成為一個律師賺
    錢還債。」

    註：die 在此指模型，cast 是打上石膏──定型了！

73. **The hell it is!**

    胡說

    ● "Where is my wallet?"

    「我的錢包呢？」

    "On the table."

    「在桌上。」

    "The hell it is."

    「胡說。」

● daughter ： "I'm going to an all night party."
（女兒）：「我要去參加一個通宵舞會。」
father ： "The hell you are."
（爸爸）：「亂來！」

74. **The idea.**
哼（對方、某人）怎敢有這種想法
● "What happened last night?"
「昨晚發生了什麼事？」
"I went to a bar with Joe and after a few drinks, he wanted me to go to bed with him."
「我跟 Joe 去酒吧喝酒，幾杯下肚，他要我跟他上床。」
"So?"
「結果呢？」
"So, I told him to go to hell. . . The idea!"
「結果，我叫他去死…哼，虧他想得出來！」

75. **The less said the better. . . .**
說得越少越好（話多易被抓語病）
● "Ida, let me explain. . ."
「 Ida ，你聽我解釋…」
"I don't want to hear it. The less said the better."
「我不想聽，少說為妙。」

76. **the last straw**
所能忍耐的最後限度
● "The reporters kept interfering with my private life. When they showed up at my house with cameras, that was the last straw."
「那些記者不斷的騷擾我的私生活。當他們拿着照相機出現在我家時，那是我所能忍耐的最後限度。」
註：放稻草在駱駝背上讓它背負，一根…千根…萬根，放到

一個數量就不能再放，否則駱駝背骨就會被壓斷了，在
此用以表示人的忍耐力。

77. **(have) the last word**

愛抬槓；愛頂嘴（喜歡回嘴，不讓別人佔上風）

- "He always has the last word."

「他永遠愛抬槓。」

78. **The proof of the pudding is in the eating.**

[pruf]

空談不如實驗（布丁的美味吃了才知道）；（試了才知好壞）

- "He has a lot of high flown theories but the proof of the
pudding is in the eating."

「他有一套大道理，但要試過才知好壞。」

79. **The real thing.**

眞品；上等貨

- "Judy, look! This is my new mink coat."

「Judy，喏！這是我新的貂皮大衣。」

"Gosh, it's the real thing."

「老天，這是眞的啊！」

80. **the same goes for you**

你也一樣！

(one person's speaking to two others)－(老板對兩位伙計說)

- (to John): "You better clean up your act."

（對 John）說：「你最好幹點正事。」

(to Bill): "The same goes for you."

（對 Bill）說：「你也是一樣。」

81. **The sky's the limit.**

（以天空爲頂）多少都沒有關係之意。

- "How much should we spend on our trip?"

「這次旅行我們該花多少錢？」

"The sky's the limit."

「多少都沒關係。」

82. **There are plenty of fish in the sea.**

天涯何處無芳草。

- "Forget her, Jim. There are plenty of fish in the sea."

「Jim, 忘了她吧！天涯何處無芳草。」

83. **There goes everything.**

一切都泡湯了；完了（如工廠倒閉；房子失火…）

- "There goes everything."

「一切都完了。」

"Don't be sad, you can start it all over again."

「別難過，你可以東山再起。」

"Yeah, but how?"

「是啊，可是怎麼東山再起呢？」

84. **There he is as large as life.**

他就在那裏（表示真實的存在，可看到，可觸摸到的）

- "Where is Jeffrey?"

「Jeffrey 在哪裏？」

"There he is, as large as life."

「喏，就在那裏。」

85. **There's a saying in Chinese (English, or Japanese. . .)**

中國有句俗話…

- There's a saying in Chinese (=The Chinese have a saying): "When a friend comes from a long distance away, how can you not be happy!"

中國有句俗話說：「有朋自遠方來不亦樂乎！」

86. **There's neither rhyme nor reason to. . . .**

[raɪm]

完全沒有道理

●"There's neither rhyme nor reason to his arguments."

「他的爭辯沒有一點道理。」

87. **There's no holding (him/me/you) back.**

沒有事能阻止（他、我、你）（去做某事）

●"I want to marry Marian, and there's no holding me back."

「我要娶 Marian，沒有任何事能攔阻我！」

88. **There you go again!**

又來了！又來這一套了！（老毛病又犯）

●"There you go again. I told you a thousand times not to bring anything, but you just won't listen."

「又來了。我告訴你上千遍了，不要帶任何東西來，你就是不聽。」

89. **thick-skinned**

皮厚（沒有羞恥心也！）

●"She's really thick-skinned. Insults roll right off her back."

「她真是厚臉皮，羞侮的話她是毫不在乎。」

90. **things**

情況；情形

●"Things are getting tough."

「情況越來越艱苦。」

91. **think big**

胸懷大志

●"We young men should think big."

「我們年青人必須胸懷大志。」

92. **(You) think of everything (=You're considerate.)**

你的顧慮真周到。

●"Do we have napkins?"

「有餐巾紙嗎？」

"Yes. Here you are."

「有，給你。」

"Kathy, you think of everything."

「Kathy , 你的顧慮真周到。」

93. **think. . . over**

仔細考慮過；再想一想

● "Before you marry her, I hope you can think it over once or twice."

「在你娶她之前，我希望你好好的想上一兩遍。」

94. **third degree**

[dɪ'gri]

修理（打罵或禁足）

● "If Dad finds out I smoke, he'll give me the third degree."

「假如老爸知道我抽煙，他會修理我。」

95. **third wheel**

[hwil]

電灯泡

● "If you and your girlfriend are going to the movies, I'll just stay at home. I don't want to be a third wheel."

「假如你跟你的女朋友要去看電影，我就留在家裏。我可不願當電灯泡。」

96. **This is a token of my esteem.**

['tokən]　　[ə'stim]

這是我一點心意（送禮時說）

● "Happy anniversary, Mr. and Mrs. Huffman. This is a token of my esteem."

「Huffman 先生，Huffman 太太，祝你們結婚週年愉快，這是我的一點心意。」

97. **This is (really) living.**

這才是人過的日子。

- "Wow, fancy car, olympic-size swimming pool. . . . This is really living."

「哇，時髦的車子，合於奧運標準的游泳池…這才是人過的日子。」

98. **through**

①完蛋。②吹了；完了；絕交（緣盡了）。③作完了；完成。

① ● "You are through!"

「你完了！」

② ● "We are through!"

「我們吹了！」

● "I'm through with you!"

「我跟你已經絕交了。」

③ ● "After I get through with school, I'm going back to Taiwan."

「在我完成學業之後，我會回到台灣。」

99. **through the grapevine**

['grep/vaɪn]

據說（謠傳）；道聽途說

● "How did you find this out?"

「你怎麼知道的？」

"I heard it through the grapevine."

「路邊聽來的。」

100. **throw (someone) a party**

替（人）開個宴會

● "We're throwing a party for Joe on Friday. It's his birthday."

「我們將要在星期五替 Joe 開個舞會。因為那天是他的生日。」

101. **throw you out the window**

[θro]

把你扔出窗外（威脅語）

● "If you do it again, I'll throw you out the window."

「如果你再犯錯，我就要把你從窗戶扔出去。」

102. thumbs down

['θʌmz]

被拒絕；被否決了

● "The decision on your proposal was thumbs down."

「你的提議被否決了。」

註：thumbs up 則是通過了。

103. ticker-tape parade

['tɪkɚ] [tep] [pəˈred]

綵帶，鮮花，英雄式的歡迎

● "If the football team wins the national championship, when they come back they'll get a ticker-tape parade."

「假如足球隊贏得了全國冠軍，當他們回來的時候將會受到英雄式的歡迎。」

104. tie

平手

● "How did the game go?"

「比賽如何？」

"It was a tie."

「平手。」

105. to tie the knot

結婚

● "They'll tie the knot in June."

「他們將在六月結婚。」

106. (be) tied to (someone's) apron strings

['epən]

聽（媽媽，太太）話的男人；受（媽媽，太太）支配的男人

● "Jack is tied to his mother's apron strings."

「Jack 很聽他媽媽的話。」

註：apron strings 是圍裙帶。

107. tied up

[taɪd]

①忙得不可開交。②纏住。

① ● "I'm sorry, I'm tied up this morning. Can you call back this afternoon?"

「對不起，今早我很忙。你能不能下午再打來。」

● "I got all tied up in red tape when I went to get my student visa."

「當我去申請學生簽證時，我被那些公文手續搞得頭昏眼花的。」

② ● "He got tied up by her."

「他被她纏住了。」

108. tight

[taɪt]

①爛醉如泥。②沒有性經驗或經驗不多的（女孩）。③緊張；不安。④小氣。

① ● "Boy, did he get tight at last night's party."

「乖乖，他在昨晚的宴會中真是爛醉如泥。」

② ● "She's really tight."

「她真是經驗不多。」

③ ● "You're too tight; relax."

「你太緊張了，放輕鬆一點。」

④ ● "You're tight."

「你真小氣。」

109. tight schedule

[taɪt/'skɛdʒul]

緊湊的行事表

● "I have a very tight schedule; I'm teaching at 3 universities."

「我的時間表很緊湊繁忙；我在三所大學教書。」

110. Your time is running out. = Time is running out on (us, you, him)

（你的）時間不多了！

● "I'll give you ten minutes. If you don't tell us where the money is, I'll blow your head off... Your time is running out. Are you ready to talk now?"

「我給你十分鐘的時間，假如你不告訴我錢在哪裏，我會打爛你的腦袋…。時間不多了，你準備說了嗎？」

111. tip

[tɪp]

①小費。②透露消息或秘密。 (=advice; clue)

① ● "Do we have to leave a tip?"

「我們需要給小費嗎？」

● "How much should we leave for a tip?"

「我們該留多少小費？」

② ● "The police have a few tips on the robbery case."

「在那件竊盜案上，警方得到一些情報。」

● "Don't bet on that horse; he never wins."

「別賭那匹馬，它從來沒贏過。」

"Thanks for the tip."

「謝謝你告訴我。」

112. tip-top

[tɪp/tɑp]

一流的；最佳的

● "This car is in tip-top condition."

「這輛車的狀況很好！」

113. tits

[tɪts]

乳房

● "She has a big pair of tits."

「她的胸部很豐滿。」

● "She has nice tits."

「她的胸部很美。」

114. To err is human.

[ˈhjumən]

犯錯是人之常情

● "I'm sorry."

「對不起。」

"Don't worry, to err is human."

「沒關係，犯錯是人之常情。」

● "To err is human; to forgive divine."

「犯錯是人之常情，原諒別人却不是件容易之事。」

115. together

同道（氣味相投）

● "That girl isn't very together. I never know what to say to her."

「那個女孩與我們志不同道不合。我總不知該對她說些什麼？」

"Yeah. It's like she's in another world."

「是啊！好像她是另外一個世界的人似的。」

116. token

①代用硬幣。②毫無價值的東西。③只露了一下臉，打個照面就走（別人請你去參加宴會，你不願去）。④樣本（展示一、兩個以表示有）。⑤象徵。

① ● "Where can I buy subway tokens?"
「我在哪兒可以買到地下火車的銅板呢？」

② ● "This is just a small token of my esteem."
「這是一點小意思不成敬意。」　　註：送禮時說。

③ ● "He put in a token appearance at the party."
「他在宴會中只露了一面。」

④ ● "The company has a token black to give the appearance of fair employment practices."
「那公司僱了一個黑人做樣子，以便讓人覺得他們是公平僱用各類人種的。」

註：美國有法律規定各大公司、工廠需要僱用相當比率的「有色人種」以保障有色人種的就業機會。

⑤ ● "Here's $20, as a token of my good faith. I'll pay you the other $80 before the end of the month."
「這是 2 0 元，表示一下我的信用，月底以前我會把剩下的 80 塊還你。」

117. told off

抱怨；責罵（有下哀的美頓書的味道，多用於男女之間）

● "She told him off."
「她責罵他。」

118. (Every) Tom, Dick, and Harry

[dɪk]
每一個人；張三李四

● "Every Tom, Dick, and Harry in this town went to that party last night."
「昨晚鎮上的每一個人都去參加那個宴會。」

● "I don't want you sleeping with every Tom, Dick, & Harry when you go to America."
「當你去美國時，我可不願你跟每一個傢伙上床啊！」

119. tomboy

['tɑm,bɔɪ]

男孩子氣的女孩

● "She's a real tomboy."

「她是個有男子氣概的女孩。」

120. (go) too far

太過份

● "You've gone too far."

「你太過份了。」

121. too much

①太過份。②眞好笑（當別人說了一連串笑話之後，你可以說："You're too much." 表示太好笑了。）

① ● "You are really too much."

「你太過份了。」

② ● "He's just too much. I can't stand it."

「他的笑話太好笑了，我眞消受不了。」

122. too much authority

超越職權，指管得太多了；權力太大，可以管很多閑事（可能會濫用職權）

● "Being a cop gives you too much authority. It's bad for you."

「當了警察，給了你太多的權力，對你是不好的。」

123. too ready/quick to suspect

[sə'spɛkt]

疑心病太重

● "You're too quick to suspect. She's only my schoolmate."

「你疑心病太重了，她只不過是我的同學罷了。」

124. top-notch

[tɑp,nɑtʃ]

頂呱呱的

● "He is top-notch student."

「他是一個頂呱呱的學生。」

125. touch the right chord/spot

觸及心弦

● "I like the blues. They touch the right chord."

「我喜歡藍調（音樂）。它們能打動我的心弦。」

126. tough

[tʌf]

①不好應付；很棘手；辛苦。②嚴格；難纏；強硬的。③遺憾（有諷刺之意）。

① ● "It's a tough job."

「那是一份很辛苦的工作。」

② ● "Oh, boy. He is very tough."

「乖乖。他真難纏。」

● "He is a tough guy."

「他是一個強硬的傢伙。」

③ ● "If you don't like it, that's just tough."

「假如你不喜歡它，那真是太遺憾了。」

127. tough world (=life is tough all over)

冷酷的世界

● "I can't believe she stood me up for that big ape."

[ep]

「我真不敢相信，她會為了那個大猩猩放我鴿子。」

"It's a tough world."

「這個世界是冷酷的。」

128. trade-in

[tred]

以舊換新物（如以舊冰箱，貼補些錢換個新冰箱）

●"I'm going to trade in my black and white T.V. for a new color T.V."

「我將要把我的舊黑白電視拿去換一架彩色電視機。」

129. train of thought

思路

●"Be quiet! I don't want to lost my train of thought."

「安靜點！我不想打斷我的思路。」

130. trap

[træp]

嘴

●"Would you shut your big trap for once?"

「請你閉上你的嘴好嗎？」

131. trash

[træʃ]

①廢物；廢紙。②搗亂。

① ●"This movie is really trash."

「這電影真是難看。」

●"You are real trash; you know nothing but eating."

「你真是個廢物；除了吃你啥也不知道。」

② ●"Let's go to his party and trash it."

「我們去他的宴會，並且搞砸它。」

132. trick

[trɪk]

①噱頭。②花樣；耍花招。⑧嫖客。

① ●"Go-Go Department Store is having a sale."

「去去百貨公司正在大拍賣。」

"Well, it's just a trick."

「啊！那只是個噱頭罷了。」

② ●"Don't play any tricks with me."

「別跟我耍花樣。」

③ ●"The whore said in the interview that she turns 20 tricks a day."

「那個妓女在接受訪問中說，她一天接20個客人。」

133. tricky

['trɪkɪ]

①奸詐的人；詭詐的；好惡作劇。②複雜的。

① ●"He is very tricky."

「他很奸詐。」

② ●"The game is very tricky."

「這種遊戲很複雜。」

134. trimmings (=the works)

['trɪmɪŋz]

（烹調的）配料

●"I'll take a hamburger with all the trimmings."

「我要一客漢堡加所有的配料。」

註：trimmings 指夾在中間的蕃茄醬、生洋蔥、黃瓜片、芥末、蕃茄片等等。

135. trouble maker

惹事生非的人；搗蛋鬼

●"My kid brother is a real trouble maker."

「我的小弟真是個搗蛋鬼。」

136. try me

（不妨）試試看

●"You're not going to believe this. ..."

「你將不會相信（我告訴你的）這件事…。」

"Try me."

「（你不妨）試試看。」

● "I don't think you will hit me."
「我不相信你會打我。」

"Try me."
「試試看。」

● "I don't think you can do it."
「我不認為你能做這件事。」

"Try me."
「(你不妨)試試看。」

137. tummy (=belly=abdomen)

['tʌmɪ]   ['æbdəmən]

肚子

● "My tummy doesn't feel good. I'm sure I ate some-thing bad."
「我的肚子覺得不舒服，我相信我一定吃了什麼東西不對勁。」

138. turkey

['tɜkɪ]

沒出息的人；驢蛋；笨蛋

● "You failed the test, you turkey."
「你考試不及格，你這沒出息的傢伙。」

139. turn

[tɜn]

輪到(誰)；該(誰)做某事

● "Is it my turn to treat you?"
「是不是該輪到我請你了？」

● "It's your turn to do the dishes."
「該你洗碟子了！」

● "Let's take turns driving."
「我們輪流開車好了。」

140. turn in (=hit the sack)

去睡覺了

● "I'm turning in now, see you tomorrow."

「我現在要去睡覺了，明兒見。」

141. turn off

①關。②出口。③令人討厭的。

① ● "Turn off the light."

「把灯關掉。」

② ● "We want the next turn-off."

「我們在下一個出口出去。」

③ ● "Girls who wear too much makeup are a real turn off."

「化粧得太濃的女孩，是討人厭的。」

142. turn sour

[saʊr]

變糟；惡化

● "The whole thing turned sour."

「事情變糟了。」

143. turn out

①結果；演變成。②趕走。

① ● "This latest experiment is turning out better than we expected."

「最近這次實驗的結果，出乎我們意料之外的好。」

● "I didn't expect things would turn out like this."

「我沒有料到事情會變成這樣。」

② ● "You're turning us out? It's only 2:00 AM!"

「你要趕我們走？現在才（凌晨）兩點！」

144. turnover

失誤

●"What an exciting game! 5 turnovers!"

「這場比賽真緊張刺激啊！竟然有 5 次失誤。」

145. (to be) two faced

兩面人（常口是心非）

●"Don't listen to him. He is two faced."

「別聽他的，他是個兩面人。」

●"That two-faced bitch. She tells us that she hates him but she always sees him when we're not around."

「那個兩面的臭娘們。她說她討厭他，但只要我們不在，她總是去找他。」

146. Two heads are better than one.

集思廣益

●"Let's work on this together. Two heads are better than one."

「讓我們一起來想法子，集思廣益嘛。」

147. Two's a company, three's a crowd.

二個人恰恰好，三個人就嫌太擠！（這句話，常用在約會中，表示不歡迎別人當電灯泡。）

●"Milton, what are you doing tonight?"

「Miltion, 今晚你打算做什麼？」

"Jane and I are going to see Star Wars."

「Jane 跟我打算去看星際大戰。」

"Oh, boy. I've been dying to see that movie. Can I go with you two?"

「乖乖，我一直想去看那電影，我能跟你們一道去嗎？」

"Sorry, buddy. Two's a company; three's a crowd."

「對不起，老朋友，二個人恰恰好，三個人就嫌太擠了。」

148. two timing (=two timer)

一隻腳踩兩條船

● "She's two timing you, I tell you. She's going out with some football player almost every night."

「我告訴你，她是一隻脚踩兩條船。她幾乎每天晚上都跟某位足球員出去玩。」

1. **Uncle Sam**

   指美國政府

   ●"I got drafted by Uncle Sam."

   「我被（美國）政府徵召入伍。」

   ●"Uncle Sam will get you, if you don't pay your income taxes."

   「（美國）政府會找到你的，如果你不付所得稅。」

2. **undercover agent**

   　　　　　['edʒənt]

   便衣警探

   ●"He is an undercover agent."

   「他是一個便衣警探。」

3. **under the table**

   ①秘密交易（非法的）②私下工作沒有報稅

   ① ●"Where did you get this bike?"

   　　「你這輛腳踏車哪兒買的？」

   　　"I got it under the table."

   　　「我是經秘密交易來的。」

   ② ●"He pays my salary under the table, so I don't pay tax."

   　　「他私下付我薪水，所以我不必報稅。」

4. **uptight (=tense)**

   緊張

   ●"Don't get uptight."

   　「別緊張。」

   ●"He's a very uptight person."

   　「他是一個很緊張的人。」

   註：lay back 則是很放鬆，不緊張。

5. **up to par**

[par]

體力夠；身體好

- "I'm not up to par lately."

「我近來身體不太好。」

- "I'm not feeling up to par."

「我覺得不太舒服。」

6. **up-and-coming**

年輕有為（有潛力將來會有前途）

- "He's an up-and-coming young man; that's why I like him."

「他是一個有前途的年輕人，所以我喜歡他。」

- "He's an up-and-coming young executive."

「他是一個年輕有為的行政官。」

7. **upset**

[ʌpˈsɛt]

沮喪

- "What are you upset about?"

「你沮喪個什麼？」

8. **(to) use (someone)**

利用

- "Be smart; he is just using you."

「放聰明點，他只是在利用你。」

- "I hate to be used by others."

「我討厭被人利用。」

1. **V.D. (or the clap)**

   [klæp]

   性病；淋病

   - "She got V.D. (=the clap) from her boyfriend."

     「她從她男朋友那裏感染了性病。」

2. **very, very touching**

   ['tʌtʃɪŋ]

   眞叫人感動（也可用來作諷刺語）

   - "I did this all for you."

     「我這樣做全是爲了你。」

     "Thank you. That's very, very touching."

     「謝謝，眞叫人感動。」

3. **vote for**

   [vot]

   選舉；贊成

   - "I believe most people will vote for you."

     「我相信絕大多數的人會投你一票。」

   - "I vote for going out for pizza and beer."

     「我贊成去吃義大利餅及喝啤酒。」

1. **walk on air**

   非常高興；洋洋得意

   ●"She heard she got a scholarship and now she's walk-ing on air."

   「她聽說她得到了獎學金，現在她高興的要命。」

2. **walk out (on)**

   ①離開。②非正式罷工（如：以請假代替罷工）

   ① ●"Please don't walk out on me."

   「請不要離開我。」

   ② ●"The workers staged a walkout to protest their low wages."

   「那些工人仍在罷工中以抗議薪水太低。」

3. **(a) walking encyclopedia/dictionary**

   [ɪnˌsaɪkləˈpidɪə]

   萬事通；活字典

   ●"That guy knows everything. He's like a walking ency-clopedia."

   「那傢伙什麼都懂，他是個萬事通。」

4. ●"If you want to know what it means. Look it up into the dictionary. I'm not your walking dictionary."

   「你假如想知道這字的意思。去查查字典。我可不是你的字典。」

4. **walking papers**

   解僱通知書

   ●"Jimmy got his walking papers this morning."

   「今早Jimmy 收到解僱的通知書。」

5. **(a) wall flower**

   壁花（舞會中一直沒人問津的女孩；或不會跳舞一直坐在那兒的女孩。通常不用來指自己。）

●"She never goes to any party, because she hates being a wall flower."

「她從不參加舞會。因為她討厭當壁花。」

6. **wall-to-wall**

全套的；完全的；全部的

●"Their house has a color TV, a fire place, a swimming pool, and wall-to-wall carpeting."

「他們家裏有一架彩色電視、一個壁爐、一個游泳池，以及全套的地毯。」

●"That party was wall-to-wall with people."

「那個宴會是人山人海。」

7. **the walls have ears**

隔牆有耳

●"Be careful what you say; the walls have ears."

「小心說話，隔牆有耳。」

8. **Want to make something of it?**

不服氣是不是？（想打架啊？）

●"Why do you keep picking on me?"

「你為什麼老找我的麻煩？」

"Because I feel like it. Want to make something of it?"

「因為我高興。怎麼，不服氣是不是？」

9. **warm up**

①熱身運動。②暖車（機器）。③態度轉好（較熱情了，不再冷冰冰）。

① ●"Before you jump into the swimming pool, don't forget to warm up first."

「在你跳入泳池之前，別忘了先做暖身運動。」

② ●"It takes me 20 minutes to warm up my car during the winter."

「在冬天，我需要 20 分鐘暖車。」

③ ● "He didn't like me at first, but he seems to have warmed up a little bit recently."

「他開始並不喜歡我，但近來好一點了。」

10. **wash out**

輸得很慘；輸得乾乾淨淨的

① ● "That baseball game was a washout for the home team."

「那場棒球賽地主隊輸得很慘。」

② ● "He got washed out in Las Vegas."

「他在 Las Vegas （賭城）輸光了錢。」

註：與 home team 相對的是 visiting team。

11. **wash your mouth out (with soap)**

洗洗嘴巴（父母在孩子講髒話之後的責備語）

● "Oh, fuck."

「哦！操！」

"Where did you learn that word? I'm going to wash your mouth out with soap."

「你從哪兒學來的字？我要用肥皂洗你的嘴巴。」

12. **watch me**

等着瞧；瞧我的

● "I don't believe you can beat him up."

「我不認為你能打倒他。」

"Just watch me."

「等着瞧！」

● "Here comes Jannie, watch me."

「Jannie 來了，瞧我的。」

13. **watch (one's) money**

不胡亂花錢；花錢很小心

● "I always watch my money."

「我花錢一向很小心。」

14. **watch your language**

[wɔtʃ] [ˈlæŋgwɪdʒ]

說話小心點；別胡說八道

- "You double crossed me; you son of a bitch."
  「你出賣了我；你這狗養的。」

  "Hey, watch your language."
  「嘿，說話小心點。」

15. **watch your step**

①小心台階；走路要小心！②小心。

① - "Peter's office in upstairs, just follow me,....watch your step."
  「Peter 的辦公室在樓上，跟我來，小心台階。」

② - "He's very tricky. When you deal with him, watch your step."
  「他很詭詐，當你跟他打交道時，小心點！」

16. **watch your tongue**

別亂嚼舌根；不要胡說八道

- "Hey, chick! Do you need company tonight?"
  「嘿，小妞，你今晚需要人陪嗎？」

  "Watch your tongue, mister."
  「老兄，說話小心啊！」

17. **way to go! (=nice going!)**

要得！

- "I was just promoted."
  「我高升了！」

  "Way to go!"
  「要得！」

18. **We can never be more than friends.**

我們只能維持朋友的關係（不能進一步成為戀人）。（這常是女孩子拒絕男孩的用語）

- "Pete, I like you very much. You're really a nice guy, but we can never be more than friends."

  「Pete 我很喜歡你。你眞是個好人，但是我們只能當朋友。」

19. **We can't take any chances.**

  我們冒不起任何風險（要小心點，別出任何差錯）

  - "Be careful; we can't take any chances."

    「小心，我們冒不起任何風險。」

20. **We'll see about that!**

  走着瞧

  - "I'm not going to let you join our group!"

    「我不會讓你參加我們這一組。」

    "We'll see about that!"

    「走着瞧。」

21. **wear the pants in the family**

  一家之主（通常是指女的爲一家之主時）

  - "She wears the pants in that family."

    「她是她們家的一家之主。」

22. **wear two hats**

  一心兩用

  - "One thing at a time, please. I can't wear two hats at one time."

    「拜託，一件一件來，我無法一心兩用。」

  - "He wears two hats. He is both the mayor and a banker."

    「他一心兩用。他又當市長又當銀行家。」

23. **weed (=marijuana)**

  [wid]

  大麻（煙）

  - "He offered me some weed."

    「他給我一些大麻。」

24. **weird**
    [wɪrd]
    古怪透頂
    - "You're weird."
      「你眞是古怪透頂。」

25. **well into the night**
    直到深更半夜
    - "We talked well into the night."
      「我們一直聊到深更半夜。」

26. **wet behind the ears**
    乳臭未乾
    - "What do you know about women? You're still wet behind the ears."
      「你對女人懂得什麼？你仍然乳臭未乾。」
    - "What can you do? You're still wet behind the ears."
      「你能做些什麼呢？你仍是乳臭未乾。」
      "Just don't underestimate me; you'll see."
      「別低估我，你等着瞧。」

27. **wet blanket**
    ['blæŋkɪt]
    澆人冷水；掃興的人
    - "We'll never make it."
      「我們成不了的。」
      "Hey, don't be a wet blanket, O.K.?"
      「嘿，別澆冷水，好嗎？」

28. **What a line!**
    [laɪn]
    多麼中聽的話（少拍馬屁了！）
    - "You are the most sweet, generous, intelligent girl in our class."

「你是我們班上最甜、最慷慨、最聰明的女孩。」

"What a line."

「多麼動聽的話啊！」

● "Mom, you are the most fabulous mother in this world."

「媽，你是世界上最棒的母親。」

"What a line! O.K. tell me what's on your mind. You need money again?"

「多動聽的話啊！好，告訴我，你心裏在想什麼？是不是又要錢了？」

29. **What a pity!**

['pɪtɪ]

真可惜！

● "Such a pretty girl turned out to be a thief, what a pity."

「那麼漂亮的一個女孩居然是個小偷，真是可惜啊！」

● "You can't go with us? What a pity."

「你不能跟我們一起去？真可惜啊！」

30. **What a shame.**

真可惜；太可惜

● "What a shame, it always rains on my day off."

「真可惜，每次我休假就下雨。」

31. **What a waste!**

真是糟蹋啊！（如：鮮花插在牛糞上）

● "Have you met her husband? . . . He is so ugly, I can't believe it."

「你見過她的先生嗎？…他真醜，我簡直不能相信。」

"Yeah, what a waste."

「是啊！真是糟蹋啊！」

32. **What about?**

怎麼辦呢？

●"We'll go to London this summer."

「我們今年夏天要去倫敦。」

"What about Lucy (dog)?"

「Lucy（狗）怎麼辦呢？（帶不帶去）」

33. **What are you looking at me for?**

①你盯着我看做什麼？②看什麼看？（不愉快的問法）；看着我做什麼？（表示不愉快，無辜）。

① ●"What are you looking at me for?"

「你看着我做什麼？」

"You're very pretty tonight."

「今晚你真漂亮。」

"Really?"

「真的嗎？」

② ●"What are you looking at me for? Never seen a girl before?"

「你幹嘛瞪着我看？沒見過女孩子啊？」

● "I didn't do it. What are you looking at me for?"

「又不是我幹的，你看我幹嘛？」

34. **What are you selling?**

你葫蘆裏賣的是什麼藥？

●"What are you selling?"

「你葫蘆裏到底賣的是什麼藥？」

"You'll see."

「等着瞧！」

35. **What (on earth) are you talking about?**

你到底是什麼意思呢？你到底在胡說些什麼？

●"You don't want to see me again? What on earth are you talking about?"

「你不想再見到我？你到底在胡扯什麼？」

●"It doesn't make any sense. What are you talking about?"

「我一點都聽不懂。你到底在胡說些什麼？」

36. **What are you yelling for?**

     [jɛlɪŋ]

     你在嚷嚷個什麼勁？

     ●"What are you yelling for? I'm on the phone."

     「你鬼叫什麼？我在打電話。」

     "I need some toilet paper."

     「我需要一些衛生紙。」

37. **What brings you here?**

     什麼風把你吹來的？

     ●"Hi! Joseph! Long time no see. What brings you here?"

     「嗨！Joseph! 好久不見，什麼風把你吹來的？」

     "Well, I just dropped in for a chat."

     「唔，我只是順道來找你聊聊。」

38. **What could be worse?**

     [wɝs]

     還能更糟嗎？還會有比這更糟的事嗎？

     ●"My money was stolen and my wife ran away. What could
     be worse?"

     「我的錢被偷了，我太太跑掉了。天下還有比這更糟的事
     嗎？」

39. **What'd (=did) I say?**

     我到底說錯了什麼？

     ●"I don't want to continue our conversation. . . . I want to go
     home."

     「我不想再繼續聊下去。我要回家了。」

     "What'd I say?"

     「我說錯了什麼？」

40. **What do (they) know?**

     （他們）知道些什麼？（他們）懂得什麼？（如：指責外行

人，局外人之批評時用）

● "They said you're not qualified for this job? What do they know?"

「他們說你不夠資格擔任這個工作？他們又懂什麼？」

41. **What do you call this?**

①你這算什麼？你這是什麼意思？（如：你好言相勸朋友，結果他却賞你一拳！）②這個東西，你們怎麼叫的？你叫這什麼？

① ● "What do you call this? Are you out of your mind?"

「你這是什麼意思？你瘋啦？」

② ● "What do you call this, Lisa?"

「Lisa, 你叫這什麼？」

" 肉粽，rice dumpling."

「肉粽。」

42. **What do you know about life?**

你對人生又懂得多少？（常是用來教訓無知的年輕人用。）

● "Life? You're talking life to me? What do you know about life?"

「人生？你在跟我談人生？你又懂得什麼叫人生？」

● "Life is boring."

「人生眞是無聊。」

"Yeah? Boring? What do you know about life? You just sit there and drink coke all day long."

「眞的嗎？無聊？你懂得什麼叫人生？你整天只會坐在那兒喝可樂。」

43. **What do you say?**

閣下意見如何？（徵求別人的意思）

● "I'll have the car, and you have the boat, what do you say?"

（在離婚分財產時，你說:)「我拿車子，你拿汽艇，如何？」

- "We'll go to the beach, and then go get a big seafood dinner. What do you say?"

「我們去海灘，然後去買一份海鮮大餐，閣下意見如何？」

44. **What do you think?**

你覺得如何？你的意見如何？

- "I think this color is too bright for me. What do you think?"

「我想這顏色對我來說太鮮艷了。你覺得呢？」

45. **What does (it) have to do with (this, it, you)?**

（這）跟（那）有什麼關係？

- "Why did they leave out the song?"

「他們為什麼取消了這首歌？」

"Because of Dorothy."

「為了 Dorothy（的緣故）。」

"What does she have to do with this?"

「她跟這事有什麼關係？」

46. **What does that have to do with the price of beans?"**

那與真正的原因又有什麼關係？那與我們現在所講的事又有什麼關係？

- "I'd like to go to graduate school at Harvard, but I'm afraid my English isn't good enough."

「我很希望到哈佛唸研究所，但我擔心我的英文不夠好。」

"What does that have to do with the price of beans? Aren't you going to graduate school in Chinese language and literature?"

「這又有什麼關係？你不是要唸中文研究所嗎？」

47. **What's done is done.**

已成事實，過去的不必再提了。

- "I told myself what's done is done, just let bygones be bygones."

「我告訴我自己，既成的事實不必再去追悔，過去的就讓它過去吧。」

48. **What for? (=for what reason?)**

為了什麼？（疑問或心有未甘）

- "You want me to give him another chance? What for?"

  「你要我再給他一次機會？為什麼？」

49. **What has she/he got that I don't have?**

（她／他）到底有什麼地方比我強？（不服氣的問話）

- "I don't know why you go for her. What has she got that I don't have?"

  「我不明白你為什麼中意她，她那點比我強？」

50. **What's it all about?**

怎麼回事？

- "You said Linda got divorced three days ago? What's it all about?"

  「你說 Linda 三天前離婚了？怎麼回事？」

- "They said you had a fight with Dick. What's it all about?"

  「他們說你跟 Dick 爭吵了，怎麼回事啊？」

51. **What's cooking?**

近況如何？

- "What's cooking?"

  「近來如何？」

  "Nothing special; how about you?"

  「沒什麼特別的事，你呢？」

52. **What's going on?**

怎麼回事啊？發生了什麼事？

- "What's going on here?"

  「這裏發生了什麼事？」

53. **What's gotten into you?**

怎麼回事？哪兒不對勁？

● "You've never acted like this before. What's gotten into you?"

「你從來沒有這樣過？到底怎麼回事？」

54. **What's he like?**

他長得如何？他的個性如何？

● "I met a guy at the party last night."

「我昨天在舞會中認識一個男孩。」

"What's he like?"

「他長得什麼樣子？」

"6 feet 2, blond, dark, strong, handsome."

「6 呎 2 吋，金髮，深色皮膚，體壯，英俊。」

"Intelligent, charming, and very friendly."

「聰明，迷人，並且十分友善。」

55. **What's next?**

①接下去是什麼？②接下去還有什麼花樣？

① ● "Three's Company is on at 7. What's next?"

「7 點鐘是三人行。接下去呢？」

② ● "I broke my leg yesterday, and lost my wallet this morning. What's next?"

「我昨天摔斷了腿，今早又丟了錢包。接下去還有什麼精彩的？」

56. **What's on (TV)?**

在演什麼？

"What's on TV. now?"

「現在電視在演什麼？」

註："What was it about?"

「內容如何？」（偵探、歌舞、功夫）

"Who's in it?"

「有哪些演員？」

"How is it?"

「好不好看？」

"What's on for tonight?"

「今晚做什麼？」（看電影？逛街？）

57. **What's on your mind?**

①什麼事？②你心裏想什麼。③你在擔心些什麼？

① ● "Oh, I haven't seen you for a long time; what's on your mind?"

「好久不見，有什麼事嗎？」

② ● "Speak up! What's on your mind?"

「說（出來）！你心裏到底在想些什麼？」

③ ● "You look worried. What's on your mind?"

「你看起來很憂慮。你在擔心什麼？」

58. **What's so funny?**

['fʌnɪ]

什麼事那麼好笑？

● "What's so funny?"

「什麼事那麼好笑？」

"Your fly is unzipped."

「你的拉鏈開了。」

註：fly 指褲子的拉鏈。

59. **What's the Chinese (French, Greek. . .) (word) for "Ouch"?**

中文 " 好痛 " 怎麼說？   [aʊtʃ]

（ Ouch 也可換成別的字如 "hot", "crazy", ... ）

60. **What's the difference?**

['dɪfərəns]

又有什麼差別／不同？又有什麼關係（表示無關緊要）

● "One day, two days, what's the difference?"
「一天（或）兩天，又有什麼差別呢？」

61. **What's the dope? (=scoop)**

　　　　[dop] [skup]
你在賣弄什麼玄虛？葫蘆裏賣什麼藥？

● "Wanda, can you come over right now? I want to show you something."
「Wanda，你能不能馬上過來一趟？我要給妳看樣東西。」

"What's the dope? Why don't you tell me now?"
「到底是什麼東西？你為什麼不在電話中告訴我？」

62. **What's the matter (or wrong) with you?**
你怎麼搞的？（不對勁！）

● "What's the matter with you today? You're very impatient."
「你今天怎麼搞的？怎麼那麼沒有耐心呢？（脾氣不好）」

"I'm sorry. I don't know what's bothering me either."
「對不起。我也不知道什麼事使我如此煩躁。」

63. **What's the point of getting angry?**
生氣有什麼用？

● "What is the point of getting angry? Let's sit down and talk it over."
「生氣有什麼用？讓我們坐下來談談。」

註："What's the point" 可當「有什麼用？」，也可當「目的何在？什麼意思？」

64. **What's the rush?**
急什麼？忙什麼？

● "I have to go now. See you."
「我該走了。再見。」

"Stay a little longer. What's the rush?"
「再待一會兒。急什麼？」

65. **What's (the) story? (=What's happened?)**

    怎麼回事？

    "What's the story between you and Marlon?"

    「你跟 Marlon 之間是怎麼一回事？」

66. **What's this all about? (=What's going on?)**

    怎麼回事？

    ● "What's this all about? My birthday is next week."

      「這是怎麼一回事啊？我的生日是在下個星期。」（他的
      朋友搞錯日子了！）

67. **What's your line/field?**

    你是幹哪一行的？

    ● "What's your line, Mr. Anson?"

      「Anson 先生，你是做什麼的？」

      "Bank robbery, why?"

      「搶銀行的，問什麼問？」

68. **What kept you so long?**

    什麼事耽誤你這麼久？你怎麼現在才來？」

    ● "What kept you so long? We have been waiting here for
      45 minutes.

      「什麼事情耽攔你這麼久？我們在這兒等了４５分鐘。」

69. **What makes you think so/that?**

    什麼事會讓你這麼想呢？

    ● "Jeffrey, I know you don't like me...."

      「Jeffrey，我知道你不喜歡我…」

      "What makes you think that? I like you!"

      「你怎會這麼想呢？我喜歡你啊！」

70. **What on earth are you (doing, talking about ....)?**

    你在胡搞些什麼？你在鬼扯些什麼？

    ● "Jennie is having an affair with Mr. Fairbanks? What
      on earth are you talking about?"

「Jennie 跟 Fairbank 先生有一手？你在胡說些什麼？」

71. **What say? (=What do you say?)**

意下如何？

- "Let's have fried chicken, what say?"

「我們吃炸雞，如何？」

"O.K."

「好！」

72. **What the heck.**

[hεk]

管他的

- "Well, are you going or not?"

「你到底去不去？」

"Oh, what the heck, I'll go."

「哦，管他的，我去。」

73. **What the heck are you (doing, talking about)?**

[hεk]

你在搞什麼鬼？你在胡說些什麼？

- "What the heck are you doing? Trying to get yourself killed?"

「你在搞什麼鬼？不想活啦？」

註：heck 是 hell 的委婉的說法，如 sugar, shoot 與 shit;
　　darn 與 damn。

74. **What the hell is this?**

[hεl]

這他媽的是怎麼一回事？

- "What the hell are you talking about?"

「你他媽的在說些什麼？」

- "What the hell are you doing?"

「你他媽的在做什麼？」

" ' Do Not Disturb' Can't you read?"

"When will you grow up and get your act together?"

75. **What was I saying?**
    我剛才說到哪？

    ● "What was I saying? Oh, I was talking about last
    night's party."
    「我剛才說到哪？哦，對了，我正在說昨天晚上宴會的事。」

76. **When in Rome, do as the Romans do.**
    入境隨俗

    ● "Sir, have you ever used chopsticks before?"
    「先生，你以前用過筷子吃飯嗎？」

    "No, but when in Rome, do as the Romans do. I'll
    give it a try."
    「沒有，入境隨俗，不妨試一試。」

    註：有些人會只講 When in Rome. 而省去後面半句。

77. **When's chow?**
    [tʃaʊ]
    什麼時候開飯？

    ● "I'm hungry. When's chow?"
    「我餓了。什麼時候開飯？」

78. **When things go wrong, smile.**
    當事情不順時，要處之泰然。

    ● "Mike, remember? When things go wrong, smile."
    「Mike, 記得嗎？當事情不順時，要處之泰然。」

79. **When will you grow up?**
    你什麼時候才長得大？（斥責人幼稚、不懂事。）

    ● "When will you grow up, Johnny?"
    「Johnny, 你什麼時候才長得大？」

80. **Where are you calling from?**
    你是從哪兒打來的？

    ● "It's so noisy, where are you calling from?"
    「你那裏好吵哦，你從哪兒打來的？」

"The train station."

「火車站。」

81. **Where did you learn your manners?**

[`mænəz]

你哪學來的？怎麼這麼無禮（斥責語）

● "How can you do this to a lady? Where did you learn your manners?"

「你怎能這樣對待一位女士？你哪學來的？」

● "That's not how you hold a knife and fork. Where did you learn your manners?"

「不是那樣拿刀叉的。你是在哪裏學來的規矩啊？」

82. **Where's your sense of humor?**

[sɛns]　[`hjumə]

你的幽默感到哪兒去了？（當你開玩笑別人不解風情勃然大怒時，你可問…）

● "Where's your sense of humor? I'm just joking."

「你的幽默感到哪裏去了？我只是開玩笑啊。」

83. **Where was I? (=Where were we?)**

我剛說到哪兒了？（話被打斷，要繼續時用）

● "Where was I? Oh, yes, I saw Billy on 5th Avenue, . . ."

「我剛說到哪裏了？哦，對了，我在第5街上看到 Billy。」

84. **whistle blower**

[hwɪsl] [bloə]

打小報告的人

● "I'm convinced (=certain) he's a whistle blower. We'll have to bump him off."

「我確信他是一個打小報告的人。我們得宰了他。」

● "Who blew the whistle?"

「誰告的密？」

85. **white trash**

     [træʃ]

   白種廢物（罵白人的話，指住在南部，較窮、落後的白人。）

   ● "Don't let him bother you. He's just a white trash."

     「別讓他煩你，他只是一個白種廢物。」

   註： white trash多半會喜歡三K黨。

86. **Who are you?**

   你算老幾？

   ● "Who are you to tell me what to do?"

   「你算老幾，還要你告訴我怎麼做？」

87. **Who are you kidding?**

     ['kɪdɪŋ]

   你在跟誰開玩笑？（你當我是傻瓜？）

   ● "I'm going to be the next chairman."

     「我會成為下一屆主席。」

   "Who are you kidding? You don't have a chance!"

     「你在騙誰？不可能！」

88. **Who cares?**

   我才不在乎呢！誰會在乎？

   ● "I heard Roland is going to get married next Sunday."

     「聽說 Roland 下禮拜天結婚。」

   "Who cares."

     「我才不在乎。」

89. **Who else?**

   除了他還會是誰呢？

   ● "Who did this?"

     「誰幹的？」

   "Johnny! Who else?"

     「（除了）Johnny! 還會有誰？」

90. **Who gives the orders around here?**

   是誰在此發號施令的？

●"Who gives the orders around here? You or I?"
「在此誰發號施令？是你還是我？」

91. **Who is it?**

誰呀？（聽到敲門時問）

●"Who is it?"
「誰呀？」

"It's me, Helen."
「是我，Helen 。」

92. **Who knows?**

誰知道？（只有天曉得）

●"Is Mary coming tonight, John?"
「John, Mary 今晚會來嗎？」

"Who knows?"
「天知道！」

93. **Why don't you just drop dead?**

你爲什麼不去死？滾開！你爲什麼不死了算了？

●"Hey, gal, do you want to make love tonight?"
「嘿，小姐，你今晚想做愛嗎？」

"Why don't you just drop dead?"
「你爲什麼不去死了算了？」

94. **Why don't you watch where you're going?**

你走路怎麼不帶眼睛？

●"Hey, why don't you watch where you're going?"
「嘿，你走路怎麼不帶眼睛？」

95. **Why me?**

爲什麼要找／選上我呢？（例如倒霉事老臨到你頭上，你就
可以抬頭問問老天 "Why me?"）

●"Leo, go and get us some more 7-up."

"I don't like this stuff."

"Why me?"

「Leo, 去幫我們再買幾瓶七喜汽水。」

"Why me? I'm not the only one drinking."

「為什麼要我去？又不是只有我一個人喝。」

96. **Why not?**

為什麼不？（反問語）好啊！

● "Mary wanted me to go to that dancing party with her."

「Mary 要我跟她去參加那個舞會。」

"Why not?"

「你為什麼不答應？」

● "Do you really want to try it?"

「你真的要試？」

"Why not? One time can't hurt."

「為什麼不？一次無妨。」

97. **wild**

[waɪld]

①狂野。②奇異的（有趣的；與衆不同的）

① ● "She is wild."

「她真野。」

② ● "It's a wild movie."

「那電影真有趣！」

98. **Will you say grace, please?**

[gres]

你來說祈禱詞好嗎？（在美國一般吃飯前總會祈禱，有時也會請客人代說祈禱詞。）

● "Robert, will you say grace, please?"

「 Robert, 你來說祈禱詞好嗎？」

"My pleasure, Mr. Seller."

「那是我的榮幸，Seller 先生。」

99. win some, lose some

[wɪn]　　[luz]

有贏有輸（得到一些也失去一些）

● "That's life. You win some, you lose some."
　「那就是人生。你得到一些，同時也會失去一些。」

● "Sometimes you win, sometimes you lose."
　「有時你贏，有時你輸。」

100. window shopping

[ˈwɪndo/ˈʃɑpɪŋ]

逛街（光看不買）

● "Let's go window shopping."
　「我們逛街去。」

101. Wish me luck.

祝我好運（當你要去做某一件事，需要大量的運氣與祝福時，就這樣對別人說，有「為我祈禱」之意。）

● "I'm going to see Dr. Triper."
　「我要去見 Triper教授。」

"Dr. Triper?!"
　「Triper 教授？」

"Yes, so wish me luck."
　「是的！所以祝我好運吧！」

"Good luck."
　「祝你好運。」

102. wise up

識相點；放聰明點

● "Wise up, boy. I don't want to kill you, so don't force me."
　「小子，放聰明點。我不想殺你，所以別逼我。」

● "You better wise up, tell us where the money is."
　「你最好放聰明點，告訴我們錢在哪兒。」

103. **with bells on**

盛裝以赴

●"Teresa went to that party with bells on."

「Teresa盛裝參加那個宴會。」

104. **with the boys**

跟男的同事／朋友…

●"I'm going to have a beer with the boys."

「我要去跟（男的）朋友喝杯酒。」

註：因女權運動也有 "with the girls" 的用法。

105. **work out**

①完成。②解決。③成功。

①② ●"I think I can work out this problem within 2 days."

「我想兩天之內，我可以辦好（解決）這個問題。」

③ ●"What happened to the romance Sue was having with Larry?"

「Sue 跟 Larry 之間的羅曼史怎麼了？」

"It just didn't work out."

「沒成！」

106. **working (or career) woman**

職業婦女（凡是有工作的人）

●"My mother is a working woman."

「我媽媽是個職業婦女。」

107. **works**

[wɜks]

①教訓。②(=trimming) 一切佐料。

① ●"If he comes again, I'll give him the works."

「假如他再來，我要教訓他一頓。」

② ●"I want a pizza with the works."

「我要一個義大利餅加上一切配料。」

註：在此 works 指 cheese, green pepper, ham, mushroom, 等東西。

108. would-be

準（歌星、作家），（有能力但或許努力不夠，諷刺有成不了的意味）

● "She's a would-be writer, however, she dislikes putting her thoughts on paper."

「她應該可以成為一個 " 作家 "，然而，她太懶於寫作了。」

109. wouldn't dream of it

連作夢都不敢想（表示遙不可及）

● "I wouldn't dream of asking her out. She'd laugh in my face."

「我連作夢都不敢想邀她出去，她會當面譏笑我的。」

110. wrong number

（電話）打錯了！

● "May I speak to Dr. Lee, Please?"

「我可以跟李醫生說話嗎？」

"Sorry, I'm afraid you've got a wrong number."

「對不起，你打錯了。」

"Oh, I'm sorry."

「對不起。」

"Never mind." /"It's O.K."

「沒關係。」

1. **xerox (=copy)**

   [ˈzirɑks]

   影印（Xerox 是美國很大的一家影印公司，現以公司名代表影印之意。）

   - "Excuse me, would you please tell me where the xerox machine is?"

     「打擾一下，你能告訴我影印機在哪兒嗎？」

   - "Could you xerox this for me please?"

     「你能幫我影印這東西嗎？」

2. **an X-rated film (=adult movie; blue movie) X-rated photograph; adult books & magazines; porn, or pornography**

   都是指成人（電影、圖片、書刊）

   - "The Godfather is an X-rated film, because it is too violent."

     「"教父"是一部成人電影，因爲它太暴戾了。」

   註：blue movies（黃色電影）一定是 X-rated movies, 但 X-rated movies 不一定是 blue movies，因爲 X-rated movies 可能因爲太暴戾，或因爲色情而被列爲成人電影。

1. **yellow**

   胆小；害怕；胆小鬼

   ● "He is. so yellow; he wouldn't dare complain."

   「他是那麼胆小；他不敢抱怨的。」

   ● "Boy, are you yellow!"

   「老天，你胆子眞小！」

22. **yes-man**

   應聲蟲；沒有主見的人；唯唯諾諾的人

   ● "I hate all yes-men."

   「我討厭所有的應聲蟲。」

3. **YIELD**

   [jild]

   幹道車先行

   ● "When you come to a YIELD sign, you have to let the cars on the main road go first."

   「當你來到寫著「幹道車先行」的路口時，你必須讓主要幹道的車子先走。」

4. **yo-yo**

   [jo jo]

   遊手好閑；無所事事的人

   ● "He's such a yo-yo. How can you expect him to be a good husband?"

   「他是這麼一個遊手好閑的人。你怎能寄望他做個好丈夫?」

5. **You're all alike.**

   你們是一丘之貉（都不是好東西）

   ● "Don't blame me. It wasn't my fault; I didn't do anything."

   「別怪我。不是我的錯；我可沒做什麼哦！」

   "You're all alike."

   「你們都是一丘之貉。」

6. **You're all mouth.**

你只有一張嘴（光會嘴說）

● "You will do it? I don't believe you. You're all mouth."

「你會做嗎？我才不相信你，你只有一張嘴。」

7. **You're just being polite!**

[pə`laɪt]

你只是客氣罷了！

● "Your casserole was delicious, Annie."

「Annie, 你的義大利烤麵條眞是好吃。」

"Who are you kidding? You're just being polite."

「你在騙誰？你只是客氣罷了。」

8. **You're my last hope.**

你是我最後的希望。

● "Kent, lend me $50 please. You're my last hope."

「Kent,請借我五十塊，你是我最後的希望。」

"No, N O — no."

「不，ㄅㄨ，ㄅㄨˋ」

9. **You're not just saying that?"**

你不光是說說罷了吧？

● "Honey, I'm so glad your mother can come this summer."

「甜心，我眞高興妳媽媽這個夏天能來。」

"You're not just saying that, are you, darling?"

「你不光是嘴巴上說說罷了吧？親愛的。」

"Of course not!"

「當然不是。」

10. **You're putting words into my mouth.**

我根本沒這個意思，是你自己講的。

● "I didn't say that at all. You're putting words in my mouth."

「我根本沒這意思，是你自己講的。」

11. **You're the boss.**

      [bɔs]

你是老闆一切聽你的；你來作主

● "What would you like to eat?"

「你想吃些什麼？」

"It's up to you, you are the boss."

「由你決定，你作主。」

12. **You're through.**

①完蛋。②過氣 (=over the hill)。

① ● "The big boss is looking for you. You are through."

「大老闆在找你，你完了！」

② ● "You are through, just face it."

「你已過氣了，面對這個事實吧！」

  ● "You're too old to play on the team. You're through."

「你太老了不能打球了。你過氣了。」

13. **You're trying my patience.**

不要惹我發火

● "Where did you get all this money?. . . .Come on, you're trying my patience."

「你哪來這麼多錢？快說，不要惹我發火。」

14. **You ain't seen (or heard) nothing yet.**

好戲還在後面

● "These planes are too noisy."

「這些飛機的聲音太吵了。」

"You ain't seen nothing yet. Just wait till the SST starts flying here."

「你還沒聽到更吵的呢！等着超音速飛機啓航吧！」

註：SST 是 supersonic transport 指超音速飛機。

15. **You bet!**

[bɛt]

當然！

- "You bet I'll go."

「當然我會去。」

- "Are you going to tell this to Jane?"

「你打算把這事告訴 Jane ？」

"You bet!"

「當然！」

16. **(Are) you blind?**

[blaɪnd]

瞎了眼？你到現在還看不見，看不清楚？

- "Did you just get a haircut?"

「你是不是剛理了髮？」

"Are you blind? I got it three weeks ago."

「你瞎了？三個星期前我就剪了。」

17. **You call this justice/fair?**

[ˈdʒʌstɪs]

你管這叫公平嗎？（不公平的意思）

- "Same work, different pay, you call this justice?"

「同工不同酬，你管這叫公平嗎？」

18. **You can't be serious.**

[ˈsɪrɪəs]

你不可能是當眞的！（你是在開玩笑吧？）

- "I want my money back now."

「我要取回我的錢。」

"Now? $30,000? You can't be serious."

「現在？三萬塊，你不會是當眞的吧？」

"I'm dead serious."

「我是絕對認眞的。」

19. **You can't please everyone.**

你不可能討好每一個人（無法面面顧到）不可能做得讓人人滿意的。

● "Oh, forget it, you can't please everyone."

「哦，算了吧，你不可能討好每一個人。」

20. **You devil**

你這魔鬼（咒詛人或撒嬌時用）

● "You devil. You'll get yours someday!"

「你這魔鬼。有一天你會得到報應的！」

● "Oh, you devil you."

「噢，你這個魔鬼。（撒嬌時用）」

21. **You don't have to yell.**

　　　　　　　　　[jɛl]

用不着窮吼。

● "I can hear you. You don't have to yell."

「我聽得見。你用不着吼。」

22. **You don't mean ‧‧‧‧**

　　　　　[min]

你不是說…

● "You don't mean you are going to chicken ou ‧‧"

「你不是說你要退出吧？（因為害怕）」

23. **You don't mean to say...**

你的意思是說…（表驚訝，不敢相信）

● "You don't mean to say she is a thief?"

「你的意思是說，她是個小偷？」

24. **You don't say.**

眞沒想到

● "He's already 45."

「他已 45 歲了！」

"You don't say."

「眞沒想到。」

25. **You got (or have) company.**

['kʌmpənɪ]

你有客人（通常指事先未約好的不速之客。）

● "Mary, you've got company."

「Mary，你有客人。」

26. **You'd better make sure.**

你最好能確定（你所說事情的眞實性）。（威脅語）

● "I saw her go into that motel."

「我看到她走進那個汽車旅社。」

"You'd better make sure or...."

「你最好確定，否則…」

27. **You've got to be kidding.**

[kɪdɪŋ]

你準是在開玩笑；你不是在開玩笑吧！（半信半疑）

● "You mean you flunked the test? You've got to be kidding."

「你是說你被當了？你準是開玩笑！」

28. **You've got to do something.**

你一定要想個法子（做點什麼）

● "He's going to kill her. You've got to do something."

「他會殺了她的。你一定要想個法子。」

"Why me? Why not you?"

「爲什麼要我想法子？你爲什麼不想想法子？」

29. **You have my word (=I give you my word. =I promise you.)**

我向你保證

● "We will return this to you right after we finish using it. You have my word."

「我向你保證，我們一用完就還你。」

30. **You hear me?**

聽到沒有？聽清楚了嗎？

- "No more drinks for you. You hear me?"

「不准再喝酒了，聽到沒有？」

31. **You know**

①你知道（表示心照不宣）。②你該知道。

① ● "You know how sloppy Mary is."

「你知道，Mary 有多邋遢。」

② ● "Well, you know....I'm tired and...."

「你是知道的，我又累又…」

- "You know, I'm not a fool."

「你該知道，我不是傻瓜。」

32. **You know better than I do.**

你比我清楚，少裝蒜了！

- "What happened here?"

「這裏怎麼了？」

"I think you know better than I do."

「我想你比我更清楚。」

33. **You know something? (=You know what?)**

你知道嗎？（在對別人講一件事前的開場白。）

- "You know something? You are a nut."

「你知道嗎？你是個瘋子。」

34. **You know the rules.**

你該明白規矩的

- "Don't play games. You know the rules."

「別要花招，你該明白規矩的。」

35. **You leave me no choice.**

你沒有留給我選擇的餘地

● "I hate to do this, but you leave me no choice."

「我不願這樣做，可是你沒有留給我任何選擇的餘地。」

36. **You listen well.**

給我好好聽着

● "You listen to me and listen well. I don't want you to go to that kind of place again."

「你給我好好聽着。我不許你再去那種地方。」

37. **You look like you've seen a ghost!**

你好像見了鬼一樣！（看到別人神色不對時的話語）

● "What's wrong, Flora? You look like you've seen a ghost."

「怎麼回事，Flora？你好像見到鬼一樣。」

38. **You look (much) younger than your age.**

你看來比你的實際年齡年輕多了！（在對方說出自己歲數時，恭維他人年輕的用語！）

● "Elizabeth, this is my mom."

「Elizabeth，這是我媽。」

"Hi, Mrs. Ford. You look so young, just like Betty's sister."

「嗨，Ford 太太。你看上去真年輕啊，好像 Betty 的姊姊。」

"Thank you, I'm already 55."

「謝謝你，我已經 55 歲了。」

"Really? you look much much younger than your age."

「真的嗎？你看上去比實際年齡年輕多了。」

39. **You lucky rascal.**

['ræskl]

你這幸運的淘氣鬼，搗蛋鬼

● "You lucky rascal. What did you do this time?"

「你這幸運的搗蛋鬼，這次你又闖下什麼禍？」

40. **You may take it anyway you like.**

你愛怎麼想都可以。（往好、往壞想隨你）

- "I'm not going to that party tonight. You may take it anyway you like."

「今晚我絕不去參加那個宴會。你要怎麼想，隨你。」

- "Does that mean we're through?"

「那是不是意味着我們之間完了？」

"You can take it anyway you like it."

「隨你怎麼想。」

41. **You must be daydreaming.**

你準是在做白日夢。

- "I just heard the phone rang a minute ago."

「我剛剛聽到電話鈴響。」

"I didn't hear anything. You must be daydreaming."

「我沒聽到什麼，你一定是在做白日夢。」

42. **You mustn't do/say that.**

你不該那樣說（做）的。〔責備別人說話（行為）不當〕

- "You mustn't say that. She is your best friend."

「你不該那樣說，她是你最要好的朋友啊！」

43. **You picked a great (or fine) time.**

[pɪkt]

你真會挑時間啊！

- "Hello, Jennifer? What took you so long to answer the phone?"

「喂，Jennifer 嗎？妳怎麼這麼久才來接電話啊？」

"You picked a great time. I was taking a shower."

「你真會挑時間，我正在洗澡。」

- "You want a divorce? You sure picked a fine time."

「你要離婚？你可真會挑時間啊。」

44. **You said it yourself.**

是你自己說的（我可沒說）

● "You called me a fool?"
「你叫我笨蛋？」

"I didn't say it. You said it yourself."
「我可沒說。是你自己說的。」

45. **You reap what you sow.**

[rip] [so]

自食其果；自作自受

● "I heard Lana left Gordon without saying good-bye."
「聽說 Lana 離開了 Gordon，連聲再見都沒說。」

"All I can say is, you reap what you sow."
「我只能說，（他）活該（自食其果也）。」

46. **You too**

你也是；彼此彼此

● "Good-bye, Joe. Have a nice day."
「Joe，再見了，祝你有個美好的一天。」

"You too, see you."
「彼此彼此，再見。」

● "You're a dummy."
「你是個笨蛋。」

"You too."
「你也一樣。」

47. **You want to bet?**

[bɛt]

你要打賭嗎？（你敢打個賭嗎？）

● "She is not coming."
「她不會來了。」

"She will."
「她會！」

"You want to bet?"

「你要打賭嗎？」

48. **You'll be sorry (=repent) for this.**

[rɪ'pɛnt]

你會後悔的（勸告，或警告語，表示要報復）

● "I swear to God, you'll be sorry for this."

「我對天發誓。你會後悔的。」

● "If you leave her now; someday you'll be sorry."

「如果你現在離開她；有一天你會後悔的。」

49. **You won't find anything out of line.**

保證絕對完美無疵

● "Are you sure everything is O.K. now?"

「你確定一切都（修）好了嗎？」

"I promise you. You won't find anything out of line."

「我保證你絕對找不出一點毛病。」

50. **You win, O.K.?**

算你贏了，行吧！

● "You win, O.K.? I don't want to argue with you anymore."

「你贏了，行吧？我不想再跟你爭論。」

51. **Your flag is at half-mast.**

[flæg]　　　[mæst]

你褲子的拉鏈開了

= "You're flying low. Zip up your fly."

「你的拉鏈開了，拉上你的拉鏈。」

52. **Your wish is my command.**

[kə'mænd]

你的心願就是我的命令（照辦也！），（奉承女孩，或巴結上司、客人之用語）

• "I want to have champagne for my birthday party."
「生日宴會上我要用香檳酒招待客人。」

"Your wish is my command, darling."
「你的心願就是我的命令，親愛的。」

1. **zit (=pimple)**

   [zɪt]

   青春痘

   - "I'm picking (or popping) my zits."

     「我正在擠青春痘。」

INDEX 索　引

D

D

E

H

I

J

L

O

P

S